THE BOOK OF THE EPIC

It is in this vast, dim region of myth and legend the sources of the literature of modern times are hidden; and it is only by returning to them, by constant remembrance that they drain a vast region of vital human experience, that the origin and early direction of that literature can be recalled.—HAMILTON WRIGHT MABIE

"This vast, dim region of myth and legend"

Fr. Stella Langdale

THE BOOK OF THE EPIC

THE WORLD'S GREAT EPICS TOLD IN STORY

BY

H. A. GUERBER

BIBLO and TANNEN
NEW YORK
1966

Reprinted, 1966, with the permission of the publishers
by
Biblo & Tannen Booksellers & Publishers, Inc.
63 Fourth Ave. New York, N. Y. 10003

Library of Congress Catalog Card Number: 66-13473

Printed in U.S.A. by
NOBLE OFFSET PRINTERS, INC.
NEW YORK 3, N. Y.

PREFACE

DERIVED from the Greek *epos*, a saying or oracle, the term 'epic' is generally given to some form of heroic narrative wherein tragedy, comedy, lyric, dirge, and idyll are skilfully blended to form an immortal work.

"Mythology, which was the interpretation of nature, and legend, which is the idealization of history," are the main elements of the epic. Being the "living history of the people," an epic should have "the breadth and volume of a river." All epics have, therefore, generally been "the first-fruits of the earliest experiences of nature and life on the part of imaginative races"; and the real poet has been, as a rule, the race itself.

There are almost as many definitions of an epic and rules for its composition as there are nations and poets. For that reason, instead of selecting only such works as in the writer's opinion can justly claim the title of epic, each nation's verdict has been accepted, without question, in regard to its national work of this class, be it in verse or prose.

The following pages, therefore, contain almost every variety of epic, from that which treats of the Deity in dignified hexameters, strictly conforms to the rule "one hero, one time, and one action of many parts," and has "the massiveness and dignity of sculpture," to the simplest idylls, such as the Japanese *White Aster*, or that exquisite French medieval compound of poetry and prose, *Aucassin et Nicolette*. Not only are both Christian and pagan epics impartially admitted in this volume, but the representative works of each nation in the epic field are grouped according to the languages in which they were composed.

Many of the ancient epics are voluminous ; one of them, printed in full, would fill twenty-four volumes as large as this. To give even the barest outline of one or two poems in each language has, therefore, required the utmost condensation ; and although the temptation to quote many choice passages has been well-nigh irresistible, space has precluded all save the scantiest quotations.

The main object of this volume consists in outlining clearly and briefly, for the use of young students or of the busy general reader, the principal examples of the time-honoured stories which have inspired our greatest poets and supplied endless material to painters, sculptors, and musicians ever since art began.

CONTENTS

ILLUSTRATIONS

THE BOOK OF THE EPIC

GREEK EPICS

THE greatest of all the world's epics, the *Iliad* and the *Odyssey*, are attributed to Homer, or Melesigenes, who is said to have lived some time between 1050 and 850 B.C. Ever since the second century before Christ, however, the question whether Homer is the originator of the poems, or whether, like the Rhapsodists, he merely recited extant verses, has been hotly disputed.

The events upon which the *Iliad* is based took placc some time before 1100 B.C., and we are told that the poems of Homer were collected and committed to writing by Pisistratus during the age of Epic Poetry, or second age of Greek literature, which ends 600 B.C.

It stands to reason that the *Iliad* must have been inspired by, or at least based upon, previous poems, since such perfection is not achieved at a single bound. Besides, we are aware of the existence of many shorter Greek epics, which either have been entirely lost or of which we now possess only fragments.

A number of these ancient epics form what is termed the Trojan Cycle, because all relate in some way to the War of Troy. Among them is the *Cypria*, in eleven books, by Stasimus of Cyprus (or by Arctinus of Miletus), wherein is related Jupiter's frustrated wooing of Thetis, her marriage with Peleus, the episode of the golden apple, the judgment of Paris, the kidnapping of Helen, the mustering of the Greek forces, and the main events of the first nine years of the Trojan War. The *Iliad* follows this epic, taking up the story where the wrath of Achilles is aroused and ending it with the funeral of Hector.

This, however, does not conclude the story of the Trojan War, which is resumed in the *Aethiopia*, in five books, by Arctinus of Miletus. After describing the arrival of Penthesilea, Queen of the Amazons, to aid the Trojans, the poet relates her death at the hand of Achilles, who, in his turn, is slain by Apollo and Paris. This epic concludes with the famous dispute between Ajax and Ulysses for the possession of Achilles' armour.

The *Little Iliad*, the authorship of which is ascribed to various poets, including Homer, next describes the madness and death of Ajax, the arrival of Philoctetes with the arrows of Hercules, the death of Paris, the purloining of the Palladium, the stratagem of the wooden horse, and the death of Priam.

In the *Ilion Persis*, or 'Sack of Troy,' by Arctinus, in two books, we find the Trojans hesitating whether to convey the wooden steed into their city, and discover the immortal tales of the traitor Sinon and of Laocoön. We then behold the taking and sacking of the city, with the massacre of the men and the carrying off into captivity of the women.

In the *Nostoi*, or 'Homeward Voyage,' by Agias of Troezene, the Atridae differ in opinion ; so, while Agamemnon delays his departure to offer propitiatory sacrifices, Menelaus sets sail for Egypt, where he is detained. This poem also contains the narrative of Agamemnon's return, of his assassination, and of the way in which his death was avenged by his son Orestes.

Next in sequence of events comes the *Odyssey* of Homer, and then the *Telegonia* of Eugamon of Cyrene, in two books. This describes how, after the burial of the suitors, Ulysses renews his adventures, and visits Thesprotia, where he marries and leaves a son. We also have his death, a battle between two of his sons, and the marriage of Telemachus and Circe, as well as that of the widowed Penelope to Telegonus, one of Ulysses' descendants.

Another sequel or addition to the *Odyssey* is found in the *Telemachia*, also a Greek poem, as well as in a far more modern work, the French classic *Télémaque*, written by Fénelon for his pupil the Dauphin in the age of Louis XIV.

Another great series of Greek poems is the Theban Cycle, which comprises the *Thebais*, by some unknown author, wherein is related in full the story of Oedipus, that of the Seven Kings before Thebes, and the doings of the Epigoni.

There exist also cyclic poems in regard to the labours of Heracles, among others one called *Oechalia*, which has proved a priceless mine for poets, dramatists, painters, and sculptors.[1]

In the *Alexandra* by Lycophron (270 B.C.), and in a similar poem by Quintus Smyrnaeus, in fourteen books, we find tedious sequels to the *Iliad*, wherein Alexander is represented as a descendant of Achilles. Indeed, the life and death of Alexander the Great are also the source of innumerable epics, as well as of romances in Greek, Latin, French, German, and English. The majority of these are based upon the epic of Callisthenes (A.D. 110), wherein an attempt was made to prove that Alexander descended directly from the Egyptian god Jupiter Ammon, or at least from his priest Nectanebus.

Besides being told in innumerable Greek versions, the tale of Troy has frequently been repeated in Latin, and it enjoyed immense popularity through-

[1] A detailed account of Oedipus, Heracles, the Argonauts, and the 'War of Troy' is given in the author's *Myths of Greece and Rome*.

out Europe in the Middle Ages. It was, however, most beloved in France, where Benoît de St Maur's interminable *Roman de Troie*, as well as his *Roman d'Alexandre*, greatly delighted the lords and ladies of his time.

Besides the works based on the story of Troy or on the adventures of Alexander, we have in Greek the *Theogony* of Hesiod in some 1022 lines, a miniature Greek mythology, giving the story of the origin and the doings of the Greek gods, as well as the Greek theory in regard to the creation of the world.

Among later Greek works we must also note the *Shield of Heracles* and the *Eoiae*, or Catalogue of the Boeotian heroines who gave birth to demi-gods or heroes.

In 194 B.C. Apollonius Rhodius at Alexandria wrote the *Argonautica* in four books, wherein he relates the adventures of Jason in quest of the golden fleece. This epic was received so coldly that the poet, in disgust, withdrew to Rhodes, where, having remodelled his work, he obtained immense applause.

The principal burlesque epic in Greek, the *Batrachomyomachia*, or 'Battle of Frogs and Mice,' was attributed to Homer, but only some 300 lines of this work remain, showing what it may have been.

THE ILIAD

Introduction

Jupiter, king of the gods, refrained from an alliance with Thetis, a sea divinity, because he was told that her son would be greater than his father. To console her, however, he decreed that all the gods should attend her nuptials with Peleus, King of Thessaly. At this wedding banquet the Goddess of Discord produced a golden apple, inscribed "To the fairest," which Juno, Minerva, and Venus claimed.

The gods refused to act as umpires in this quarrel, so Paris, son of the King of Troy, was chosen. As an oracle had predicted before his birth that he would cause the ruin of his city, Paris had been abandoned on a mountain to perish, but had been rescued by kindly shepherds.

Upon Juno offering him worldly power, Minerva boundless wisdom, and Venus the most beautiful wife in the world, Paris bestowed the prize of beauty upon Venus. She therefore bade him return to Troy, where his family was ready to welcome him, and sail thence to Greece to kidnap Helen, daughter of Jupitor and Leda and wife of Menelaus, King of Sparta. So potent were this lady's charms that her stepfather had made all her suitors swear never to carry her away from him who should win her hand, and to aid in her recovery should she ever be abducted.

Shortly after his arrival at Sparta and during a brief absence of its king, Paris induced Helen to elope with him. On his return the outraged husband summoned the suitors to redeem their pledge, and collected a huge force at Aulis, where Agamemnon, his brother, became leader of the expedition. Such was the popularity of this war that even heroes who had taken no oath were anxious to take part in the punitive expedition, the most famous of these warriors being Achilles, son of Thetis and Peleus.

After many adventures the Greeks, landing on the shores of Asia Minor, began the siege of the city, from the ramparts of which Helen watched her husband and his allies measure their strength against the Trojans. Such was the bravery displayed on both sides that the war raged nine years without any decisive advantage being obtained. At the end of this period, during a raid, the Greeks secured two female captives, who were awarded to Agamemnon and to Achilles in recognition of past services.

Although the above events are treated in a number of other Greek poems and epics—which no longer exist entire, but form part of a cycle—the *Iliad*, accredited to Homer, takes up the story at this point, and relates the wrath of Achilles, together with the happenings of some fifty days in the ninth year.

Book I

After invoking the Muse to aid him sing the wrath of Achilles, the poet relates how the priest of Apollo came in person to the Greek camp to ransom his captive daughter, only to be treated with contumely by Agamemnon. In his indignation this priest besought Apollo to send down a plague to decimate the enemy's forces, and the Greeks soon learned from their oracles that its ravages would not cease until the maiden was restored to her father.

> Nor shall we cease his heavy hand to feel,
> Till to her sire we give the bright-ey'd girl,
> Unbought, unransom'd, and to Chrysa's shore
> A solemn hecatomb despatch ; this done,
> The God, appeas'd, his anger may remit.[1]

In a formal council Agamemnon is therefore asked to relinquish his captive, but violently declares that he will do so only on condition that he receives

[1] All the quotations from the *Iliad* are taken from Lord Derby's translation.

The Leaders of the Greeks
Christian G. Heyne

Achilles' slave. This insolent claim so infuriates the young hero that he is about to draw his sword, when Minerva, unseen by the rest, bids him hold his hand, and state that should Agamemnon's threat be carried out he will withdraw from the war.

Although the aged Nestor employs all his honeyed eloquence to soothe this quarrel, both chiefs angrily withdraw, Agamemnon to send his captive back to her father, and Achilles to sulk in his tent.

It is while he is in this mood that Agamemnon's heralds appear and lead away his captive. Mindful of Minerva's injunctions, Achilles allows her to depart, but registers a solemn oath that, even were the Greeks to perish, he will lend them no aid. Then, hastening down to the shore, he summons his mother from the watery deep, and implores her to use her influence to avenge his wrongs. Knowing his life will prove short though glorious, Thetis promises to visit Jupiter on Olympus to plead for him. There she wins from the Father of the Gods a promise that the Greeks shall suffer defeat so long as her son does not fight in their ranks—a promise confirmed by his divine nod. This, however, arouses the wrath and jealousy of Juno, whom Jupiter is compelled to chide so severely that peace and harmony are restored in Olympus only when Vulcan, acting as cup-bearer, rouses the inextinguishable laughter of the gods by his awkward limp.

Book II

That night, while all are sleeping, Zeus sends a deceptive dream to Agamemnon to suggest that the moment has come to attack Troy. At dawn, therefore, Agamemnon calls an assembly, and the chiefs decide to test the mettle of the Greeks by ordering a return home, and, in the midst of these preparations, summoning the men to fight.

These signs of imminent departure incense Juno and Minerva, who, ever since the golden apple was bestowed upon Venus, are sworn foes of Paris and Troy. In disguise, therefore, Minerva urges Ulysses, wiliest of the Greeks, to silence the clown Thersites, and admonish his companions that if they return home empty-handed they will be disgraced. Only too pleased, Ulysses reminds his countrymen how, just before they left home, a serpent crawled from beneath the altar and devoured eight young sparrows and the mother who tried to defend them, adding that this was an omen that for nine years they would vainly besiege Troy but would triumph in the tenth.

His eloquent reminder, reinforced by patriotic speeches from Nestor and Agamemnon, determines the Greeks to attempt a final attack upon Troy. So, with the speed and destructive fury of a furious fire, the Greek army, whose forces and leaders are all named, sweeps on toward Troy, whither Iris has flown to warn the Trojans of their approach.

> As when the Lord of thunder, in his wrath,
> The earth's foundations shakes, in Arimi,
> Where, buried deep, 'tis said, Typhœus lies ;
> So at their coming, groan'd beneath their feet
> The earth, as quickly o'er the plain they spread.

It is in the form of one of Priam's sons that this divinity enters the palace, where, as soon as Hector hears the news, he musters his warriors, most conspicuous among whom are his brother Paris, and Aeneas, son of Venus and Anchises.

Book III

Both armies now advance toward each other, the Trojans uttering shrill cries like migratory cranes, while the Greeks maintain an impressive silence. When near enough to recognize his wife's seducer, Menelaus rushes forward to attack Paris, who, terrified, takes refuge in the ranks of the Trojan host. So cowardly a retreat, however, causes Hector to express the bitter wish that his brother had died before bringing disgrace upon Troy. Although conscious of deserving reproof, Paris, after reminding his brother that all men are not constituted alike, offers to redeem his honour by fighting Menelaus, provided Helen and her treasures are awarded to the victor. This proposal proves so welcome that Hector checks the advance of his men and proposes this duel to the Greeks, who accept his terms, provided Priam will swear in person to the treaty.

Meanwhile Iris, in the guise of a princess, has entered the Trojan palace and bidden Helen hasten to the ramparts to see the two armies—instead of fighting—offering sacrifices as a preliminary to the duel, of which she is to be the prize. Donning a veil and summoning her attendants, Helen seeks the place whence Priam and his ancient counsellors gaze down upon the plain. On beholding her even these aged men admit that the two nations are excusable for so savagely disputing her possession, while Priam, with fatherly tact, ascribes the war to the gods alone.

> Helen they saw, as to the tow'r she came;
> And, "'Tis no marvel," one to another said,
> "The valiant Trojans and the well-greav'd Greeks
> For beauty such as this should long endure
> The toils of war; for goddess-like she seems."

Then he invites Helen to sit beside him and name the Greeks that he points out, among whom she recognizes, with bitter shame, her brother-in-law Agamemnon, Ulysses the wily, and Ajax the bulwark of Greece. While she is vainly seeking the forms of her twin brothers, messengers summon Priam down to the plain to swear to the treaty. As soon as he has taken the oath, he drives back to Troy, leaving Hector and Ulysses to measure out the ground and to settle by lot which champion shall strike first.

Fate having favoured Paris, he advances in brilliant array, and soon shatters Menelaus' sword. Deprived of a weapon, Menelaus boldly grasps his adversary by his plumed helmet and drags him away, until, seeing her *protégé* in danger, Venus breaks the fastenings of his helmet, which alone remains in Menelaus' hands. Then she spirits Paris back to the Trojan palace, where she leaves him resting on a couch, and hurries off, in the guise of an old crone, to twitch Helen's veil, whispering that Paris awaits her at home. Recognizing the goddess in spite of her disguise, Helen reproaches her, declaring that she has no desire ever to see Paris again, but Venus, awing Helen into submission, leads her back to the palace. There Paris, after artfully ascribing Menelaus' triumph to the aid of Minerva, proceeds to woo Helen anew. Meanwhile Menelaus vainly ranges to and fro, seeking his foe and hotly accusing the Trojans of screening him, while Agamemnon clamours for the immediate surrender of Helen, asserting that the Greeks have won.

Book IV

The gods on Mount Olympus, who have witnessed all, now taunt each other with abetting the Trojans or the Greeks, as the case may be. After this quarrel has raged some time, Jupiter bids Minerva go down and violate the truce ; so, in the guise of a warrior, she prompts a Trojan archer to aim at Menelaus a dart which produces a slight wound. This is enough to excite Agamemnon to avenge the broken treaty. A moment later the Greek phalanx advances, urged on by Minerva, while the Trojans, equally inspired by Mars, rush to meet them with similar fury. Streams of blood now flow, the earth trembles beneath the crash of falling warriors, and the roll of war chariots is like thunder. Although for a while the Greeks seem to gain the advantage, Apollo spurs the Trojans to new efforts by reminding them that Achilles, their most dreaded foe, is absent.

Book V

Seeing the battle well under way, Minerva now drags Mars out of the fray, suggesting that the mortals settle their quarrel unaided. Countless duels now occur, many lives are lost, and various miracles are performed. Diomedes, for instance, is instantly healed of a grievous wound by Minerva, plunges back into the fray, and fights until Aeneas bids an archer check his destructive career. But this man is slain before he can obey, and Aeneas himself would be killed by Diomedes did not Venus snatch him away from the battle-field. While she is rescuing Aeneas, Diomedes wounds her in the hand, causing her to drop her son, who is rescued by Apollo, while Venus hastens off to obtain from Mars the loan of his chariot, and drives back to Olympus. There, on her mother's breast, Venus sobs out the tale of her fright, and is sarcastically advised to leave fighting to the other gods and busy herself only with the pleasures of love.

> Thus she: and smil'd the Sire of Gods and men;
> He call'd the golden Venus to his side,
> And, "Not to thee, my child," he said, "belong
> The deeds of war; do thou bestow thy care
> On deeds of love, and tender marriage ties;
> But leave to Mars and Pallas feats of arms."

Having snatched Aeneas out of danger, Apollo conveys him to Pergamus to be healed, leaving on the battlefield in his stead a phantom to represent him. Then Apollo challenges Mars to avenge Venus' wound, and the fray which ensues becomes so bloody that 'Homeric battle' has been ever since the accepted term for fierce fighting. Mars and Bellona protect Hector, and the Trojans now gain some advantage, until Juno and Minerva hasten to the rescue of the Greeks. Arriving on the battle-field, Juno, assuming the form of Stentor (whose brazen tones have become proverbial), directs the Greek onslaught. Meanwhile, instigated by Minerva, Diomedes attacks Mars, who, receiving a wound, emits such a roar of pain that both armies shudder. Then he too is miraculously conveyed to Olympus, where, after exhibiting his wound, he denounces Minerva who caused it. Although Jupiter sternly rebukes his son he takes such prompt measures to relieve his suffering that Mars is soon seated at the Olympian board, where before long he is joined by Juno and Minerva.

Book VI

Meanwhile the battle rages, and in the midst of broken chariots, flying steeds, and clouds of dust we descry Menelaus and Agamemnon doing wonders and hear Nestor cheering on the Greeks. The Trojans are about to yield before their onslaught, when a warrior warns Hector and the newly returned Aeneas of their dire peril. After conferring hastily with his friends, Hector returns to Troy to direct the women to implore Minerva's favour, while Aeneas goes to support their men. At the Scaean Gate Hector meets the mothers, wives, and daughters of the combatants, who, at his bidding, gladly prepare costly offerings to be borne in solemn procession to Minerva's temple.

Then Hector himself rushes to the palace, where, refusing all refreshment, he goes in quest of Paris, whom he finds in the company of Helen and her maids, idly polishing his armour. Indignantly Hector informs his brother that the Trojans are perishing without the walls in defence of the quarrel which he kindled, but which he is too cowardly to uphold. Admitting that he deserves reproach, Paris declares that he is about to return to the battle-field, for Helen has rekindled all his ardour. As Hector does not answer, Helen timidly expresses her regret at having caused these woes, bitterly wishing that fate had bound her to a man noble enough to feel and resent an insult. With a curt recommendation to send Paris after him as soon as possible, Hector hastens off to his own dwelling, for he longs to embrace his wife and son, perhaps for the last time.

At his home he finds none but the servants, who inform him that his wife has gone to the watch-tower, whither he now hastens. The meeting between Hector and Andromache, her tender reproaches at the risk he runs, and her passionate reminder that since Achilles deprived her of her kin he is her sole protector, form the most touching passage in the *Iliad*. Gently reminding her that he must go where honour calls, and sadly admitting that he is haunted by visions of fallen Troy and of her plight as a captive, Hector adds that to protect her from such a fate he must even fight. But when he holds out his arms to his child, the little one, terrified by the plumes on his helmet, refuses to come to him until he lays it aside. Having embraced his infant son, Hector fervently prays that he may grow up to defend the Trojans, and hands him back to Andromache, from whom also he takes tender leave.

> Thus as he spoke, great Hector stretch'd his arms
> To take his child ; but back the infant shrank,
> Crying, and sought his nurse's shelt'ring breast,
> Scar'd by the brazen helm and horsehair plume,
> That nodded, fearful, on the warrior's crest.
> Laugh'd the fond parents both, and from his brow
> Hector the casque remov'd, and set it down,
> All glitt'ring, on the ground ; then kissed his child,
> And danc'd him in his arms ; then thus to Jove
> And to th' Immortals all address'd his pray'r :
> " Grant, Jove, and all ye Gods, that this my son
> May be, as I, the foremost man of Troy,
> For valour fam'd, his country's guardian King ;
> That men may say, 'This youth surpasses far
> His father,' when they see him from the fight,
> From slaughter'd foes, with bloody spoils of war
> Returning, to rejoice his mother's heart ! "

Then, resuming his helmet, Hector drives out of the Scaean Gate and is joined by his brother Paris, now full of ardour to fight.

Book VII

Joyfully the Trojans hail the arrival of the two brothers, before whose fierce onslaught the Greeks

soon fall back in their turn. Meanwhile Minerva and Apollo, siding with opposite forces, decide to inspire the Trojans to challenge the Greeks to a single combat, and perch upon a tree, in the guise of vultures, to watch the result. Calling for a suspension of hostilities, Hector dares any Greek to fight him, stipulating that the arms of the vanquished shall be the victor's prize, but that his remains shall receive honourable burial. Conscious that none of their warriors—save Achilles—match Hector, the Greeks at first hesitate, but nine finally volunteer, and Ajax is chosen by lot to be the Greek champion. Overjoyed at this opportunity to distinguish himself, Ajax advances with boastful confidence to meet Hector, who, undismayed by his size and truculent speeches, enters into the fight. The duel is, however, not fought to a finish, for the heralds interrupt it at nightfall, pronouncing the champions equal in strength and skill and postponing its issue until the morrow.

In his elation Ajax offers thanks to Jupiter before attending a banquet, at which Nestor prudently advises his friends to fortify their camp by erecting earthworks. While the Greeks are feasting, the Trojans debate whether it would not be wise to apologize for the broken truce and to restore Helen and her treasures to the Greeks. But this suggestion is angrily rejected by Paris, and Priam suggests that they propose instead an armistice of sufficient length to enable both parties to bury their dead.

At dawn, therefore, Trojan heralds visit Agamemnon's tent to propose a truce, and offer any indemnification save the return of Helen. But, although the Greeks consent to an armistice, they feel so confident of success that they refuse all offers

of indemnity. Both parties now bury their dead, a sight witnessed by the gods, who, gazing down from Olympus, become aware of the earthen ramparts erected during the night to protect the Greek fleet. This sight prompts Neptune to express jealous fears lest these may eclipse the walls he built round Troy, but Jupiter pacifies him by assuring him that he can easily bury them beneath the sand as soon as the war is over.

Book VIII

At daybreak Jupiter summons the gods, forbidding them to lend aid to either party, under penalty of perpetual imprisonment in Tartarus. Having uttered this decree, Jupiter betakes himself to Mount Ida, whence he proposes to watch the contest. It is there, at noon, that he takes out his golden balances, and places in opposite scales the fates of Troy and Greece. A moment later a loud clap of thunder proclaims that the day's advantage will remain with the Trojans, whose leader, Hector, is protected by Jupiter's thunderbolts each time that Diomedes attacks him. This manifestation of divine favour strikes terror into the hearts of the Greeks, but encourages the Trojans. They therefore hotly pursue the Greeks to their ramparts, which Hector urges them to scale when the foe seeks refuge behind them.

Seeing the peril of the Greeks, Juno urges Agamemnon to visit Ulysses' tent, and there proclaim, in such loud tones that Achilles cannot fail to overhear him, that their vessels will soon be in flames. Then, fearing for his companions, Agamemnon prays so fervently for aid that an eagle flies over the camp and drops a lamb upon the Greek altar. This omen

of good fortune renews the courage of the Greeks, and stimulates the archer Teucer to cause new havoc in the Trojan ranks with his unfailing arrows, until Hector hurls a rock which lays him low, and rushes into the Greek camp.

Full of anxiety for their *protégés*, Juno and Minerva forget Jupiter's injunctions, and are about to hurry off to their rescue, when the king of the gods bids them stop, assuring them that the Greeks will suffer defeat until, Patroclus having fallen, Achilles arises to avenge him. When the setting sun signals the close of the day's fight the Greeks are still in possession of their tents, but the Trojans bivouac in the plain, just outside the trench, to prevent their escape.

Book IX

Such anxiety reigns in the Greek camp that Agamemnon holds a council in his tent. There, almost choked by tears, he declares that no alternative remains save flight, but Diomedes so hotly contradicts him that the Greeks decide to remain. At Nestor's suggestion, Agamemnon then tries to atone for his insult to Achilles by gifts and apologies, instructing the bearers to promise the return of the captive and to offer an alliance with one of his daughters, if Achilles will only come to their aid. Wending their way through the moonlit camp, these emissaries find Achilles idly listening to the music of Patroclus. After delivering the message, Ulysses makes an eloquent appeal on behalf of his countrymen, but Achilles coldly replies that the Greeks must defend themselves, as he is about to depart. Such is his resentment that he refuses to forgive Agamemnon, although his aged tutor urges him to

be brave enough to conquer himself. Most reluctantly, therefore, Ulysses and Ajax return, and, although sleep hovers over Achilles' tent, dismay reigns within that of Agamemnon, until Diomedes vows they will yet prove that they do not need Achilles' aid.

Book X

Exhausted by the day's efforts, most of the Greeks have fallen asleep, when Agamemnon, after conversing for a while with Menelaus, arouses Nestor, Ulysses, and Diomedes to inspect their posts. In the course of these rounds Nestor suggests that one of their number steal into the camp of the Trojans to discover their plans. This suggestion is eagerly seized by Diomedes and Ulysses, who, on their way to the enemy's camp, encounter Dolon, a Trojan spy, who is coming to find out what they are planning. Crouching among the corpses, Diomedes and Ulysses capture this man, from whom they wring all the information they require, together with exact directions where to find the steeds of Rhesus. To secure this prize, Ulysses and Diomedes steal into the Trojan camp, where, after slaying a few sleepers, they capture the steeds and escape in safety, thanks to the aid of Minerva. On seeing his friends emerge from the gloom with so glorious a prize, Nestor, who has been anxiously watching, expresses great joy, and invites his companions to refresh themselves after their exertions.

Book XI

At daybreak Jupiter sends Discord to waken the Greeks and, when they appear in battle array,

hurls a thunderbolt as a signal for the fight to begin. Stimulated by Hector's ardour, the Trojans now pounce like ravening wolves upon their foes, but, in spite of their courage, are driven back almost to the Scaean Gate. To encourage Hector, however, Jupiter warns him that once Agamemnon is wounded the tide will turn. Soon after a javelin strikes Agamemnon, and Hector, seeing him borne to his tent, urges his men on with new vehemence until he forces back the Greeks in his turn. In the ensuing medley both Diomedes and Ulysses are wounded, and Achilles, moodily lounging on the prow of his ship, sees Nestor bring them into camp. Wishing to ascertain who has been hurt, he sends Patroclus to find out. This warrior learns how many of the Greeks are wounded, and is persuaded to try to induce Achilles to assist their countrymen, or at least to allow his friend to lead his forces to their rescue.

Book XII

Although the Trojans are now fiercely trying to enter the Greek camp, their efforts are baffled until Hector, dismounting from his chariot, attacks the mighty wall which the gods are to level as soon as the war is over. Thanks to his efforts, its gates are battered in, and the Trojans pour into the Greek camp, where many duels occur, and where countless warriors are slain on both sides.

Book XIII

Having effected an entrance into the camp, the Trojans rush forward to set fire to the ships, hoping thus to prevent the escape of their foes. Perceiving the peril of the Greeks, Neptune, in the guise of a priest, urges them to stand fast.

> So spake th' Earth-shaker, Circler of the Earth,
> And with his sceptre touching both the chiefs,
> Fill'd them with strength and courage, and their
> limbs,
> Their feet and hands, with active vigour strung ;
> Then like a swift-wing'd falcon sprang to flight,
> Which down the sheer face of some lofty rock
> Swoops on the plain to seize his feather'd prey :
> So swiftly Neptune left the chiefs.

But the advantage does not remain continuously with the Trojans, for Hector is soon beaten back, and, seeing his people's peril, again hotly reviles Paris, whose crime has entailed all this bloodshed.

Book XIV

In the midst of the gloom caused by a new irruption of the Trojans in the Greek camp, Nestor hastens to the spot where the wounded Agamemnon, Ulysses, and Diomedes are watching the fight. But, although Agamemnon renews his former suggestion that they depart, Diomedes and Ulysses, scorning it, prepare to return to the fray, in spite of their wounds. This renewal of Greek courage pleases Juno, who, fearing that Jupiter will again interfere in behalf of the Trojans, proceeds by coquettish wiles, and with the aid of the God of Sleep, to lull him into a state of forgetfulness. Juno then sends Sleep to urge the Greeks to make the most of this respite, and, thus stimulated, they fight on, until Ajax hurls a rock which lays Hector low. But, before he and his companions can secure this victim, Hector is rescued by his men, who speedily convey him to the river, where the cool waters soon restore his senses.

Book XV

Thus temporarily deprived of a leader, the Trojans fall back to the place where they left their chariots. They are mounting in confusion in order to flee, when Jupiter, waking from his sleep, and realizing how he has been tricked, discharges his wrath upon Juno's head. Hearing her lay the blame on Neptune, Jupiter wrathfully orders his brother back to his realm and despatches Apollo to cure Hector. Then he reiterates that the Greeks shall be worsted until Patroclus, wearing Achilles' armour, takes part in the fray. He adds that, after slaying his son Sarpedon, this hero shall succumb beneath Hector's sword, and that, to avenge Patroclus' death, Achilles will slay Hector and thus ensure the fall of Troy.

Once more the Trojans drive back the Greeks, who would have given up the contest in despair had not Jupiter encouraged them by a clap of thunder. When the Trojans again burst into the camp, Patroclus rushes out of Achilles' tent and sees Teucer winging one deadly arrow after another among the foe. But, in spite of his skill, and although Ajax fights like a lion at bay, Hector and the Trojans press fiercely forward, torch in hand, to fire the Greek ships.

Book XVI

Appalled by this sight, Patroclus rushes back to Achilles, and, after vainly urging him to fight, persuades him to lend him his armour, chariot, and men. But, even while furthering his friend's departure, Achilles charges him neither to slay Hector nor take Troy, as he wishes to reserve that double honour for himself. The first vessels are already enveloped in flames when Patroclus rushes to the rescue of his countrymen. At the sight of a warrior whom they mistake for Achilles, and at this influx of fresh troops, the Trojans beat a retreat, and the Greeks, fired with new courage, pursue them across the plain to the very gates of Troy. Such is Patroclus' ardour that, forgetting Achilles' injunctions, he is about to attack Hector, when Sarpedon challenges him to a duel. Knowing that this fight will prove fatal to his beloved son, Jupiter causes a bloody dew to fall upon the earth, and despatches Sleep and Death to take charge of his remains, which they are to convey first to Olympus to receive a fatherly kiss and then to Lycia for burial. No sooner is Sarpedon slain than a grim fight ensues over his spoil and remains, but while the Greeks secure his armour, his corpse is borne away by Apollo, who, after purifying it from the stains of battle, entrusts it to Sleep and Death.

Meantime, renewing his pursuit of the Trojans, Patroclus is about to scale the walls of Troy, when Apollo reminds him that the city is not to fall a prey either to him or to his friend. Then, in the midst of a duel in which Patroclus engages with Hector, Apollo snatches the helmet off the Greek hero's head, leaving him exposed to his foe's deadly blows. Mortally wounded, Patroclus declares that had not the gods betrayed him he would have triumphed, and predicts that Achilles will avenge his death. In the meantime, pleased with having slain so redoubtable a foe, Hector makes a dash to secure Achilles' chariot and horses, but fails because the driver (Automedon) speeds away.

Book XVII

On seeing Patroclus fall Menelaus rushes forward to defend his remains and rescue Achilles' armour from the foe. Hector therefore abandons the vain pursuit of Achilles' chariot, and returns to claim his spoil. He is attacked by Menelaus and Ajax, and a fierce battle takes place over Patroclus' remains, while Achilles' horses weep for the beloved youth who so often caressed them.

Book XVIII

No sooner is the death of Patroclus known in Achilles' tent than the female captives break into lamentation, while the hero groans so loudly that Thetis hears him. Rising from the depths of the sea, she hurries to his side, regretting that his brief life should be marred by so much sorrow. When he swears to avenge his friend, she entreats him to wait until the morrow, that she may procure him new armour from Vulcan. Having obtained this promise, she hastens away to visit the god and bespeak his aid in behalf of her son.

Meanwhile the Greeks, who are trying to bear away the remains of Patroclus, are hard pressed by the Trojans, and Juno sends word that Achilles must intervene. Hampered by the lack of armour and by his promise to his mother, the hero ventures only as far as the trench, where, however, he utters so threatening a war-cry that the Trojans flee, and the Greeks are thus able to bring Patroclus' body safely into camp, just as the sun sets and the day's fighting ends.

Having unharnessed their steeds, the Trojans assemble to consider whether it will not be best to retreat within their walls, for they know that Achilles will appear on the morrow to avenge Patroclus. But Hector so vehemently insists upon their maintaining the advantage gained, that they encamp on the plain, where Jupiter predicts that Juno's wish will be granted and that her favourite Achilles will win great glory.

That night Thetis visits Vulcan's forge, and in the attitude of a suppliant implores the divine blacksmith to make new armour for her son. Vulcan not only consents, but hurries off to his anvil, where he and the Cyclopes labour to such good purpose that a magnificent suit of armour is ready by dawn.

Book XIX

Aurora has barely risen from the bosom of the sea, when Thetis enters her son's tent, bearing these wonderful weapons. Finding him still weeping over his friend's remains, Thetis urges him to rouse himself and fight. At the sight of the armour she brings, Achilles' ardour is so kindled that he vows he will avenge his friend. Pleased to think that the Greeks will have the help of this champion, Agamemnon humbly apologizes for the past, proffering gifts and a feast, which latter Achilles refuses to attend so long as Patroclus is unavenged. Before entering into battle, however, our hero implores his divine steeds to do their best, only to be warned by one of them (Xanthus) that, although they will save him to-day, the time is fast coming when he too will fall a victim to the anger of the gods. Undaunted by this prophecy, Achilles jumps into his chariot and sets out for the fray.

> "Xanthus, why thus predict my coming fate ?
> It ill beseems thee ! Well I know myself
> That I am fated here in Troy to die,
> Far from my home and parents ; yet withal
> I cease not, till these Trojans from the field
> Before me fly." He said, and to the front,
> His war-cry shouting, urg'd his fiery steeds.

Helen on the Walls of Troy 34

Lord Leighton

By Permission of Henry Graves and Co., Ltd.

Book XX

The gods, assembled on Mount Olympus, are told by Jupiter that, whereas he intends merely to witness the fight, they may all take part in it, provided they remember that Achilles is to reap the main honours of the day. The gods dart off to side with Troy and Greece, as their inclinations prompt, and thus take an active part in the battle, for which Jupiter gives the signal by launching a thunderbolt. The gods not only fight against each other on this day, but use all their efforts to second their favourites in every way. Before long, however, it becomes so evident they are merely delaying the inevitable issue, that they agree to withdraw from the field, leaving the mortals to settle their own destinies.

There are vivid descriptions of personal encounters, including one between Achilles and Aeneas, wherein both heroes indulge in boastful speeches before coming to blows. At one time, when Aeneas is about to be worsted, the gods, knowing that he is reserved for greater things, snatch him from the battle-field and convey him to a place of safety. Thus miraculously deprived of his antagonist, Achilles resumes his quest for Hector, who has hitherto been avoiding him, but who, on seeing one of his brothers fall beneath the Greek's blows, meets him bravely. But, as the moment of Hector's death has not yet come, the gods separate these two fighters, although their hatred is such that whenever they catch a glimpse of each other, they rush forward to renew the fight.

Book XXI

Fleeing before the Greeks, the Trojans reach the river Xanthus, into which Achilles plunges after them, and where, after killing hosts of enemies, he secures a dozen prisoners to sacrifice on his friend's tomb. Hearing Achilles refuse mercy to a young Trojan, and enraged because his bed is choked with corpses, the River God suddenly rises to chide him, but Achilles is now in so defiant a mood that he is ready to fight even the gods themselves. In spite of his courage he would, however, be drowned did not Neptune and Minerva come to his rescue; they assure him that Hector will soon lie lifeless at his feet, and Vulcan is summoned to fight the waters with fire.

His fair stream bubbling up,
As when a cauldron, on a blazing fire,
Fill'd with the melting fat of well-fed swine,
Boils up within, and bubbles all around,
With well-dried wood beneath, so bubbling up
The waters of the lovely River boil'd :
Nor onward would he flow, but check'd his course,
By the hot blast o'er-borne, and fiery strength
Of skilful Vulcan.

The course of this day's fighting is anxiously watched by old King Priam from the ramparts of Troy, and, when he sees Achilles' forces pursuing his fleeing army across the plain, he orders the gates to be opened to admit the fugitives, and quickly closed again so that the foe cannot follow. To facilitate this move, Apollo assumes the guise of Hector and decoys Achilles away from the gates until the bulk of the Trojan army is safe.

Book XXII

Meanwhile the real Hector is stationed beside the gate, and Achilles, suddenly realizing that he has been pursuing a mere phantom, darts with a cry of wrath toward his foe. Hector's parents implore him to seek refuge within the walls, but the young man is too brave to accept such advice. Still, when he sees the fire in Achilles' eyes, he cannot resist an involuntary recoil, and turning, flees, with Achilles in close pursuit, hurling taunts at him.

These warriors circle the citadel, until the gods, who are looking on, knowing they can no longer defer Hector's death, but wishing it to be glorious, send Apollo down to urge him to fight. In the guise of one of Hector's brothers, this god offers to aid him, and, thus supported, Hector turns to meet Achilles, with whom before fighting he tries to bargain that the victor shall respect the remains of the vanquished. But Achilles refuses to listen to terms, and in the course of the ensuing duel is ably seconded by Minerva, while Hector, who depends upon his supposed brother to supply him with weapons when his own fail, is basely deserted by Apollo.

Hector is disarmed, and Achilles finally deals him a deadly blow, loudly proclaiming that he shall be a prey to vultures and wolves. Hector curses his conqueror and dies, predicting that Achilles shall be slain by Paris. His victim having breathed his last, Achilles ties him by the heels to his chariot, and drives off with Hector's noble head trailing in the dust!

Meantime Andromache, who is preparing for her husband's return, is so startled by loud cries that she rushes toward the ramparts to find out what has occurred. Arriving there just in time to see her husband dragged away, she faints at the pitiful sight, and, on coming back to her senses, bewails her sad lot, foresees an unhappy fate for her infant son, and laments that she cannot bury her beloved husband.

Book XXIII

On reaching his tent with his victim, Achilles drags it round Patroclus' remains, apostrophizing him and assuring him that twelve Trojans shall be executed on his pyre, while his slayer's body shall be cast to the dogs. Then, having thrown Hector's corpse on the refuse heap, Achilles assembles the Greeks in his tent for a funeral repast, after which they retire, leaving him to mourn. That night he is visited by Patroclus' spirit, which warns him that he also must soon die, and bespeaks funeral rites. This vision convinces Achilles that the human soul does not perish with the body, and impels him to rouse his companions at dawn to erect a huge pyre on the shore, where innumerable victims are to be sacrificed to satisfy his friend's spirit. Then he renews his promise that Hector's body shall be a prey to the dogs, unaware that Venus has mounted guard over it so that no harm may befall it.

In describing the building and lighting of the pyre, the poet relates how the flames were fanned by opposite winds, depicts the sacrifices offered, the funeral games celebrated, and sets forth how the ashes were finally placed in an urn, which was destined to receive also the remains of Achilles.

Book XXIV

While most of the Greek warriors are resting after the strenuous exertions of the day, Achilles weeps in his tent until daybreak, when he harnesses his horses to his chariot and again drags Hector's body around Patroclus' tomb, still unaware that Venus and Apollo guard it from all harm. It is only on the twelfth day after Patroclus' death, that the gods interfere in behalf of the Trojans, and send Iris to Priam to guide him to Achilles' tent, where they assure him his prayers will obtain his son's body. The rainbow goddess brings the mourning father unseen into Achilles' tent, where, falling at the hero's feet, the aged Priam sues in such touching terms that the Greek warrior's heart melts and tears stream down his cheeks. He willingly grants Priam's request, and assures him that he is far happier than Peleus, since he still has several sons to cheer him although Hector has been slain.

Within Achilles' breast
Fond mem'ry of his father rose ; he touch'd
The old man's hand, and gently put him by ;
Then wept they both, by various mem'ries stirr'd :
One, prostrate at Achilles' feet, bewail'd
His warrior son ; Achilles for his sire,
And for Patroclus wept, his comrade dear ;
And through the house their weeping loud was heard.
But when Achilles had indulg'd his grief,
And eas'd the yearning of his heart and limbs,
He rose, and with his hand the aged sire
He rais'd.

Still guided by Iris, Priam conveys the body of his son back to Troy, where his mother, his wife, and the other Trojan women utter a touching lament. Then a funeral pyre is built, and the *Iliad* of Homer closes with brave Hector's obsequies.

THE ODYSSEY

Book I

Homer's second great epic covers a period of forty-two days. After the opening invocation he proceeds to relate the adventures of Ulysses. Nearly ten years have elapsed since the taking of Troy, when the gods looking down from Olympus behold him—sole survivor of his troop—stranded on the Island of Calypso. After some mention of the fate of the other Greeks, Jupiter decrees that Ulysses shall return to Ithaca, where many suitors are besieging his wife Penelope. In obedience to this decree, Pallas (Minerva) dons golden sandals—which permit her to flit with equal ease over land and sea—and visits Ithaca, where Ulysses' son, Telemachus, mournfully views the squandering of his father's wealth. Here she is hospitably received, and, after some conversation, urges Telemachus to visit the courts of Nestor and Menelaus to inquire of these kings whether his father is dead.

Telemachus has just promised to follow the advice of the goddess, when the suitors' bard begins the recital of the woes which have befallen the various Greek chiefs on their return from Troy. These sad strains attract Penelope, who passionately beseeches the bard not to enhance her sorrows by his songs!

Assuming a tone of authority for the first time, Telemachus bids his mother retire and pray, then, addressing the suitors, vows that unless they depart he will call down upon them the vengeance of the gods. His words are resented by these men, who continue their revelry until the night, when Telemachus retires, to dream of his projected journey.

Book II

At dawn, Telemachus rises and betakes himself to the market-place, where in public council he complains of the suitors' depredations, and announces that he is about to depart in quest of his sire. In reply to his denunciations the suitors accuse Penelope of deluding them, instancing how she promised to choose a husband as soon as she had finished weaving a winding sheet for her father-in-law Laertes. But, instead of completing this task as soon as possible, she unravelled by night the work done during the day, until the suitors discovered how they were being tricked.

"Thus then all of the day at the spacious loom she was weaving;
During the night she unravelled the web with her torches beside her.
Three long years with her secret device she befooled the Achaeans;
Till, when the fourth year came, and as season was followed by season,
Then at the last (since one of her women, who knew it, had told us),
While at the loom her magnificent web she unravelled, we caught her.
Thus was she forced, though sorely unwilling, to finish her labour."[1]

They now suggest that Telemachus send Penelope back to her father, but the youth indignantly refuses, and the council closes while he prays for vengeance. That he has not been unheard is proved by the appearance of two eagles, which peck out the eyes of some of the spectators. This is interpreted by an old man as an omen of Ulysses' speedy return, and he admonishes all present to prove faithful, lest they incur their master's wrath.

The assembly having dispersed, Telemachus hastens down to the shore, where Minerva visits him in the guise of his tutor Mentor, and instructs him to arrange for secret departure. Telemachus, therefore, returns to the palace, where the suitors are preparing a new feast. Refusing to join their

[1] The quotations from the *Odyssey* are taken from H. B. Cotterill's translation (George G. Harrap & Company).

revels, he seeks his old nurse Eurycleia, to whom he entrusts the provisioning of his vessel, bidding her if possible conceal his departure from Penelope for twelve days. Meantime, in the guise of Telemachus, Minerva scours the town to secure skilful oarsmen, and at sunset has a vessel ready to sail. Then, returning to the palace, she enchains the senses of the suitors in such deep slumber that Telemachus effects his departure unseen, and embarking with Mentor sets sail, his vessel speeding smoothly over the waves all night.

Book III

At sunrise Telemachus reaches Pylos and finds Nestor and his friends offering a sacrifice on the shore. Joining the feasters—who gather by fifties round tables groaning under the weight of nine oxen apiece—Telemachus makes known his name and errand. In return, Nestor mentions the deaths of Patroclus and Achilles, the taking of Troy, and the Greeks' departure from its shores. He adds that, the gods having decreed they should not reach home without sore trials, half the army lingered behind with Agamemnon to offer propitiatory sacrifices, while the rest sailed away. Among these were Nestor and Ulysses, but, while the former pressed on and reached home, the latter, turning back to pacify the gods, was seen no more. Since his return, Nestor has been saddened by the death of Agamemnon, slain on his arrival at Mycenae by his faithless wife Clytemnestra and her lover Aegisthus. His brother, Menelaus, more fortunate, has recently reached home, having been long delayed in Egypt by contrary winds.

While Nestor recounts these tales, day declines,

so he invites Telemachus to his palace for the night, promising to send him on the morrow to Sparta, where he can question Menelaus himself. Mentor urges Telemachus to accept this invitation, but declares that he must return to the ship, and vanishes in the shape of a bird, thus revealing to all present his divine origin. A sumptuous meal in the palace follows, and the guest, after a night's rest, participates at break of day in a solemn sacrifice.

Book IV

Riding in a chariot skilfully guided by one of Nestor's sons, Telemachus next speeds on to Sparta, where he finds Menelaus celebrating the marriages of a daughter and son. On learning that strangers have arrived, Menelaus orders every attention to be shown them, and after they have been refreshed by food and drink, inquires their errand. He states that he himself reached home only after wandering for seven years, and adds that he often yearns to know what has become of Ulysses. At this name the tears of Telemachus flow, and Helen, who has just appeared, is struck by his resemblance to his father. When Telemachus admits his identity, Menelaus and Helen mingle their tears with his, for the memory of the past overwhelms them with sorrow. To banish care, Helen casts 'nepenthe' into the wine, and, thanks to this beneficent drug, all soon forget their woes. She next relates how Ulysses once entered Troy in the guise of a beggar, and how she alone recognized him in spite of his disguise. This reminds Menelaus of the time when Ulysses restrained him and the other Greeks in the wooden horse, and when Helen circled round it mimicking the voices of their wives!

Soothed by 'nepenthe,' all retire to rest, and when morning dawns Telemachus inquires whether Menelaus knows aught of his father. All the information Menelaus can vouchsafe is that when he surprised Proteus counting sea-calves on the island of Pharos, he was told he would reach home only after making due sacrifices in Egypt to appease the gods, that his brother had been murdered on arriving at Mycenae, and that Ulysses—sole survivor of his crew—was detained by Calypso in an island, whence he had no means of escape. The sea-god had further promised that Menelaus should never die, stating that, as husband of Helen and son-in-law of Jupiter, he should enjoy everlasting bliss in the Elysian Fields. Then, after describing the sacrifices which ensured his return to Sparta, Menelaus invites Telemachus to tarry with him, although the youth insists that he must return home.

Meantime the suitors in Ulysses' palace entertain themselves with games, in the midst of which they learn that Telemachus has gone. Realizing that if he were dead Penelope's fortunate suitor would become possessor of all Ulysses' wealth, they decide to man a vessel to guard the port and slay Telemachus on his return. This plot is overheard by a servant, who hastens to report it to Penelope. On learning that her son has ventured out to sea, she wrings her hands, and reviles the nurse who abetted his departure, until this wise woman advises her rather to pray for her son's safe return. While Penelope is offering propitiatory sacrifices, the suitors dispatch a vessel in Antinous' charge to lie in wait for the youth. But, during the sleep which overcomes Penelope after her prayers, she is favoured by a vision, in which her sister assures her that Telemachachus will soon be restored to her, although she refuses to give her any information in regard to Ulysses.

Book V

Aurora has barely announced the return of day to gods and men, when Jupiter assembles his council on Mount Olympus. There Minerva pleads in favour of Ulysses, demanding that he be at last allowed to return home and that his son be saved from the suitors' ambush. In reply Jupiter sends Mercury to bid Calypso provide her unwilling guest with the means to leave her shores. Donning his golden sandals, the messenger-god flits to the island of Ogygia, enters Calypso's wonderful cave, and delivers his message. Although reluctant to let Ulysses depart, Calypso—not daring to oppose the will of Jupiter—goes in quest of her guest. Finding him gazing tearfully in the direction of home, she promises to supply him with the means to build a raft which, thanks to the gods, will enable him to reach Ithaca.

After a copious repast and a night's rest, Ulysses fells twenty trees and constructs a raft, in which, after it has been provisioned by Calypso, he sets sail. For seventeen days the stars serve as his guides, and he is nearing the island of Phaeacia, when Neptune becomes aware that his hated foe is about to escape. One stroke of the sea-god's mighty trident then stirs up a tempest which dashes the raft to pieces, and Ulysses is in imminent danger of perishing, when the sea-nymph Leucothea gives him her life-preserving scarf, bidding him cast it back into the waves when it has borne him safely to land! Buoyed up by this scarf, Ulysses finally reaches land.

On to the rock-bound shore he was borne by a billow enormous.
Here had his skin been stript and his bones all broken in pieces,
Had not the thought been put in his heart by the goddess Athene
Suddenly forward to dart and to clutch with his hands on a boulder,
Clinging to which with a groan he awaited the rush of the roller.
This he withstood and escaped it; but seaward recoiling the billow
Leapt on him, smote him and hurled him away far out on the ocean.
E'en as it haps when a cuttle is dragged from its hole by a fisher
While to its tentacle-tips full many a pebble is clinging,
Thus by the jags of the rock from the strong bold hands of Odysseus
Stript was the skin as the mountainous billow descended upon him.
Now had the hapless Odysseus despite all destiny perished,
Had not a fortunate thought been sent by the goddess Athene.
Steering him clear of the surf of the surge that was thundering landward,
Further he coasted along and he gazed at the land to discover
Beaches that slope to the water or sheltering creeks of the ocean.
Then at the last to the mouth of a river of beautiful waters
Swimming he came.

Having reached the shore, and returned to the ocean the sea-nymph's scarf, Ulysses buries himself in dead leaves and sinks into an exhausted sleep.

Book VI

While Ulysses is thus sleeping, Minerva, in a dream, admonishes Nausicaa, daughter of Alcinous, King of Phaeacia, to wash her garments in readiness for her wedding. On awakening, the Princess, after bespeaking a chariot with mules to draw the clothes to the washing place, departs with her maids for the shore.

The clothes having been washed and hung out

to dry, the Princess and her attendants play ball, until their loud merriment awakens Ulysses. Veiling his nakedness behind leafy branches he timidly approaches the maidens, and addresses them from afar. Convinced that he is, as he represents, a shipwrecked man in need of aid, the Princess provides him with garments, and directs him to follow her chariot to the confines of the city. There he is to wait until she has reached home before presenting himself before her parents, as she does not wish his presence in her company to cause gossip in the town.

Book VII

Having left Ulysses behind her, Nausicaa returns to her home, where her chariot is unloaded; but shortly after she has retired, Ulysses, guided by Minerva in disguise, enters the town and palace unseen. It is only when, obeying Nausicaa's instructions, he seeks her mother's presence and beseeches her aid, that he becomes visible to all. King and Queen gladly promise their protection to the suppliant, who, while partaking of food, describes himself as a shipwrecked mariner and asks to be sent home. After he has refreshed himself, the Queen, who has recognized the clothes he wears, learning how he obtained them, delights in her daughter's charity and prudence. Then she and her husband promise the wanderer their protection before retiring to rest.

Book VIII

At daybreak the King conducts his guest to the public square, where Minerva has summoned all the inhabitants. To this assembly Alcinous makes known that a nameless stranger bespeaks their aid, and proposes that after a banquet, where blind Demodocus will entertain them with his songs, they load the suppliant with gifts and send him home.

The festive meal is in progress when the bard begins singing of a quarrel between Ulysses and Achilles, strains which so vividly recall happier days that Ulysses, drawing his cloak over his head, gives way to tears. Noting this emotion, Alcinous checks the bard and proposes games. After displaying their skill in racing, wrestling, discus-throwing, etc., the contestants mockingly challenge Ulysses to give an exhibition of his proficiency in games of strength and skill. Stung by their covert taunts the stranger casts the discus far beyond their best mark, and avers that although out of practice he is not afraid to match them in feats of strength, admitting, however, that he cannot compete with them in fleetness of foot or in the dance. His prowess in one line and frank confession of inferiority in another disarm further criticism, and the young men dance until the bard begins singing of Vulcan's stratagem to punish a faithless spouse.[1]

All the Phaeacians now present gifts to the stranger, who finds himself rich indeed, but who assures Nausicaa he will never forget that she was the first to lend him aid. Toward the close of the festivities the blind bard sings of the wooden horse devised by Ulysses and abandoned on the shore by the retreating Greeks. Then he describes its triumphant entry into Troy, where for the first time in ten years all sleep soundly without dread of a surprise. But,

[1] See chapter on Venus in the author's *The Myths of Greece and Rome*.

while the too confident Trojans are thus resting peacefully upon their laurels, the Greeks, emerging from this wooden horse, open the gates to their comrades, and the sack of Troy begins.

Such was the story he sang, this singer renowned ; and Odysseus
Melted in tears and the great drops fell on his cheeks from his eyelids.
E'en as a woman with wailings her well-loved husband embraceth
Fallen in front of the city, in front of the host of the fighters, . . .
So did the pitiful tears fall fast from the eyes of Odysseus.
Thus then weeping he sat and unnoted of all of the others,
All save Alcinous, who alone was aware and observed it,
Sitting anigh to his side ; and hearing him heavily groaning,
Quickly he turned to the lovers of oars, Phaeacia's princes :
"Hearken, I pray, to my words, Phaeacian leaders and chieftains !
Time is for Demodocus from his clear-toned lute to refrain him,
Seeing that not to us all seems pleasing the song that he singeth.
Since our supper began and the godlike singer aroused him
Never as yet hath the stranger with pitiful grieving and groaning
Ceased to lament."

Alcinous asks the stranger guest whether he has lost some relative in the war of Troy, and finally begs him to relate his adventures.

Book IX

Thus invited to speak, Ulysses, after introducing himself and describing his island home, relates how, when the ruin of Troy was completed, he and his men left the Trojan shores. Driven by winds to Ismarus, they sacked the town, but, instead of sailing off immediately with their booty as Ulysses urged, tarried there until surprised by their foes, from whom they were glad to escape with their lives. Tossed by a tempest for many days, the Greek ships next neared the land of the Lotus-Eaters, people who feasted upon the buds and blossoms of a narcotic lotus. Sending three men ashore to reconnoitre, Ulysses vainly awaited their return; finally, suspecting what had happened, he went in quest of them himself, only to find that having partaken of the lotus they were dead to the calls of home and ambition. Seizing these men, Ulysses conveyed them bound to his ship, and, without allowing the rest to land, sailed hastily away from those pernicious shores.

Before long he came to the land of the Cyclopes, and disembarked on a small neighbouring island to renew his stock of food and water. Then, unwilling to depart without having at least visited the Cyclopes, he took twelve of his bravest men, a skin-bottle full of delicious wine, and set out to find Polyphemus, chief of the Cyclopes. On entering the huge cave where this giant pursued his avocation of dairyman, Ulysses and his companions built a fire, round which they sat awaiting their host's return. Before long a huge one-eyed monster drove in his flocks, and, after closing the opening of his cave with a rock which no one else could move, proceeded to milk his ewes and make cheese.

It was only while at supper that he noticed Ulysses and his men, who humbly approached him as suppliants. After shrewdly questioning them to ascertain whether they were alone, believing Ulysses' tale that they were shipwrecked men, he seized and devoured two of them before he lay down to rest. Although sorely tempted to slay him while he was thus at their mercy, Ulysses refrained, knowing that he and his companions would never be able to move the rock.

At dawn the giant again milked his flock, and

devoured two more Greeks. Then he easily rolled aside the rock, which he replaced when he and his flock had gone out for the day, thus imprisoning Ulysses and his eight surviving men.

During that long day Ulysses sharpened to a point a young olive, and, after hardening this weapon in the fire, secured by lot the helpers whom he needed to execute his plan. That evening Polyphemus, having finished his household tasks and his cannibal repast, graciously accepted the wine which Ulysses offered him. Pleased with its taste, he even promised the giver a reward if he would only state his name. The wily Ulysses declaring that he was called Noman, the giant facetiously promised to eat him last, before he fell into a drunken sleep. Then Ulysses and his four men, heating the pointed pine, bored out the eye of Polyphemus, who howled with pain:

> "Then did I thrust me the stake in the midst of the embers to make it
> Fiery hot, and with comforting words I addressed my companions,
> Giving them courage lest any in fear might fail and desert me.
> So, when at last that stake sharp-pointed of olive was almost
> Bursting to flame, though green was the wood, and was terribly glowing,
> Then did I fetch it anigh from the fire, and around it my comrades
> Posted themselves, and courage immense some deity gave us.
> Seizing the stake all glowing and sharp at the point, with a strong thrust
> Into the eye full deeply they drove it; and I at the top end
> Twisted it round, as a man that is boring the beam of a vessel
> Bores with an auger, and others below with the leather revolve it,
> Holding by both ends fast, as the auger is ceaselessly spinning.
> Thus in his eye did we bore, and the stake sharp-pointed and glowing
> Twisted about, red-hot; and the blood ran spluttering round it.

Then did the breath of the flame scorch all of his eyelid and eyebrow,
While consumed was the ball of the eye, and the roots of it crackled."

His fellow Cyclopes, awakened by his cries, gathered without his cave, asking what was the matter. But, hearing him vehemently howl that Noman was hurting him, they all declared that he was evidently being punished by the gods and left him to his plight!

When morning came, the groaning Cyclops rolled aside the rock, standing beside it with arms outstretched to catch his prisoners should they attempt to escape. But Ulysses tied his men under the sheep, and, clinging to the fleece of the biggest ram, was thus also dragged out of the cave. Passing his hand over the backs of the sheep to make sure that the strangers were not riding on them, Polyphemus recognized by touch his favourite ram, and feelingly ascribed its slow pace to sympathy with his woes.

"Last of the flock came slowly the ram, and he paced to the doorway
Cumbered with all of his wool and weighted with me and my cunning.
Him too handled and thus accosted the huge Polyphemus:
'What is the reason, my pet, thou art issuing forth from the cavern
Last of the flock? Not ever before wast led by the others,
Nay, but afar in the front didst graze fresh blooms of the meadows
Mightily striding, and first didst come to the streams of the rivers;
First too ever 'tis thou who at eveningtide to the homestead
Longst to return—while now thou art last! Ay surely thou grievest,
Mourning the eye of thy lord, that an impious mortal hath blinded,
He and his fellows accursèd, my wits with his wine overcoming—

Ulysses and Polyphemus
Patten Wilson

Nobody. . . . Ah, but I deem he is not yet safe from destruction!
Verily, hadst thou but feeling as I and the power of speaking,
So as to tell me the place where shunning my wrath he is skulking,
Then all over the cavern his brains were this way and that way
Dashed on the ground as I crushed him to death, and happy my heart were,
Lightened of all the woe that a worthless Nobody brought me.' "

Once out of the cave, Ulysses cut the bonds of his men, with whose aid he drove part of Polyphemus' flock on board his ship, which he had hidden in a cove. He and his companions were scudding safely past the headland where blind Polyphemus idly sat, when Ulysses tauntingly raised his voice to make known his escape and real name. With a cry of rage, the giant flung huge masses of rock in the direction of his voice, hotly vowing that his father Neptune would yet avenge his wrongs!

Book X

After leaving the island of the Cyclopes, Ulysses visited Aeolus, king of the winds, and was hospitably entertained in his cave. In token of friendship and to enable Ulysses to reach home quickly, Aeolus confined all the contrary winds, letting loose only those which would speed him on his way. On leaving Aeolus, Ulysses so carefully guarded the skin-bottle containing the adverse gales that his men believed it must contain jewels of great price. For nine days and nights Ulysses guided the rudder, and only when the shores of Ithaca came in sight closed his eyes in sleep. This moment was seized by his crew to open the bottle, whence the captive winds escaped with a roar, stirring up a hurricane which finally drove them back to the isle of Aeolus.

"'Many a treasure he bringeth from Troy, magnificent prizes
Out of the booty; but we, who the selfsame journey have ended,
Homeward return nought having withal save hands that are empty.
This too sure is a gift which lately hath lavished in friendship
Aeolus. Come now, quick let us spy what is here and discover
How great treasure of gold and of silver is stowed in the wallet.'
Thus did they speak, and the men were won by the counsel of mischief.
Loosing the bag they untied it—and out rushed every storm-wind,
Seized them with might of a tempest and carried them suddenly seaward
Wailing and weeping, afar from the land of their fathers; whereat I
Waked from my slumber, and straight with my spirit unerring I communed
Whether to leap from the ship and to seek for my death in the waters,
Or to endure it in silence and still to remain with the living.
Well—I endured and remained, and wrapt in my cloak on the vessel
Lay, as the ships went on, by the terrible blast of the storm-wind
Back to the isle Aeolian borne, midst groans of my comrades."

On seeing them return with tattered sails, Aeolus was convinced that they had incurred the wrath of some god and therefore drove them away from his realm. Toiling at the oar, they reached, after seven days, the harbour of the Laestrygonians, cannibal giants, from whose clutches only a few ships escaped. Sorrowing for their lost friends, the Greeks next landed in the island of Circe, where Ulysses remained with half his men by the ships, while the rest set out to renew their supplies. This party soon discovered the abode of the enchantress Circe, who, aware of their approach, had prepared a banquet and a magic drug. Enticed by her sweet voice, all the men save one sat down to her banquet, and ate so greedily that the enchantress, contemptuously waving her wand over them, bade them assume the forms of the animals they most resembled! A moment later a herd of grunting pigs surrounded her, pigs which, however, retained a distressing consciousness of their former human estate.

"Bringing them into her palace she set them on chairs and on couches,
Mixed them of cheese and of meal and of yellow honey a batter
Mingled with Pramnian wine, and noxious drugs of enchantment
Added, that all might utterly fail to remember their homeland.
Now so soon he had drained what she gave him, behold, of a sudden
Smiting the man with her wand she imprisoned him close in a pig-sty,
Having already the head of a pig and the voice and the bristles,
Ay and the body, but reason remaining unchanged as aforetime.
Thus imprisoned in sties they made lamentation, and Circe
Flung to them acorns and mast of the ilex and fruit of the cornel,
Food that by wallowing swine is at all times greedily eaten."

This dire transformation was viewed with horror by the man lurking outside, who fled back to the ships, imploring Ulysses to depart. Unwilling to desert his men, Ulysses on the contrary set out for Circe's dwelling, meeting on the way thither Mercury in disguise, who gave him an herb to annul the effect of Circe's drugs and directed him how to free his companions.

Following these instructions, Ulysses entered Circe's abode, partook of the refreshments offered him, and, when she waved her wand over him, threatened to kill her unless she restored his men to their wonted forms! The terrified Circe not only complied, but detained Ulysses and his companions with her a full year. As at the end of that time the men pleaded to return home, Ulysses told his hostess that he must leave her. She then informed him that he must first visit the Cimmerian shore and consult the shade of the blind seer Tiresias. The prospect of such a journey greatly alarmed Ulysses, but when Circe had instructed him how to proceed, he bravely set out.

Wafted by favourable winds, Ulysses' ship soon reached the country of eternal night. On landing there he dug a trench, slew the black victims which Circe had given him, and with drawn sword awaited the approach of a host of shades, among whom he recognized a man killed by accident on Circe's island, who begged for proper funeral rites. By Circe's order, Ulysses, after allowing the ghost of Tiresias to partake of the victims' blood, learned from him that, although pursued by Neptune's vengeance, he and his men would reach home safely, provided they respected the Cattle of the Sun on the island of Trinacria. The seer added that all who attacked them would perish, and that, even if he should escape death and return home, he must slay his wife's insolent suitors before he could rest in peace.

After this had been accomplished Ulysses was to resume his wanderings until he came to a land where the oar which he carried would be mistaken for a winnowing fan. There he was to offer a propitiatory sacrifice to Neptune, after which he would live to serene old age and die peacefully among his own people. His conversation with Tiresias finished, Ulysses interviewed his mother—of whose demise he had not been aware—and conversed with the shades of women noted for having borne sons to gods or to famous heroes.

Book XI

This account had been heard with breathless interest by the Phaeacians, whose king now implored Ulysses to proceed. The hero then described his interview with the ghost of Agamemnon—slain by his wife and her paramour on his return from Troy—who predicted his safe return home, and begged for tidings of his son Orestes, of whom Ulysses knew nought. Ulysses next beheld Achilles, who, although ruler of the dead, bitterly declared that he would rather be the meanest labourer on earth than monarch among shades!

> " 'Speak not smoothly of death, I beseech, O famous Odysseus !
> Better by far to remain on the earth as the thrall of another,
> E'en of a portionless man that hath means right scanty for living,
> Rather than reign sole king in the realm of the bodiless phantoms.' "

To comfort him, Ulysses described how bravely his son had fought at the taking of Troy, where he had been one of the men in the wooden horse. The only shade which refused to approach Ulysses was that of Ajax, who still resented his having won the armour of Achilles. Besides these shades, Ulysses beheld the judges of Hades and the famous culprits of Tartarus. But, terrified by the " innumerable nation of the dead " crowding around him, he finally fled in haste to his vessel, and was soon wafted back to Circe's shore.

Book XII

There Ulysses buried his dead companion, and, after describing his visit to Hades, begged his hostess' permission to depart. Circe consented, warning him to beware of the Sirens, of the threatening rocks, of the monster Scylla and the whirlpool Charybdis on either side of the Messenian Strait, and of the cattle of Trinacria, giving him minute directions how to escape unharmed from all these perils.

Morning having come, Ulysses took leave of Circe, and, on nearing the reef of the Sirens, directed his men to bind him fast to the mast, paying no heed to his gestures, after he had stopped their ears with soft wax. In this way he heard, without perishing, the Sirens' wonderful song, and it was only when it had died away in the distance and the spell had ceased that his men unbound him from the mast.

> "Thus did they call as they sang with a beautiful voice, and within me
> Fain was the heart to obey, and to loose me I ordered my comrades,
> Frowning and nodding—but forward they bent them, incessantly rowing,
> While rose Eurylochus, rose also his mate Perimedes,
> Bound me with bonds still more and with cordage fettered me firmly.
> Then, so soon we had gotten us further, nor heard in the distance
> Longer was sound of the words or the voice of the song of the Sirens,
> Quickly my well-loved mates from their ears unloosened the beeswax
> Which I had smeared them withal, and out of my bonds they released me."

Not daring describe to his companions the threatened horrors of Charybdis and Scylla, Ulysses bade his steersman avoid the whirlpool, and, fully armed, prepared to brave the monster Scylla. But, notwithstanding his preparations, she snatched from his galley six men who were seen no more. Although reluctant to land on Trinacria, lest his sailors should steal the Cattle of the Sun, Ulysses was constrained to do so to allow them to rest. During their stay on the island, unfavourable winds began to blow, and continued so long that the Greeks consumed all their provisions, and, in spite of their efforts to supply their larder by hunting and fishing, began to suffer from hunger. During one of Ulysses' brief absences the men, breaking their promises, slew some of the Cattle of the Sun, which although slain moved and lowed as if still alive! Undeterred by such miracles, the men feasted, but, on embarking six days later, they were overtaken by a tempest in which all perished save Ulysses. Clinging to the mast of his wrecked ship, he drifted between Charybdis and Scylla, escaping from the whirlpool only by clinging to the branches of an overhanging fig-tree. Then, tossed by the waves for nine days longer, Ulysses was finally cast on the isle of Ogygia, whence he had come directly to Phaeacia as already described.

Book XIII

Having finished this account of his ten years' wanderings, Ulysses, after banqueting with Alcinous, was conveyed with his gifts to the ship which was to take him home. Then, while he slept in the prow, the skilful Phaeacian rowers entered a sheltered Ithacan bay, where they set sleeper and gifts ashore and departed without awaiting thanks. They were about to re-enter their own port when Neptune, discovering they had conveyed his enemy home, struck their vessel with his trident, thus transforming it into the galley-shaped rock still seen there to-day.

Meantime Ulysses, awakening, hid his treasures away in a cave. Then, accosted by Minerva in disguise, he gave a fantastic account of himself, to which she lent an amused ear, before revealing her identity and assuring him of his wife's fidelity.

She then told him of the insolence of the suitors lying in wait to murder Telemachus at his return, and suggested that Ulysses, in the guise of an aged beggar, should visit his faithful swineherd until the time should come to make his presence known.

Book XIV

Transformed by Minerva into a ragged beggar, Ulysses next visits the swineherd, who sets before him the best he has, complaining that the greedy suitors deplete his herds. This old servant is comforted when the beggar assures him that his master will soon return, and states that he has seen him lately. Ulysses' fictitious account of himself serves as entertainment until the hour for rest, when the charitable swineherd covers his guest with his best cloak.

Book XV

Meantime Minerva, hastening to Sparta, awakens in the heart of the sleeping Telemachus a keen desire to return home, warns him of the suitors' ambush, instructs him how to avoid it, and cautions him on his return to trust none save the women on whose fidelity he can depend. At dawn, therefore, Telemachus, after offering a sacrifice and receiving Menelaus' and Helen's parting gifts, sets out, cheered by favourable omens. Without pausing to visit Nestor—whose son is to convey his thanks—Telemachus embarks, and, following Minerva's instructions, lands near the swineherd's hut.

Book XVI

The swineherd is preparing breakfast, when Ulysses warns him that a friend is coming, for his dogs fawn upon the stranger and do not bark. A moment later Telemachus enters the hut, and is warmly welcomed by his servant, who wishes him to occupy the place of honour at his table. But Telemachus modestly declines it in favour of the aged stranger, to whom he promises clothes and protection as soon as he is master in his own house. Then he bids the swineherd notify his mother of his safe arrival, directing her to send word to Laertes of his return. This man has no sooner gone than Minerva restores Ulysses to more than his wonted vigour and good looks, bidding him make himself known to his son and concert with him how to dispose of the suitors. Amazed to see the beggar transformed into an imposing warrior, Telemachus is overjoyed to learn who he really is. The first transports of joy over, Ulysses advises his son to return home, lull the suitors' suspicions by specious words, and, after removing all weapons from the banquet hall, await the arrival of his father, who will appear in mendicant's guise.

While father and son are thus laying their plans, Telemachus' vessel reaches port, and the suitors mourn the escape of their victim. They dare not, however, attack Telemachus openly, for fear of forfeiting Penelope's regard, and assure her that they intend to befriend him. Meantime, having delivered his message to his mistress, the swineherd returns to his hut, where he spends the evening with Telemachus and the beggar, little suspecting that the latter is his master.

Book XVII

At daybreak Telemachus hastens back to the palace, whither the swineherd is to guide the stranger later in the day, and is rapturously embraced by his mother. After a brief interview, Telemachus sends her back to her apartment to efface the trace of her tears, adding that he is on his way to the market-place to meet a travelling companion whom he wishes to entertain. After welcoming this man with due hospitality, Telemachus gives his mother an account of his voyage. While he is thus occupied, Ulysses is wending his way to the palace, where he arrives just as the suitors' wonted revels reach their height. But as he enters the court-yard, his favourite hunting dog expires for joy on recognizing him.

> There he was lying—the poor old Argus, infested with vermin.
> Yet e'en now, as he looked and was ware that his master was present,
> Both of his ears down-dropping and wagging his tail he attempted
> Nearer to come to Odysseus his lord, but was wholly unable
> Thither to creep; and Odysseus averted his eyes as he saw it,
> Drying a tear, that he easily hid from his swineherd.

Humbly making the rounds of the tables like the beggar he seems, Ulysses is treated kindly by Telemachus, but grossly insulted by the suitors, one of whom, Antinous, actually flings a stool at him. Such a violation of the rights of hospitality causes some commotion in the palace, and so rouses the indignation of Penelope that she expresses a wish to converse with the beggar, who may have heard of her absent husband.

Book XVIII

Meantime Ulysses has also come into conflict with the town-beggar (Irus), a lusty youth, who challenges him to fight. To his dismay, Ulysses displays such a set of muscles on laying aside his

Ulysses and Irus
Patten Wilson

robe that the insolent challenger wishes to withdraw. He is, however, compelled by the suitors to fight, and is thoroughly beaten by Ulysses, whose strength arouses the suitors' admiration. Then, in reply to their questions, Ulysses favours them with another of those tales which do more honour to his imagination than to his veracity.

Penelope, meanwhile, has lain down to rest, and during her slumber Minerva restores all her youthful charms. Then she descends into the hall, to chide Telemachus for allowing a stranger to be insulted beneath his father's roof. She next remarks that she foresees she will soon have to choose a husband among the suitors present, as it is only too evident that Ulysses is dead, and, under pretext of testing their generosity, she induces them all to bestow upon her gifts, which she thriftily adds to her stores. Beside themselves with joy at the prospect that their long wooing will soon be over, the suitors sing and dance, until Telemachus advises them to return home.

Book XIX

The suitors having gone, Ulysses helps Telemachus to remove all the weapons, while the faithful nurse mounts guard over the palace women. Secretly helped by Minerva, father and son accomplish their task, and they are sitting before the fire when Penelope comes to ask the beggar to relate when and how he met Ulysses. This time the stranger gives so accurate a description of Ulysses, that Penelope, wishing to show him some kindness, summons the old nurse to bathe his feet. As she herself dozes while this homely task is being performed, she is not aware that the old nurse recognizes her master by a scar on his leg, and is cautioned by him not to make his presence known.

Now as the flat of her hand passed o'er it, the agéd attendant
Knew it at once by the touch. Down dropt she the foot she was holding.
On to the edge of the basin the leg struck sharply. The vessel
Clattered and rang as it fell on its side, upsetting the water.
Joy overwhelmed her together with grief, while gathering tear-drops
Flooded her eyes, and the flow of her clear-voiced utterance failed her.
Then, to the chin of Odysseus uplifting her hand, she addressed him:
"Yea, thou art truly Odysseus—my child! my belovéd! my master!"

Penelope wakens and resumes her conversation with the beggar, telling him she has been favoured by a dream portending the death of the suitors. Still, she realizes there are two kinds of dreams,—those that come true issuing from Somnus' palace by the gate of horn, while deceptive dreams pass through an ivory gate. After providing for the beggar's comfort, Penelope retires, and as usual spends most of the night mourning for her absent partner.

Book XX

Sleeping beneath the portico on the skins of the animals slain to feast the horde of suitors, Ulysses sees the maids slip out of the palace to join the suitors, who have wooed them surreptitiously. Then he falls asleep and is visited by Minerva, who infuses new strength and courage in his veins. At dawn Ulysses is awakened by Telemachus, and soon after the house is once more invaded by the suitors, who with their own hands slay the animals provided for their food. Once more they display their malevolence by ill-treating the beggar, and taunt Telemachus, who apparently pays no heed to their words.

Book XXI

Meanwhile Minerva has prompted Penelope to propose to the suitors to string Ulysses' bow and shoot an arrow through twelve rings. Armed with this weapon, and followed by handmaids bearing bowstring and arrows, Penelope appears in the banquet-hall, where the suitors eagerly accept her challenge. But, after Antinous has vainly striven to bend the bow, the others warily try various devices to ensure its pliancy.

Meantime, noticing that the swineherd and one of his companions—upon whose fidelity he counts—have left the hall, Ulysses follows them, makes himself known by his scar, and directs them how to act. Then, returning into the hall, he silently watches the suitors' efforts to bend the bow, and, when the last has tried and failed, volunteers to make the attempt, thereby rousing general ridicule. All gibes are silenced, however, when the beggar not only spans the bow, but sends his first arrow through the twelve rings. At the same time the faithful servants secure the doors of the apartment, and Telemachus, darting to his father's side, announces that he is ready to take part in the fray.

Book XXII

Casting his beggarly raiment aside, deep-plotting Odysseus
Leapt on the threshold of stone, still holding the bow and the quiver
Laden with bolts; and before him the swift-winged arrows he poured out

Close to his feet on the floor; and he spake, addressing the suitors:
"Lo, this fatal, calamitous contest is done—it is finished!
Now for a mark far other—a mark ne'er smit by a bowman!
This will I choose me, and see if renown shall be sent by Apollo."
Spake, and at Antinous directed the sharp-fanged arrow,
Just as he paused at the moment of lifting a beautiful goblet,
Golden, with handles at both of its sides; and already he held it,
Meaning to drink of the wine; and of death no thought or suspicion
Troubled his mind. (Would any believe in the midst of a banquet
One man, single among so many, however audacious,
Thus might compass his doom and plunge him in death and in darkness?)
Steadily aimed was the bolt of Odysseus: it struck on the gullet.
Pierced was the delicate neck right through by the point of the arrow.
Over he lurched; from his hand dropt crashing the cup, and he lay there
Mortally struck, while jetted a thick red stream of his life-blood
Out of his nostrils.

Gazing wildly around them for weapons or means of escape, the remaining suitors discover how cleverly they have been trapped. One after another now falls beneath the arrows of Ulysses, who bids his son hasten to the storeroom and procure arms for them both as there are not arrows enough to dispose of his foes. Through Telemachus' heedlessness in leaving the doors open, the suitors contrive to secure weapons too, and the fight in the hall rages until they all have been slain. Then the doors are thrown open, and the faithless maids are compelled to remove the corpses and purify the room, before they are hanged.

Book XXIII

The old nurse has in the meantime had the privilege of announcing Ulysses' safe return to his faithful retainers, and last of all to the sleeping Penelope. Unable to credit such tidings,—although the nurse assures her that she has seen his scar,—Penelope imagines that the suitors must have been slain by some god who has come to her rescue. She decides, therefore, to go down and congratulate her son upon being rid of those who preyed upon his wealth. Seeing that she does not immediately fall upon his father's neck, Telemachus hotly reproaches her, but she rejoins that she must have some proof of the stranger's identity, and is evidently repelled by his unprepossessing appearance. Ulysses thereupon suggests that all present purify themselves, don fresh garments, and partake of a feast, enlivened by the songs of their bard. While he is attended by the old nurse, Minerva sheds upon him such grace that, when he reappears, looking like a god, he dares reproach Penelope for not recognizing him. Then, hearing her order that his bed be removed to the portico, he asks who cut down the tree which formed one of its posts? As this fact is known only to Penelope and to the builder of the bed, she now falls upon Ulysses' neck, begging his forgiveness. Their joy at being united is marred only by Ulysses' determination soon to resume his travels, which he must pursue until Tiresias' prediction has been fulfilled. That night is spent in mutual confidences regarding all that has occurred during their twenty years' separation, and when morning dawns Ulysses and his son go to visit Laertes.

Book XXIV

Mindful of his office as conductor of souls to Hades, Mercury has meanwhile entered the palace of Ulysses, and, waving his wand, has summoned the spirits of the suitors, who, uttering plaintive cries, follow him down to the infernal regions.

Now were summoned the souls of the dead by Cyllenian Hermes,
Even the souls of the suitors. A rod in his hand he was holding,
Beautiful, golden, with which men's eyes he entranceth to slumber
Just as he wills, while others again from their sleep he awaketh.
Touched by the wand they awoke and obeyed him, and followed him squealing.
Even as bats in the dark mysterious depths of a cavern
Squeal as they flutter around, should one from the cluster be fallen
Where from the rock suspended they hung all clinging together,
So did the souls flock squealing behind him as Hermes the Helper
Guided them down to the gloom through dank and mouldering pathways.
Passing the Ocean's stream and the White Rock's glittering portal,
Passing the gates of the Sun and the shadowy regions of Dreamland,
Soon at the world of the dead they arrived and the asphodel meadow,
Where dwell spirits—the phantoms of those whose labour is ended.

There they overhear Ajax giving Achilles a minute account of his funeral—the grandest ever seen—and when questioned describe Penelope's stratagem in regard to the web and to Ulysses' bow.

Meanwhile Ulysses has arrived at his father's farm, where the old man is busy among his trees. To prepare Laertes for his return, Ulysses describes himself as a friend of the wanderer ere he makes himself known. Like Penelope, Laertes proves incredulous, until Ulysses points out the trees given him when a child and exhibits his scar.

Thus as he spake were loosened the knees and the heart of Laertes,
Since to himself he confessed that the token was sure that he gave him.
Stretching his arms to embrace him he sank in a swoon, but was holden
Clasped to the breast of his son, long-suffering godlike Odysseus.

To celebrate their reunion, a banquet is held, which permits the Ithacans to show their joy at their master's return. Meanwhile the friends of the suitors, having heard of the massacre, determine to avenge them by slaying father and son. But, aided by Minerva and Jupiter, these two heroes present so formidable an appearance, that the attacking party concludes a treaty, which restores peace to Ithaca and ends the *Odyssey*.

LATIN EPICS

LATIN literature took its source in the Greek, to which it owes much of its poetic beauty, for many of its masterpieces are either translations or imitations of the best Greek writings. There have been, for instance, numerous translations of the *Iliad* and *Odyssey*, the first famous one being by the 'father of Roman dramatic and epic poetry,' Livius Andronicus, who lived in the third century B.C. He also attempted to narrate Roman history in the same strain, by composing an epic of some thirty-five books which are lost.

Another poet, Naevius, a century later composed the *Cyprian Iliad*, as well as a heroic poem on the first Punic war (*Bellum Punicum*), of which only fragments have come down to us. Then, in the second century before our era, Ennius made a patriotic attempt to sing the origin of Rome in the *Annals*, in eighteen books, of which only parts remain, while Hostius wrote an epic entitied *Istria*, which has also perished. Lucretius' epic *On the Nature of Things* is considered an example of the astronomical or physical epic.

The Augustan age proved rich in epic poets, such as Publius Terentius Varro, translator of the *Argonautica* and author of a poem on Julius Caesar; Lucius Varius Rufus, whose poems are lost; and, greatest of all, Virgil, of whose last and greatest work, the *Aeneid*, a complete synopsis follows. Next to this greatest Latin poem ranks Lucan's *Pharsalia*, wherein he relates in ten books the rivalry between Caesar and Pompey, while his contemporary Statius, in his *Thebais*, and unfinished *Achilleis*, works over the time-honoured cycles of Thebes and Troy.

During the same period Silius Italicus supplied a lengthy poem on the second Punic war, and Valerius Flaccus a new translation or adaptation of the *Argonautica.*

In the second century of our own era Quintius Curtius composed an epic on Alexander, and in the third century Juvencus penned the first Christian epic, using the Life of Christ as his theme. In the fifth century Claudianus harked back to the old Greek myths of the battle of the Giants and of the Abduction of Persephone, although by that time Christianity was well established in Italy. From that epoch Roman literature practically ceased to exist, for although various attempts at Latin epics were made by mediaeval poets, none of them proved of sufficient merit to claim attention here.

THE AENEID

Book I

After stating that he is about to sing the deeds of the heroic ancestor of the Romans, Virgil describes how, seven years after escaping from burning Troy, Aeneas' fleet was overtaken by a terrible storm off the coast of Africa. This tempest, raised by the turbulent children of Aeolus at Juno's request, threatened before long to destroy the Trojan fleet. But, disturbed by the commotion overhead and by Aeneas' prayers for help, Neptune suddenly arose from the bottom of the sea, angrily ordered the winds back to their cave, and summoned sea-nymphs and tritons to the Trojans' aid. Soon thereafter seven of the vessels came to anchor in a sheltered bay, where Aeneas landed with his friend Achates. While reconnoitring, they killed seven stags with which to satisfy the hunger of their men, whom Aeneas further cheered by the assurance that they were the destined ancestors of a mighty people.

Meanwhile Venus, beholding the plight of her son Aeneas, had hastened off to Olympus to remind Jupiter of his promise to protect the remnant of the Trojan race. Bestowing a kiss, the King of the Gods assured her that after many vicissitudes Aeneas would reach Italy, where in due time his son would found Alba Longa. Jupiter added a brief sketch of what would befall this hero's race, until, some three hundred years after his death, one of his descendants, the Vestal Ilia, would bear twin sons to Mars, god of War. One of these, Romulus, would found the city of Rome, where the Trojan race would continue its heroic career and where Caesar would appear to fill the world with his fame.

> " From Troy's fair stock shall Caesar rise,
> The limits of whose victories
> Are ocean, of his fame the skies." [1]

Having thus quieted Venus' apprehensions in regard to her son, Jupiter directed Mercury to hasten off to Carthage to warn Dido that she is to receive hospitably the Trojan guests.

After a sleepless night Aeneas again set out with Achates to explore, and encountered in the forest his goddess mother in the guise of a Tyrian huntress. In respectful terms—for he suspected that she was some divinity in disguise—Aeneas begged for information, and learned that he had landed in the realm of Dido. Warned in a vision that her brother had secretly slain her husband and was plotting against her life, this Tyrian queen had fled from Tyre with

[1] All the quotations from the *Aeneid* are from Conington's translation.

Aeneas carrying his Father out of burning Troy
Gilbert Bayes

friends and wealth, and, on reaching this part of Africa, had, thanks to a clever device, obtained land enough to found the city of Byrsa or Carthage. In return Aeneas told the strange huntress his name, relating how the storm had scattered all his vessels save the seven anchored close by. To allay his anxiety regarding his friends, Venus assured him that twelve swans flying overhead were omens of the safety of his ships; but it was only when she turned to leave him that Aeneas recognized his mother, who, notwithstanding his desire to embrace her, vanished from his sight.

The two Trojans now walked on in the direction which she had indicated until they were dazzled by the beauty of the new city of Carthage, which was rising rapidly, through the exertions of Dido's subjects. In its centre stood a wonderful temple, whose brazen gates were decorated with scenes from the War of Troy. Hidden from all eyes by a divine mist, Aeneas and Achates tearfully gazed upon these reminders of past glories and mingled with the throng until Queen Dido appeared.

She was no sooner seated upon her throne than she summoned into her presence some prisoners just secured, in whom Aeneas recognized with joy the various captains of his missing ships. Then he overheard them bewail the storm which had robbed them of their leader, and was pleased because Dido promised them entertainment and ordered a search to be made for their chief.

The right moment having come, the cloud enveloping Aeneas and Achates parted, and Dido thus suddenly became aware of the presence of other strangers in their midst. Endowed by Venus with special attractions so as to secure the favour of the

Libyan Queen, Aeneas stepped forward, made himself known, and, after paying due respect to the Queen, joyfully greeted his comrades. Happy to harbour so famous a warrior, Dido invited Aeneas to a banquet in her palace, an invitation which he gladly accepted, charging Achates to hasten back to the ships to announce their companions' safety and to summon Iulus or Ascanius to join his father. To make quite sure that Aeneas should captivate Dido's heart, Venus now substituted Cupid for Iulus, whom she meantime conveyed to one of her favourite resorts. In the guise of the Trojan prince, Cupid, during the banquet, caressingly nestled in Dido's arms, and stealthily effaced from her heart all traces of her former husband's face, filling it instead with a resistless passion for Aeneas, which soon impelled her to invite him to relate his escape from Troy.

Book II

With the eyes of all present upon him, Aeneas related how the Greeks finally devised a colossal wooden horse, wherein their bravest chiefs remained concealed while the remainder of their forces pretended to sail home, although they anchored behind a neighbouring island to await the signal to return and sack Troy. Overjoyed by the departure of the foe, the Trojans hastened down to the shore, where, on discovering the huge wooden horse, they joyfully proposed to drag it into their city as a trophy. In vain their priest, Laocoon, implored them to desist, hurling his spear at the horse to prove that it was hollow and hence might conceal some foe. This daring act and apparent sacrilege horrified the Trojans, who, having secured a Greek fugitive in a swamp near by, besought him to disclose what purpose the horse was to serve. Pretending to have suffered great injustice at the Greeks' hands, the slave (Sinon) replied that if they removed the wooden horse into their walls the Trojans would greatly endanger the safety of their foes, who had left it on the shore to propitiate Neptune. Enticed by this prospect, the Trojans proved more eager than ever to drag the horse into their city, even though this necessitated pulling down part of their walls. Meanwhile part of the crowd gathered about Laocoon, who was to offer public thanks on the seashore, but, even while he was standing at the altar, attended by his sons, two huge serpents arose out of the sea, and coiling fiercely around priest and both acolytes, throttled them in spite of their efforts.

> He strains his strength their knots to tear,
> While gore and slime his fillets smear,
> And to the unregardful skies
> Sends up his agonizing cries.

The horror-stricken Trojans immediately concluded that Laocoon was being punished for having attacked the wooden horse, which they joyfully dragged into Troy, although the prophet-princess, Cassandra, besought them to desist, foretelling all manner of woe.

Night now fell upon the city, where, for the first time in ten years, all slept peacefully without fear of surprise. At midnight Sinon released the captive Greeks from the wooden steed, and, joined by their companions, who had noiselessly returned, they swarmed all over the undefended city. Aeneas graphically described for Dido's benefit his peaceful sleep, during which the phantom of the slaughtered Hector bade him arise and flee with his family, because the Greeks had already taken possession of Troy! At this moment loud clamours awakened him, confirming what he had just heard in his dream. Aeneas immediately rushed to the palace to defend his King, he and his men stripping the armour from fallen Greeks to enable them to get there unmolested. But they arrived only in time to see Achilles' son rush into the throne-room and cruelly murder the aged Priam after killing his youngest son. They also beheld the shrieking women ruthlessly dragged off into captivity, Cassandra wildly predicting the woes which would befall the Greek chiefs on their voyage home.

> Ah see! the Priameian fair,
> Cassandra, by her streaming hair
> Is dragged from Pallas' shrine,
> Her wild eyes raised to Heaven in vain;
> Her eyes, alas! for cord and chain
> Her tender hands confine.

The fall of aged Priam and the plight of the women reminding Aeneas of the danger of his own father, wife, and son, he turned to rush home. On his way thither he met his mother, who for a moment removed the mortal veil from his eyes, to let him see Neptune, Minerva, and Juno zealously helping to ruin Troy. Venus passionately urged her son to escape while there was yet time, and Aeneas, on reaching home, besought his father Anchises to depart, but it was only when the old man saw a bright flame hover over the head of his grandson, Iulus, that he realized that heaven intended to favour his race and consented to leave. Seeing him too weak to walk, his son bade him hold the household gods, and carried him off on his back, leading his boy by the hand and calling to his wife and servants to follow. Thus burdened, Aeneas reached a ruined fane by the shore, only to discover that his beloved wife was missing. Anxiously retracing his footsteps, he encountered her shade, which bade him cease from seeking for her among the living and hasten to Hesperia, where a new wife and home awaited him.

> "Then, while I dewed with tears my cheek,
> And strove a thousand things to speak,
>   She melted into night:
> Thrice I essayed her neck to clasp:
> Thrice the vain semblance mocked my grasp,
>   As wind or slumber light."

Thus enlightened in regard to his consort's fate and wishes, Aeneas hastened back to his waiting companions, and with them prepared to leave the Trojan shores.

Book III

Before long Aeneas' fleet landed on the Thracian coast, where, while preparing a sacrifice, our hero was horrified to see blood flow from the trees he cut down. This phenomenon was explained by an underground voice, which related how a Trojan was robbed and slain by the inhabitants of this land, and how trees had sprung from the javelins stuck in his breast.

Unwilling to linger in such a neighbourhood, Aeneas sailed to Delos, where an oracle informed him that he would be able to settle only in the land whence his ancestors had come. Although Anchises interpreted this to mean that they should proceed to Crete, the household gods informed Aeneas, during the journey thither, that Hesperia was their destined goal. After braving a three-days' tempest, Aeneas landed on the island of the Harpies, horrible monsters who defiled the travellers' food each time a meal was spread. They not only annoyed Aeneas in this way, but predicted, when attacked, that he should find a home only when driven by hunger to eat boards.

> " But ere your town with walls ye fence,
> Fierce famine, retribution dread
> For this your murderous violence,
> Shall make you eat your boards for bread."

Sailing off again, the Trojans next reached Epirus, which they found governed by Helenus, a Trojan, for Achilles' son had already been slain. Although Hector's widow was now queen of the realm where she had been brought a captive, she still mourned for her noble husband, and gladly welcomed the fugitives for his sake. During the parting sacrifice Helenus predicted that, after long wanderings, his guests would settle in Italy, in a spot where they would find a white sow suckling thirty young. He also cautioned Aeneas about the hidden dangers of Charybdis and Scylla, and bade him visit the Cumaean Sibyl, to induce her, if possible, to lend him her aid.

Restored and refreshed by this brief sojourn among kinsmen, Aeneas and his followers resumed their journey, steering by the stars and avoiding all landing in eastern or southern Italy, which was settled by Greeks. After passing Charybdis and Scylla unharmed, and after gazing in awe at the plume of smoke crowning Mount Aetna, the Trojans rescued one of the Greeks who had escaped with Ulysses from the Cyclops' cave but who had not contrived to sail away.

To rest his weary men, Aeneas finally landed at Drepanum, in Sicily, where his old father died and was buried with all due pomp. It was shortly after leaving this place that Aeneas' fleet had been overtaken by the terrible tempest which had driven his vessels to Dido's shore.

So king Aeneas told his tale
While all beside were still,
Rehearsed the fortunes of his sail,
And fate's mysterious will:
Then to its close his legend brought
And gladly took the rest he sought.

Book IV

While Aeneas rested peacefully, Dido's new-born passion kept her awake, causing her at dawn to rouse her sister Anna, in order to impart to her the agitated state of her feelings. Not only did Anna encourage her sister to marry again, but united with her in a prayer to which Venus graciously listened, although Juno reminded her that Trojans and Carthaginians were destined to be foes. Still, as the Goddess of Marriage, Juno finally consented that Aeneas and Dido should be brought together in the course of that day's hunt.

We now have a description of the sunrise, of the preparations for the chase, of the Queen's dazzling appearance, and of the daring huntsmanship of the false Iulus. But the brilliant hunting expedition is somewhat marred in the middle of the day by a sudden thunderstorm, during which Aeneas and Dido accidentally seek refuge in the same cave, where we are given to understand their union takes place. So momentous a step, proclaimed by the hundred-mouthed Goddess of Fame, rouses the ire of the native chiefs, one of whom fervently hopes that Carthage may rue having spared these Trojan refugees. This prayer is duly registered by Jupiter, who further bids Mercury remind Aeneas that his new realm is to be founded in Italy and not on the African coast.

Thus divinely ordered to depart, Aeneas dare not disobey, but, dreading Dido's reproaches and tears, he prepares to depart secretly. His plans are, however, detected by Dido, who vehemently demands how he dare forsake her now ? By Jupiter's orders, Aeneas remains unmoved by her reproaches, and sternly reminds her that he always declared he was bound for Italy. So, leaving Dido to brood over her wrongs, Aeneas hastens down to the shore to hasten his preparations. Dido implores her sister to detain her lover, and, as her entreaties prove vain, orders a pyre to be erected, on which she places all the objects which Aeneas has used.

That night the gods arouse Aeneas from slumber to bid him sail without taking leave of the Tyrian queen. In obedience to this command, our hero cuts with his sword the rope which moors his vessel to the Carthaginian shore, and sails away, closely followed by the rest of his fleet. From the watch-tower at early dawn, Dido discovers his vanishing sails, and is so overcome by grief, that, after rending " her golden length of hair " and calling down vengeance upon Aeneas, she stabs herself and breathes her last in the midst of the burning pyre. The Carthaginians, little expecting so tragical an end, witness the agony of their beloved Queen in speechless horror, while Anna wails aloud. Gazing down from heaven upon this sad scene, Juno directs Iris to hasten down and cut off a lock of Dido's hair,

The Death of Dido

G. B. Tiepolo

for it is only when this mystic ceremony has been performed that the soul can leave the body. Iris speedily obeys, saying:

> "This lock to Dis I bear away
> And free you from your load of clay:"
> So shears the lock: the vital heats
> Disperse, and breath in air retreats.

Book V

Sailing on, Aeneas, already dismayed by the smoke rising from the Carthaginian shore, is further troubled by rapidly gathering clouds. His weather-wise pilot, Palinurus, suggests that, since "the west is darkening into wrath," they run into the harbour of Drepanum, which they enter just one year after Anchises' death. There they show due respect to the dead by a sacrifice, of which a serpent takes his tithe, and proceed to celebrate funeral games. We now have a detailed account of the winning of prizes for the naval, foot, horse and chariot races, and the boxing and archery matches.

While all the men are thus congenially occupied, the Trojan women, instigated by Juno in disguise, set fire to the ships, that they may no longer wander over seas which they have learned to loathe. One of the warriors, seeing the smoke, raises the alarm, and a moment later his companions dash down to the shore to save their ships. Aeneas wrings his hands, and prays with such fervour that a cloud-burst drenches his burning vessels. Four, however, are beyond repair; so Aeneas, seeing he no longer has ship-room for all his force, allows the Trojans most anxious to rest to settle in Drepanum, taking with him only those who are willing to share his fortunes.

Before he leaves, his father's ghost appears to him, bidding him, before he settles in Latium, descend into Hades by way of Lake Avernus, and visit him in the Elysian Fields to hear what is to befall his race.

When Aeneas leaves Drepanum on the next day, his mother pleads so successfully in his behalf that Neptune promises to exact only one life as toll.

> "One life alone shall glut the wave;
> One head shall fall the rest to save."

Book VI

Steering to Cumae, where the Sibyl dwells, Aeneas seeks her cave, the entrance to which is barred by bronze gates, whereon is represented the story of Daedalus,—the first bird man,—who, escaping from the Labyrinth at Crete, gratefully laid his wings on this altar. We are further informed that the Sibyl wrote her oracles on separate oak leaves, which were set in due order in her cave, but which the wind, as soon as the doors opened, scattered or jumbled together, so that most of her predictions proved unintelligible to those who visited her shrine. After a solemn invocation, Aeneas besought her not to baffle him by writing on oak leaves, and was favoured by her apparition and the announcement that, after escaping many perils by land and sea and reddening the Tiber with blood, he would, thanks to Greek aid, triumph over his foes and settle in Latium with a new bride. Undaunted by the prospect of further trials, Aeneas besought the Sibyl to guide him down to Hades, to enable him to visit his father, a journey which she flatly refused to undertake, unless he procured the Golden Bough which served as a key to that region, and unless he showed due respect to the corpse of his friend. Although both conditions sounded mysterious when uttered, Aeneas discovered, on rejoining his crew, that one of his Trojans had been slain. After celebrating his funeral, our hero wandered off into a neighbouring forest, where some doves—his mother's birds—guided him to the place where grew the Golden Bough.

Armed with this talisman and escorted by the Sibyl, Aeneas, by way of Lake Avernus, entered the gloomy cave which formed the entrance to Hades. Following the flying footsteps of his mystic guide, he there plunged into the realm of night, soon reaching the precinct of departed souls, where he saw innumerable shades. Although he immediately crossed the river in Charon's leaky bark, many spirits were obliged to wait a hundred years, because they could not pay for their passage. Among these unfortunates Aeneas recognized his recently drowned pilot, who related how he had come to his death and by what means he was going to secure funeral honours.

In spite of the three-headed dog, Cerberus, and other gruesome sights, Aeneas and his guide reached the place where Minos holds judgment over arriving souls, and viewed the region where those who died for love were herded together. Among these ghosts was Dido, but, although Aeneas pityingly addressed her, she sullenly refused to answer a word. Farther on Aeneas came to the place of dead heroes, and there beheld brave Hector and clever Teucer, together with many other warriors who took part in the Trojan War.

After allowing him to converse a brief while with these friends, the Sibyl vouchsafed Aeneas a passing glimpse of Tartarus and of its great criminals, then she hurried him on to the Elysian Fields, the home of "the illustrious dead, who fighting for their country bled," to inquire for Anchises. The visitors were immediately directed to a quiet valley, where they found the aged Trojan, pleasantly occupied in contemplating the unborn souls destined to pass gradually into the upper world and animate the bodies of his progeny. On beholding his son, who, as at Drepanum, vainly tried to embrace him, Anchises revealed all that he had learned in regard to life, death, and immortality, and gave a synopsis of the history of Rome for the next thousand years, naming its great worthies, from Romulus, founder of Rome, down to Augustus, first Emperor and ruler of the main part of the world.

This account of the glories and vicissitudes of his race takes considerable time, and when it is finished the Sibyl guides Aeneas back to earth by one of the two gates which lead out of this dismal region. Pleased that he has accomplished his errand so successfully, and duly encouraged by all he has learned, Aeneas returns to his fleet and sets sail for the home which he is so anxious to reach.

Book VII

We now skirt with Aeneas the west coast of Italy, sail past Circe's island, and see his ships driven up the winding Tiber by favourable winds. On his first landing the Muse Erato rehearses for our benefit the history of the Latins, whose royal race, represented at present by Latinus, claims to descend from Saturn. Although Latinus has already betrothed his daughter Lavinia to Turnus, a neighbouring prince, he is favoured by an omen at the moment when the Trojans land. On seeking an interpretation of this sign, he learns that he is not to bestow his daughter upon Turnus, but is to reserve her hand for a stranger, whose descendants will be powerful indeed.

Meantime the Trojans feast upon meat which is served to each man on a wheaten cake. Young Iulus, greedily devouring his, exclaims playfully that in his hunger he has actually eaten the board on which his meal was spread! Hearing these significant words, his happy father exclaims that they have reached their destined goal, since the Harpies' terrifying prophecy has been fulfilled.

> "Hail, auspicious land!" he cries,
> "So long from Fate my due!
> All hail, ye Trojan deities,
> To Trojan fortunes true!
> At length we rest, no more to roam.
> Here is our country, here our home."

Then the Trojans begin to explore, and, discovering Latinus' capital, send thither an embassy of a hundred men, who are hospitably entertained. After hearing all they have to say, Latinus assures them that men of his race once migrated from Asia, and that the gods have just enjoined upon him to bestow his daughter upon a foreign bridegroom. When he proposes to unite Lavinia to Aeneas, Juno, unable to prevent a marriage decreed by Fate, tries to postpone it by infuriating Amata, mother of the bride, and causing her to flee into the woods with her daughter.

Not satisfied with one manifestation of power, Juno despatches Discord to ask Turnus if he will tamely allow his promised bride to be given to another man? Such a taunt is sufficient to determine hot-headed Turnus to make war, but, as a pretext is lacking, one of the Furies prompts Iulus to pursue and wound the pet stag of a young shepherdess called Sylvia. The distress of this rustic maid so excites her shepherd brothers that they fall upon the Trojans, who, of course, defend themselves, and thus the conflict begins. Having successfully broken the peace, Discord hastens back to Juno, who, seeing Latinus would fain remain neutral, compels him to take part in the war by opening with her own hand the gates of the temple of Janus. Here the poet recites the names of the various heroes about to distinguish themselves on either side, specially mentioning in the Rutules' force Mezentius, his son Lausus, and the Volscian maid Camilla, who prefers the stirring life of a camp to the peaceful avocations of her sex.

Book VIII

As Turnus is reinforced by many allies, Aeneas is anxious to secure some also, and sets out to seek the aid of Evander, King of Etruria, formerly a Greek. On his way to this realm, Aeneas perceives on the banks of the Tiber a white sow with thirty young, which he sacrifices to the gods in gratitude for having pointed out to him the spot where his future capital will rise. On reaching the Etruscan's stronghold, Aeneas readily secures the promise of a large contingent of warriors, who prepare to join him under the command of Pallas, son of the King. He then assists at a great Etruscan banquet in honour of one of the triumphs of Hercules, and while he is sleeping there his mother Venus induces her blacksmith husband, Vulcan, to make him a suit of armour.

Dawn having appeared, Evander entertains his guests with tales, while his son completes his preparations. Aeneas' departure, however, is hastened by Venus, who warns her son that his camp is in danger when she delivers to him the armour which she has procured. This is adorned by many scenes in the coming history of Rome, among which special mention is made of the twins suckled by the traditional wolf, of the kidnapping of the Sabines, and of the heroic deeds of Cocles, Cloelia, and Manlius, as well as battles and festivals innumerable.

Book IX

Meanwhile, obedient to Turnus's orders, the Rutules have surrounded the Trojan camp and set fire to Aeneas' ships. But, as Fate has decreed that these vessels shall be immortal, they sink beneath the waves as soon as the flames touch them, only to reappear a moment later as ocean-nymphs and swim down the Tiber to warn Aeneas of the danger of his friends. This miracle awes the foe, until Turnus boldly interprets it in his favour, whereupon the Rutules attack the foreigners' camp so furiously that the Trojans gladly accept the proposal made by Nisus and Euryalus to slip out and summon Aeneas to return.

Stealing out of the Trojan camp by night, these two heroes bravely thread their way through their sleeping foes, killing several famous warriors as they go, and appropriating their spoil. Leaving death in their wake, the two Trojans pass through the enemy's ranks and enter a forest, where they are pursued by a troop of the Volscians, who surround and slay Euryalus. Nisus at first manages to escape from their hands, but he returns to defend his comrade, and is slain also. The Volscians therefore bear two bloody heads to the Rutules' camp to serve as their war standards on the next day. It is thus that Euryalus' mother becomes aware of the death of her son, whom she mourns in touching terms.

> "Was it this, ah me,
> I followed over land and sea?
> O slay me, Rutules! if ye know
> A mother's love, on me bestow
> The tempest of your spears!
> Or thou, great Thunderer, pity take,
> And whelm me 'neath the Stygian lake,
> Since otherwise I may not break
> This life of bitter tears!"

To recount all the deeds of valour performed on this day would require much space, but, although Mars inspires the party of Aeneas with great courage, it is evidently on the verge of defeat when Jupiter orders Turnus to withdraw.

Book X

Having convoked his Olympian council, Jupiter forbids the gods to interfere on either side, and decrees that the present quarrel shall be settled without divine aid. Venus vehemently protests that, having promised that her son should found a new realm in Italy, he is bound to protect him, while Juno argues with equal force that the Trojans should be further punished for kidnapping Helen. Silencing both goddesses, Jupiter reiterates his orders and dissolves the assembly.

The scene now changes back to earth, where the Trojans, closely hemmed in by foes, long for Aeneas' return. He, on his way back, encounters the sea-nymphs, who explain that they were once his ships and bid him hasten to the rescue of his son.

Thus admonished, Aeneas hurries back, to take part in a battle where many heroic deeds are performed, and where Turnus, Mezentius, and Lausus prove bravest on the enemy's side, although they find their match in Aeneas, Pallas, and Iulus. Among the brilliant duels fought, mention must be made of one between Pallas and Turnus, in which, notwithstanding his courage, the Etruscan prince succumbs. After stripping his opponent of his armour, Turnus abandons the corpse to the Trojans, who mourn to think that he lost his life while helping them. Vowing to avenge him, Aeneas now attacks his foe with such fury that it seems as if Turnus' last day had come, but Juno pleads so eloquently in his behalf, that, although Fate has decreed his death, she grants him a brief respite.

To preserve Turnus from the deadly blows of the real Aeneas, Juno causes him to pursue a phantom foe on board a ship, whose moorings she loosens, thus setting him adrift upon the Tiber. Perceiving only then how he has been tricked, Turnus threatens to slay himself, but is restrained by Juno, who after a while allows him to land and return to the battle. Thus deprived of his principal foe, Aeneas ranges over the battlefield, where he wounds Mezentius and kills Lausus. Seeing his beloved son is gone, Mezentius is so anxious to die that he now offers an unresisting throat to Aeneas, who slays him on the spot.

> "One boon (if vanquished foe may crave
> The victor's grace) I ask, a grave.
> My wrathful subjects round me wait:
> Protect me from their savage hate,
> And let me in the tomb enjoy
> The presence of my slaughtered boy."

Book XI

Having made a trophy of the enemies' spoil, Aeneas, even before proceeding to bury his own comrades, adorns the body of Pallas and sends it back to Etruria. Then he bargains with Turnus' ambassadors for a twelve-days' truce, during which both parties celebrate magnificent funerals, the finest of all being that of Pallas.

Hoping to check further bloodshed, Latinus now proposes a peace, the terms of which Aeneas is willing to accept, but which Turnus angrily rejects since they deprive him of his promised bride. The conflict is therefore resumed, and the next interesting episode refers to Camilla, the warrior maid, whose father when she was only a babe tied her to the shaft of his spear and flung her across a torrent which he was unable to stem with her in his arms. Having thus saved her from the enemy's clutches, this father taught Camilla to fight so bravely, that she causes dire havoc among the Trojans before she dies, using her last breath to implore Turnus to hasten to the rescue.

> "Go: my last charge to Turnus tell,
> To haste with succour, and repel
> The Trojans from the town—farewell."
> She spoke, and speaking, dropped her rein,
> Perforce descending to the plain.
> Then by degrees she slips away
> From all that heavy load of clay:
> Her languid neck, her drowsy head
> She droops to earth, of vigour sped:
> She lets her martial weapons go:
> The indignant soul flies down below.

THE AENEID

Book XII

Unappeased by Latinus' reiterated assertions that he is bestowing Lavinia upon a stranger merely to obey the gods, or by the entreaties in which Amata now joins, Turnus still refuses peace. More fighting therefore ensues, during which Aeneas is wounded in the thigh. While his leech is vainly endeavouring to stanch his blood, Venus drops a magic herb into the water used for bathing his wounds and thus miraculously cures him. Plunging back into the fray, which becomes so horrible that Amata brings Lavinia home and commits suicide, Turnus and Aeneas finally meet in duel, but, although Juno would fain interfere once more in behalf of her *protégé*, Jupiter refuses to allow it. But he grants instead his wife's petition that the Trojan name and language shall forever be merged into that of the Latin race.

> "Let Latium prosper as she will,
> Their thrones let Alban monarchs fill;
> Let Rome be glorious on the earth,
> The centre of Italian worth;
> But fallen Troy be fallen still,
> The nation and the name."

Toward the end of this momentous encounter, during which both heroes indulge in boastful speeches, a bird warns Turnus that his end is near, and his sister Juturna basely deserts him. Driven to bay and deprived of all other weapons, Turnus finally hurls a rock at Aeneas, who, avoiding this missile, deals him a deadly wound. Turnus now pitifully begs for mercy, but the sight of Pallas' belt, which his foe wears, so angers Aeneas that, after wrathfully snatching it from him, he deals his foe the deadly blow which ends this epic.

"What! in my friend's dear spoils arrayed
  To me for mercy sue?
'Tis Pallas, Pallas guides the blade:
From your cursed blood his injured shade
  Thus takes the atonement due."
Thus as he spoke, his sword he drave
  With fierce and fiery blow
Through the broad breast before him spread:
The stalwart limbs grow cold and dead:
One groan the indignant spirit gave,
  Then sought the shades below.

FRENCH EPICS

THE national epic in France bears the characteristic name of *chanson de geste*, or song of deed, because the *trouvères* in the north and the troubadours in the south wandered from castle to castle singing the prowess of the lords and of their ancestors, whose reputations they thus made or ruined at will.

In their earliest form these *chansons de geste* were invariably in verse, but in time the most popular were turned into lengthy prose romances. Many of the hundred or more *chansons de geste* still preserved were composed in the northern dialect, or *langue d'oïl*, and, although similar epics did exist in the *langue d'oc*, they have the "great defect of being lost," and only fragments of *Flamença*, etc., now exist.

There are three great groups or cycles of French epics: first the cycle of France, dealing specially with Charlemagne—the champion of Christianity—who, representing Christ, is depicted surrounded by twelve peers instead of twelve disciples. Among these, to carry out the scriptural analogy, lurks a traitor, Ganelon; thus also, in the course of the poems, we are favoured with biblical miracles, the sun pausing in its course until pagans can be punished, and angels appearing to comfort dying knights. The finest sample of this cycle is without doubt the famous *Chanson de Roland*, of which a complete synopsis follows. Other remarkable examples of this cycle are *Aliscans*, *Raoul de Cambrai*, *Garin le Lorrain*, *Guillaume d'Orange*, *Les Quatre Fils d'Aymon*, *Ogier le Danois*, etc.

Even the character of the hero varies from age

to age, for whereas Charlemagne in the *Chanson de Roland*—which dates perhaps as far back as the tenth century—is a heroic figure, he becomes during later periods, when vassals rise up against their overlords,—an object of contempt and ridicule. A marked example of this latter style of treatment is furnished by *Les Quatre Fils d'Aymon.*[1]

The second group, or cycle of Brittany, animated by a chivalrous spirit, and hence termed court epic, finds its greatest exponent in the poet Chrestien de Troyes, whose hero Arthur, King of Brittany, gathers twelve knights round his table, one of whom, Mordred, is to prove traitor. The principal poems of this cycle are *Lancelot du Lac*, *Ivain le Chevalier au Lion*, *Erec et Enide*, *Merlin*, *Tristan*, and *Perceval.* These poems all treat of chivalry and love, and introduce the old pagan passion-breeding philtre, as well as a whole world of magic and fairies. These epics will be noticed at greater length when we treat of the English versions of Arthur and the Knights of the Round Table, because many of the poems have been reworked in modern English and are hence most popular in that language.

Besides the *chansons de geste* pertaining to various phases of this theme, the Breton cycle includes many shorter works termed *lais*, which also treat of love, and were composed by Marie de France or her successors. The best known of all these "cante-fables" is the idyllic *Aucassin et Nicolette*, of which a full account is embodied in this volume.

One of the best samples of the domestic epic in this cycle is the twelfth-century *Amis et Amiles*, in which two knights, born and baptized on the same day, prove so alike as to become interchangeable.

[1] See the author's *Myths and Legends of the Middle Ages.*

Charlemagne 94

Stella Langdale

Brought up in separate provinces, Amis and Amiles meet and become friends only when knighted by Charlemagne, whose graciousness toward them rouses the jealousy of the felon knight Hardré. When Charlemagne finally offers his niece to Amiles (who, through modesty, passes her on to Amis), the felon accuses the former of treacherously loving the King's daughter Bellicent, and thereupon challenges him to fight. As he is indeed guilty of loving the Princess, although he has not betrayed her, Amiles dare not accept this challenge, and changes places with Amis, who personates him in the lists. Because Amis thus commits perjury to rescue his friend from a dilemma, he is in due time stricken with leprosy, deserted by his wife, and sorely ill-treated by his vassals. After much suffering, he discovers that his sole hope of cure consists in bathing in the blood of the children which in the meanwhile have been born to Amiles and his wife, Bellicent. When the leper Amis reluctantly reveals this fact to his friend Amiles, the latter, although broken-hearted, unhesitatingly slays his children. Amis is immediately cured, and both knights hasten to church together to return thanks and inform the mother of the death of her little ones. The Princess rushes to their chamber to mourn over their corpses, only to discover that meantime they have been miraculously restored to life! This story is very touchingly told in the old *chanson*, which contains many vivid and interesting descriptions of the manners of the time.

In this cycle are also included *Gérard de Roussillon*, *Hugues Capet*, *Macaire* (wherein occurs the famous episode of the Dog of Montargis), and *Huon de Bordeaux*, which latter supplied Shakespeare, Wieland, and Weber with some of the *dramatis personae* of their well-known comedy, poem, and opera. We must also mention what are often termed the Crusade epics, of which the stock topics are quarrels, challenges, fights, banquets, and tournaments, and among which we note *Les Enfances de Godefroi*, *Antioche*, and Tudela's Song of the Crusade against the Albigenses.

The third great cycle is known as *Matiére de Rome la grand*, or as the antique cycle. It embodies Christianized versions of the doings of the heroes of the *Iliad*, *Odyssey*, *Aeneid*, *Thebais*, *Alexandreid*, etc. In their prose forms the *Roman de Thebes*, *Roman de Troie*, and *Roman d'Alexandre* contain innumerable mediaeval embellishments, among others the first mention in French of the quest for the Fountain of Youth.

Later on in French literature we come across the animal epic, or *Roman de Renard*, a style of composition which found its latest and most finished expression in Germany at the hands of Goethe, and the allegorical epic, *Le Roman de la Rose*, wherein abstract ideas were personified, such as Hope, Slander (Malebouche), Danger, etc.

There are also epic poems based on *Le Combat des Trente* and on the doings of Du Guesclin. Ronsard, in his *Franciade*, claims the Franks as lineal descendants from Francus, a son of Priam, and thus connects French history with the war of Troy, just as Wace, in the *Roman de Brut*, traces a similar connexion between the Trojan Brutus and Britain. Later French poets have attempted epics, more or less popular in their time, among which are *Alaric* by Scudéri, *Clovis* by St Sorlin, and a poem on *La Pucelle* by Chapelain.

Next comes *La Henriade* by Voltaire, a half

bombastic, half satirical account of Henry IV's wars to gain the crown of France. This poem also contains some very fine and justly famous passages, but is too long and too artificial, as a whole, to please modern readers.

The most popular of all the French prose epics is, without dispute, Fénelon's *Télémaque*, or account of Telemachus' journeys to find some trace of his long-absent father Ulysses.

Les Martyrs by Chateaubriand, and *La Légende des Siècles* by Victor Hugo, complete the tale of important French epics to date.

THE SONG OF ROLAND[1]

Introduction

The earliest and greatest of the French epics, or *chansons de geste*, is *The Song of Roland*, of which the oldest copy now extant is preserved in the Bodleian Library and dates back to the twelfth century. Whether the Turoldus (Théroulde) mentioned at the end of the poem is poet, copyist, or mere reciter remains a matter of conjecture.

The poem is evidently based on popular songs which no longer exist. It consists of 4002 verses, written in *langue d'oïl*, grouped in stanzas or ' laisses ' of irregular length, in the heroic pentameter, having the same assonant rhyme, and each ending with ' aoi,' a word no one has succeeded in translating satisfactorily. It was so popular that it was translated into Latin and German (1173–1177), and our version may be the very song sung by Taillefer at the battle of Hastings in 1066.

[1] Another version of this story is given in the author's *Myths and Legends of the Middle Ages*.

It has inspired many poets, and Roland's death has been sung again by Goethe, Schiller, Pulci, Boiardo, Ariosto, Berni, Bornier, De Vigny, etc. History claims that French armies, once in the reign of Dagobert and once in that of Charlemagne, were attacked and slaughtered in the Pyrenees, though not by the Saracens, and Charlemagne's secretary, Eginhart, briefly mentions in his chronicles that in 778, Roland, prefect of the Marches of Brittany, was slain there. Although the remainder of the story has no historical basis, *The Song of Roland* is a poetical asset we would not willingly relinquish.

Part I

A Council held by King Marsile at Saragossa.—*The Song of Roland* opens with the statement that, after spending seven years in Spain, Charlemagne is master of all save the city of Saragossa.

> The King, our Emperor Carlemaine,
> Hath been for seven full years in Spain.
> From highland to sea hath he won the land;
> City was none might his arm withstand;
> Keep and castle alike went down—
> Save Saragossa, the mountain town.[1]

It is in Saragossa that King Marsile, holding an open-air council, informs his followers that he no longer has men to oppose to the French. When he inquires what he shall do, the wisest of his advisers suggests that, when might fails, craft can gain the day. Therefore, he advises that gifts be sent to Charlemagne, with a promise to follow him to France to do homage and receive baptism. Even should Charle-

[1] All the quotations from *The Song of Roland* are taken from John O'Hagan's translation.

magne exact hostages, this councillor volunteers to give his own son, since it is better that a few should fall than that Spain should be lost forever. This advice is adopted by Marsile, who then despatches bearers of olive branches and gifts to Charlemagne.

Council held by Charlemagne at Cordova.—The Saracen emissaries find the French Emperor seated on a golden throne in an orchard, his peers around him, watching the martial games of fifty thousand warriors. After receiving Marsile's message, Charlemagne dismisses the ambassadors for the night, promising answer on the morrow. When he bids his courtiers state their opinions, Roland impetuously declares that, as Marsile has tricked them once, it would not become them to believe him now. His stepfather, Ganelon, thereupon terms him a hotheaded young fool, who prizes his own glory more than his fellow-men's lives. The wisest among Charlemagne's advisers, however, Duke Naimes, argues that the Saracen's offers of submission should be met half-way, and, as the remainder of the French agree with him, Charlemagne calls for a messenger to bear his acceptance to Marsile. Although Roland, Oliver, and Naimes eagerly sue for this honour, Charlemagne, unwilling to spare his peers, bids them appoint a baron. When Roland suggests his stepfather, Ganelon—who deems the expedition hazardous—becomes so angry that he reviles his stepson in the Emperor's presence, asserting that the youth is maliciously sending him to his death, and muttering threats of revenge. Roland merely laughs at this outburst, and Charlemagne checks the quarrel by delivering message and emblems of office to Ganelon. To the dismay of all present, he, however, drops the glove which his master hands him, an accident viewed as an omen of ill luck. Then, making speedy preparations and pathetically committing his wife and son to the care of his countrymen, Ganelon starts out, fully expecting never to return.

The Embassy and the Crime of Ganelon.—On his way to Saragossa, Ganelon converses with the Saracens, who express surprise that Charlemagne —whom they deem 200 years old—should still long for conquest. In return Ganelon assures them that his master will never cease fighting as long as Roland is one of his peers, for this knight is determined to conquer the world. The Saracens, noticing his bitter tone, now propose to rid Ganelon of his step-son, provided he arranges that Roland shall command the rear-guard of the French army. Thus riding along, they devise the plot whereby this young hero is to be led into an ambush in the Valley of Roncevaux (Roncesvalles), where, by slaying him, they will deprive Charlemagne of his principal strength.

> " For whoso Roland to death shall bring,
> From Karl his good right arm will wring,
> The marvellous host will melt away,
> No more shall he muster a like array."

Arriving in the presence of the Saracen King, Ganelon states that Charlemagne is ready to accept his offers provided he shall do homage for one half of Spain and abandon the other to Roland. As Ganelon adds the threat that, should this offer be refused, Charlemagne proposes to seize Saragossa and bear Marsile a prisoner to Aix, the Saracen King angrily orders the execution of the insolent messenger. But the Frenchmen's truculent attitude forbids the guards' approach, and thus gives the ambassadors time to inform Marsile that Ganelon has promised to help them to outwit Charlemagne by depriving him of his most efficient general. Marsile's anger is disarmed; and he not only agrees to their plan to surprise Roland while crossing the Pyrenees, but sends Ganelon back laden with gifts.

On rejoining his master at the foot of the mountains, Ganelon delivers the keys of Saragossa, and reports that the Caliph has sailed for the East with a hundred thousand men, none of whom care to dwell in a Christian land. Charlemagne, imagining his task finished, returns thanks to God, and prepares to wend his way back to France, whither he expects Marsile to follow him and do homage for Spain.

> Karl the Great hath wasted Spain,
> Her cities sacked, her castles ta'en;
> But now "My wars are done," he cried,
> "And home to gentle France we ride."

The Rear-guard and Roland condemned to Death.—On the eve of his return to "sweet France," Charlemagne's rest is disturbed by horrible dreams, in one of which Ganelon breaks his lance, while in the other wild animals are about to attack him. On awaking from this nightmare, Charlemagne divides his army so as to thread his way safely through the narrow passes of the mountains, arranging that a force shall remain twenty miles in his rear to make sure he shall not be surprised by the foe. When he inquires to whom this important command shall be entrusted, Ganelon eagerly suggests that, as Roland is the most valiant of the peers, the task be allotted to him. Anxious to keep his nephew by him, Charlemagne resents this suggestion, but, when he prepares to award the post to some one else, Roland eagerly claims it, promising that France shall lose nothing through him.

> "God be my judge," was the Count's reply,
> "If ever I thus my race belie.
> But twenty thousand with me shall rest,
> Bravest of all your Franks and best;
> The mountain passes in safety tread,
> While I breathe in life you have nought to dread."

As it is patent to all that his stepfather proposed his name through spite, Roland meaningly remarks that he at least will not drop the insignia of his rank, and in proof thereof proudly clutches the bow which Charlemagne hands him, and boastfully declares that twelve peers and twenty thousand men will prove equal to any emergency.

Fully armed and mounted on his steed (Veillantif), Roland, from an eminence, watches the vanguard of the French army disappear in the mountain gorges, calling out to the last men that he and his troop will follow them soon! This vanguard is led by Charlemagne and Ganelon, and, as it passes on, the heavy tramp of the mailed steeds causes the ground to shake, while the clash of the soldiers' arms is heard for miles around. They have already travelled thirty miles and are just nearing France, whose sunny fields the soldiers greet with cries of joy, when Duke Naimes perceives tears flowing down the Emperor's cheeks, and learns that they are caused by apprehension for Roland.

> High were the peaks, and the valleys deep,
> The mountains wondrous dark and steep;
> Sadly the Franks through the passes wound,
> Fully fifteen leagues did their tread resound.
> To their own great land they are drawing nigh,
> And they look on the fields of Gascony.

They think of their homes and their manors there,
Their gentle spouses and damsels fair.
Is none but for pity the tear lets fall;
But the anguish of Karl is beyond them all.
His sister's son at the gates of Spain
Smites on his heart, and he weeps amain.

The evident anxiety of Charlemagne fills the hearts of all the Frenchmen with nameless fear, and some of them whisper that Ganelon returned from Saragossa with suspiciously rich gifts. Meanwhile Roland, who has been waiting for the vanguard to gain some advance, also sets out to cross the mountains, where, true to his agreement with Ganelon, Marsile has concealed a force of 100,000 men, led by twelve Saracen generals, who are considered fully equal to the French peers, and who have vowed to slay Roland in the passes of Roncevaux.

Part II

Prelude to the Great Battle.—It is only when the Saracen army is beginning to close in upon the French, that the peers become aware of their danger. Oliver, Roland's bosom friend, the first to descry the enemy, calls out that this ambush is the result of Ganelon's treachery, only to be silenced by Roland, who will not allow his stepfather to be accused without proof. Then, hearing of the large force approaching, Roland exclaims, "Cursed be he who flees," and admonishes all present to show their mettle and die fighting bravely.

The Pride of Roland.—As the enemies' force greatly outnumbers theirs, Oliver suggests that Roland sound his horn to summon Charlemagne to his aid; but, unwilling to lose any glory, this hero refuses, declaring he will strike one hundred thousand such doughty blows with his mighty sword (Durendal), that all the pagans will be laid low.

> " Roland, Roland, yet wind one blast !
> Karl will hear ere the gorge be passed,
> And the Franks return on their path full fast."
> " I will not sound on mine ivory horn :
> It shall never be spoken of me in scorn,
> That for heathen felons one blast I blew ;
> I may not dishonour my lineage true.
> But I will strike, ere this fight be o'er,
> A thousand strokes and seven hundred more,
> And my Durindana shall drip with gore.
> Our Franks will bear them like vassals brave.
> The Saracens flock but to find a grave."

Oliver thrice implores Roland to summon aid, and Roland thrice refuses ; so his friend, since he will not yield, finally declares they must do their best, and adds that, should they not get the better of the foe, they will at least die fighting nobly. Then Archbishop Turpin—one of the peers—assures the soldiers that, since they are about to die as martyrs, they will earn Paradise, and pronounces the absolution, thus inspiring the French with such courage that, on rising from their knees, they rush forward to earn a heavenly crown.

Riding at their head, Roland now admits to Oliver that Ganelon must have betrayed them, grimly adding that the Saracens will have cause to rue their treachery. Then he leads his army down the valley to a more open space, where, as soon as the signal is given, both friends plunge into the fray, shouting their war-cry " Montjoi."

The Medley.—In the first ranks of the Saracens is a nephew of Marsile, who loudly boasts that Charlemagne is about to lose his right arm ; but, before he can repeat this taunt, Roland, spurring forward, runs his lance through his body and hurls it to the ground with a turn of his wrist. Then, calling out to his men that they have scored the first triumph, Roland proceeds to do tremendous execution among the foe. The poem describes many of the duels which take place,—for each of the twelve peers specially distinguishes himself,—while the Saracens, conscious of vastly superior numbers, return again and again to the attack. Even the Archbishop fights bravely, and Roland, after dealing fifteen deadly strokes with his lance, resorts to his sword, thus meeting the Saracens at such close quarters that every stroke of his blade hews through armour, rider, and steed.

> At the last it brake ; then he grasped in hand
> His Durindana, his naked brand,
> He smote Chernubles' helm upon,
> Where, in the centre, carbuncles shone :
> Down through his coif and his fell of hair,
> Betwixt his eyes came the falchion bare,
> Down through his plated harness fine,
> Down through the Saracen's chest and chine,
> Down through the saddle with gold inlaid,
> Till sank in the living horse the blade,
> Severed the spine where no joint was found,
> And horse and rider lay dead on ground.

In spite of Roland's doughty blows, his good sword suffers no harm, nor does that of Oliver (Hauteclaire), with which he does such good work that Roland assures him he will henceforth consider him a brother. Although the French slay the pagans by thousands, so many of their own warriors fall, that, by the time they have repulsed the first Saracen division, only sixty of Roland's men remain alive.

All nature seems to feel the terrible battle raging in the valley of Roncevaux, for a terrible storm breaks forth in France, where, hearing the roll of the thunder, seeing the flash of the lightning, and feeling the earth shake beneath their feet, the French fear the end of the world has come. These poor warriors are little aware that all this commotion is due to "nature's grief for the death of Roland."

Now a wondrous storm o'er France hath passed,
With thunder-stroke and whirlwind's blast;
Rain unmeasured, and hail, there came,
Sharp and sudden the lightning's flame;
And an earthquake ran—the sooth I say,
From Besançon city to Wissant Bay;
From Saint Michael's Mount to thy shrine, Cologne,
House unrifted was there none.
And a darkness spread in the noontide high—
No light, save gleams from the cloven sky.
On all who saw came a mighty fear.
They said, "The end of the world is near."
Alas, they spake but with idle breath,—
'Tis the great lament for Roland's death.

The Horn.—During the brief respite allowed them, Roland informs Oliver that he wishes to notify Charlemagne that France has been widowed of many men. In reply, Oliver rejoins that no Frenchman will leave this spot to bear such a message, for all prefer death and honour to safety! Such being the case, Roland proposes to sound his horn, whereupon Oliver bitterly rejoins, had his friend only done so at first they would have been reinforced by now, and that the Emperor can no longer reach them in time. He can, however, avenge them and give them an honourable burial, Roland argues, and he and his friend continue bickering until the Archbishop silences them, bidding Roland blow his horn. Placing Olifant to his lips, the hero, after

Roland at Roncesvalles

Evelyn Paul

drawing a powerful breath, blows so mighty a blast that it re-echoes thirty miles away.

This sound, striking Charlemagne's ear, warns him that his army is in danger, although Ganelon insists that Roland is hunting. While blowing a second blast, Roland makes so mighty an effort that he actually bursts the blood-vessels in his temples, and the Frenchmen, hearing that call, aver with awe that he would never call that way unless in dire peril. Ganelon, however, again insists that his stepson is in no danger and is merely coursing a hare.

> With deadly travail, in stress and pain,
> Count Roland sounded the mighty strain.
> Forth from his mouth the bright blood sprang,
> And his temples burst for the very pang.
> On and onward was borne the blast,
> Till Karl hath heard as the gorge he passed,
> And Naimes and all his men of war.
> " It is Roland's horn," said the Emperor,
> " And, save in battle, he had not blown."

With blood pouring from mouth and ears, Roland sounds his horn a third and last time, producing so long and despairing a note, that Naimes vows the French must be at the last extremity, and that unless they hurry they will not find any alive! Bidding all his horns sound as a signal that he is coming, Charlemagne—after ordering Ganelon to be bound and left in charge of the baggage train—leads his men back to Spain to Roland's rescue.

The day is already far advanced, and helmets and armour glitter beneath the rays of the setting sun as the Frenchmen spur along, tears coursing down their cheeks, for they apprehend what must have befallen Roland, who was evidently suffering when he blew that third blast!

The Rout.—Meanwhile, casting his eyes over the battlefield, now strewn with corpses, Roland mourns his fallen companions, praying God to let their souls rest in Paradise on beds of flowers. Then, turning to Oliver, he proposes that they fight on as long as breath remains in their bodies, and plunges back into the fray, still uttering his war-cry.

By this time the French are facing a second onslaught of the pagans, and Roland has felled twenty-four of their bravest fighters before Marsile challenges him to a duel. Although weak and weary, Roland accepts, and with his first stroke hews off the Saracen's right hand ; but, before he can follow this up with a more decisive blow, Marsile is borne away by his followers. Seeing their master gallop off toward Spain, the remainder of the Saracens, crying that Charlemagne's nephew has triumphed, cease fighting and flee. Thus, 50,000 men soon vanish in the distance, leaving Roland temporary master of the battle-field, which he knows the Emperor will reach only after he has breathed his last.

The Death of Oliver.—Although the Saracens have fled, some Moors remain to charge the Frenchmen, whom they wish to annihilate before Charlemagne can arrive. Once more, therefore, Roland urges his followers to do their best, cursing those who dream of yielding. Not daring approach the small handful of doughty Frenchmen, the pagans attack them from a distance with lance, arrow, and spear, tauntingly crying that Charlemagne will have no cause to pride himself upon having appointed them to guard his rear ! Mortally wounded by one of these spears, Oliver, blindly cutting down the foes nearest him, bids Roland hasten to his rescue, as it will not be long before they part. Seeing the stream of blood which flows from his friend's wounds, and catching a glimpse of his livid face, Roland so keenly realizes Oliver's end is near that he swoons in his saddle. The wounded man, no longer able to see, meanwhile ranges wildly around the battle-field, striking madly right and left. In doing so he runs against Roland, and, failing to recognize him, deals him so powerful a blow that he almost kills him. Gently inquiring why his friend thus attacks one he loves, Roland hears Oliver gasp, "I hear you, friend, but do not see you. Forgive me for having struck you,"—a more than ample apology—ere he dies.

> See Roland there on his charger swooned,
> Olivier smitten with his death wound.
> His eyes from bleeding are dimmed and dark,
> Nor mortal, near or far, can mark;
> And when his comrade beside him pressed,
> Fiercely he smote on his golden crest;
> Down to the nasal the helm he shred,
> But passed no further, nor pierced his head.
> Roland marvelled at such a blow,
> And thus bespake him soft and low:
> "Hast thou done it, my comrade, wittingly?
> Roland who loves thee so dear, am I,
> Thou hast no quarrel with me to seek."
> Olivier answered, "I hear thee speak,
> But I see thee not. God seeth thee.
> Have I struck thee, brother? Forgive it me."
> "I am not hurt, O Olivier;
> And in sight of God, I forgive thee here."
> Then each to other his head has laid,
> And in love like this was their parting made.

On seeing that his friend has passed away, the heart-broken Roland again swoons in his saddle, but his intelligent steed stands still until his master recovers his senses. Gazing around him, Roland now ascertains that only two other Frenchmen are still alive, and, seeing one of them severely wounded, he binds up his cuts before plunging back into the fray, where he accounts for twenty-five pagans, while the Archbishop and the wounded soldier dispose of eleven more.

Charlemagne approaches.—The last Frenchmen are fighting madly against 1000 Moors on foot and 4000 on horseback, when the spears flung from a distance lay low the wounded man and deal a mortal wound to the Archbishop. But, even while dying, Turpin joins Roland in declaring they must continue to fight, so that when the Emperor finds their bodies he can see they have piled hundreds of corpses around them. This resolve is carried out, however, only at the cost of dire suffering, for the Archbishop is dying and Roland's burst temples cause him intense pain. Nevertheless, he once more puts his horn to his lips, and draws from it this time so pitiful a blast that, when it reaches the ears of Charlemagne, he woefully exclaims: "All is going ill; my nephew Roland will die to-day, for the sound of his horn is very weak!"

Again bidding his 60,000 trumpets sound, the Emperor urges his troops to even greater speed, until the noise of his horns and the tramp of his steeds reaches the pagans' ears and admonishes them to flee. Realizing that, should Roland survive, the war will continue, a few Moors make a final frantic attempt to slay him before fleeing. Seeing them advance for a last onslaught, Roland—who has dismounted for a moment—again bestrides his steed and, accompanied by the staggering Archbishop, bravely faces them. They, however, only fling missiles from a distance, until Roland's shield drops useless from his hand and his steed sinks lifeless beneath him! Then, springing to his feet, Roland defies these cowardly foes, who, not daring to linger any longer, turn and flee, crying that Roland has won and Spain is lost unless the Emir comes to their rescue!

The Last Blessing of the Archbishop.—While the pagans are spurring toward Saragossa, Roland remains on the battle-field, for, having lost his steed and being mortally wounded, he cannot attempt to pursue them. After tenderly removing the Archbishop's armour, binding up his wounds, and placing him comfortably on the ground, Roland brings him the twelve peers, so that he may bless them for the last time. Although Archbishop Turpin admonishes him to hasten, Roland is so weak, that he slowly and painfully collects the corpses from mountain and valley, laying them one by one at the feet of the Archbishop, who, with right hand raised, bestows his blessing. While laying Oliver at Turpin's feet, Roland faints from grief, so the prelate painfully raises himself, and, seizing the hero's horn, tries to get down to the brook to bring him some water. Such is his weakness, however, that he stumbles and falls dead, face to the ground, before he can fulfil his kindly intention.

On recovering consciousness and seeing nothing save corpses around him, Roland exults to think that Charlemagne will find forty dead Saracens for every slain Frenchman! Then, feeling his brain slowly ooze out through his ears, Roland—after reciting a prayer for his dead companions—grasps his sword in one hand and his horn in the other, and begins to climb a neighbouring hill. He tries to reach its summit because he has always boasted he would die face toward the enemy, and he longs to look defiance toward Spain until the end.

Painfully reaching the top of this eminence, Roland stumbles and falls across a Saracen, who has been feigning death to escape capture. Seeing the dreaded warrior unconscious, this coward seizes the hero's sword, loudly proclaiming he has triumphed; but, at his first touch, Roland—recovering his senses—deals him so mighty a blow with his horn, that the Saracen falls with crushed helmet and skull. Having thus recovered his beloved Durendal, Roland, to prevent it from again falling into the enemy's hands, vainly tries to break it by hewing at the rocks around him, but, although he uses all the strength he has left to deal blows that cut through the stone, the good sword remains undinted. Full of admiration, Roland then recalls the feats Durendal has enabled him to perform, and, lying down on the grass, places beneath him sword and horn, so as to defend them dead as well as alive! Then, having confessed his sins and recited a last prayer, Roland holds out his glove toward heaven, in token that he surrenders his soul to God, and begs that an angel be sent to receive it from his hand. Thus, lying beneath a pine, his face toward Spain, his last thoughts for France and for God, Roland dies in the presence of the angels, who bear his soul off to Paradise.

Roland feeleth his hour at hand;
On a knoll he lies towards the Spanish land.
With one hand beats he upon his breast:
"In thy sight, O God, be my sins confessed.
From my hour of birth, both the great and small,
Down to this day, I repent of all."
As his glove he raises to God on high,
Angels of heaven descend him nigh.

Part III

Reprisals.—Roland has barely breathed his last when Charlemagne arrives on the battle-field and, gazing around him, perceives nothing but corpses. Receiving no answer to his repeated call for the twelve peers, Charlemagne groans that it was not without cause he felt anxious, and mourns that he was not there to take part in the fray. He and his men weep aloud for their fallen companions, and 20,000 soldiers swoon from grief at the sight of the havoc which has been made!

Still, only a few moments can be devoted to sorrow, for Duke Naimes, descrying a cloud of dust in the distance, eagerly suggests that if they ride on they can yet overtake and punish the foe! Detailing a small detachment to guard the dead, Charlemagne orders the pursuit of the Saracens, and, seeing the sun about to set, prays so fervently that daylight may last, that an angel promises he shall have light as long as he needs it. Thanks to this miracle, Charlemagne overtakes the Saracens just as they are about to cross the Ebro, and, after killing many, drives the rest into the river, where they are drowned.

It is only when the last of the foe has been disposed of that the sun sets, and, perceiving it is too late to return to Roncevaux that night Charlemagne gives orders to camp on the plain. While his weary men sleep peacefully, the Emperor himself spends the night mourning for Roland and for the brave Frenchmen who died to defend his cause, so it is only toward morning that he enjoys brief slumber, during which visions foreshadow the punishment to be inflicted upon Ganelon and all who uphold him.

In the mead the Emperor made his bed.
With his mighty spear beside his head,
Nor will he doff his arms to-night,
But lies in his broidered hauberk white.
Laced is his helm, with gold inlaid,
Girt on Joyeuse, the peerless blade,
Which changes thirty times a day
The brightness of its varying ray.

Meanwhile the wounded Marsile has returned to Saragossa, where, while binding up his wounds, his wife comments that it is strange no one has been able to get the better of such an old man as Charlemagne, and the last hope of the Saracens now rests in the Emir, who has just landed in Spain.

At dawn the Emperor returns to Roncevaux, and there begins his sad search for the bodies of the peers. Sure that Roland will be found facing the foe, he seeks for his corpse in the direction of Spain, and, discovering him at last on the little hill, swoons from grief. Then, recovering his senses, Charlemagne prays God to receive his nephew's soul, and, after pointing out to his men how bravely the peers fought, gives orders for the burial of the dead, reserving only the bodies of Roland, Oliver, and the Archbishop, for burial in France.

The last respects have barely been paid to the fallen, when a Saracen herald summons Charlemagne to meet the Emir. So the French mount to engage in a new battle. Such is the stimulus of Charlemagne's words and of his example, that all his men do wonders. The aged Emperor himself finally engages in a duel with the Emir, in the midst of which he is about to succumb, when an angel bids him strike one more blow, promising he shall triumph. Thus stimulated, Charlemagne slays the Emir, and the Saracens, seeing their leader slain, flee, closely pursued by the Frenchmen, who enter Saragossa in their wake. There, after killing all the men, they pillage the town.

On discovering that Marsile has meantime died of his wound, Charlemagne orders his widow to France, where he proposes to convert her through the power of love. The remainder of the pagans are compelled to receive baptism, and, when Charlemagne again wends his way through the Pyrenees, all Spain bows beneath his sceptre.

At Bordeaux, Charlemagne deposits upon the altar of St Severin Roland's Olifant, filled with gold pieces, before personally escorting the three august corpses to Blaye, where he sees them interred ere he hurries on to Aix-la-Chapelle to judge Ganelon.

The Chastisement of Ganelon.—On arriving in his palace, Charlemagne is confronted by Alda or Aude, a sister of Oliver, who frantically questions: "Where is Roland who has sworn to take me to wife?" Weeping bitterly, Charlemagne informs her his nephew is no more, adding that she can marry his son, but Audc rcjoins that, since her beloved is gone, she no longer wishes to live. These words uttered, she falls lifeless at the Emperor's feet.

From Spain the Emperor made retreat,
To Aix in France, his kingly seat;
And thither, to his halls, there came,
Alda, the fair and gentle dame.
"Where is my Roland, sire," she cried,
"Who vowed to take me for his bride?"
O'er Karl the flood of sorrow swept;
He tore his beard, and loud he wept.
"Dear sister, gentle friend," he said,
"Thou seekest one who lieth dead:
I plight to thee my son instead,—

Louis, who lord of my realm shall be."
"Strange," she said, "seems this to me.
God and His angels forbid that I
Should live on earth if Roland die."
Pale grew her cheek—she sank amain,
Down at the feet of Carlemaine.
So died she. God receive her soul!
The Franks bewail her in grief and dole.

The time having come for the trial, Ganelon appears before his judges, laden with chains and tied to a stake as if he were a wild beast. When accused of depriving Charlemagne of 20,000 Frenchmen, Ganelon retorts he did so merely to avenge his wrongs, and hotly denies having acted as a traitor. Thirty of his kinsmen sustain him in this assertion, one of them even volunteering to meet the Emperor's champion in a judicial duel. As the imperial champion wins, Ganelon and his relatives are adjudged guilty, but, whereas the latter thirty are merely hanged, the traitor himself is bound to wild horses until torn asunder.

Having thus done justice, Charlemagne informs his courtiers they are to attend the baptism of a Saracen lady of high degree, who is about to be received into the bosom of the Church.

The men of Bavaria and Allemaine,
Norman and Breton return again,
And with all the Franks aloud they cry,
That Gan a traitor's death shall die.
They bade be brought four stallions fleet;
Bound to them Ganelon, hands and feet:
Wild and swift was each savage steed,
And a mare was standing within the mead;
Four grooms impelled the coursers on,—
A fearful ending for Ganelon.
His every nerve was stretched and torn,
And the limbs of his body apart were borne;

The bright blood, springing from every vein,
Left on the herbage green its stain.
He dies a felon and recreant:
Never shall traitor his treason vaunt.

End of the Song.—Having thus punished the traitor and converted the heathen, Charlemagne, lying in his chamber one night, receives a visit from the angel Gabriel, who bids him go forth and do further battle against the pagans. Weary of warfare and longing for rest, the aged Emperor moans, "God, how painful is my life!" for he knows he must obey.

When the Emperor's justice was satisfied,
His mighty wrath did awhile subside.
Queen Bramimonde was a Christian made.
The day passed on into night's dark shade;
As the King in his vaulted chamber lay,
Saint Gabriel came from God to say,
"Karl, thou shalt summon thine empire's host,
And march in haste to Bira's coast;
Unto Impha city relief to bring,
And succour Vivian, the Christian king.
The heathens in siege have the town essayed,
And the shattered Christians invoke thine aid."
Fain would Karl such task decline.
"God! what a life of toil is mine!"
He wept; his hoary beard he wrung.

Here ends the Song of Théroulde.

AUCASSIN AND NICOLETTE[1]

Who would list a tale to know
Fashioned in a captive's woe?
How two little children met,
Aucassin and Nicolete;

[1] All the quotations from *Aucassin and Nicolette* are taken from the version by Michael West (George G. Harrap & Co.).

How he suffered grievous pain,
And did prowess all to gain
Nicolete of face so clear.
Sweet the song and soft to hear,

Very curteous, fairly set;
Listen and your cares forget.
Never man of malady
Torn and tried so grievously,
But he is made well and hale,
And forgetteth all his pain,
And is full of joy again,
At this sweet tale.

This popular mediaeval ballad is in alternate fragments of verse and prose, and relates how the Count of Valence made desperate war against the Count of Biaucaire, a very old and frail man, who saw that his castle was in imminent danger of being taken and sacked. In his distress, this old lord besought his son Aucassin, who so far had taken no interest in the war, to go forth and fight. The youth, however, refused to do so, saying his heart was wrapped up in love for Nicolette, a fair slave belonging to a captain in the town. This man, seeing the delicacy of his slave and realizing she must belong to some good family, had her baptized and treated her as if she were an adopted daughter.

On account of Nicolette's lowly condition, Aucassin's father refuses to listen when the young man proposes to marry her, and sternly bids him think of a wife better suited to his rank. The young lover, however, vehemently insists that Nicolette is fit to be an empress, and vows he will not fight until he has won her for his own. On seeing how intractable the youth is, the father beseeches the owner of the slave to clap her in prison, so that Aucassin will not be able to get at her in any way.

Heart-broken to think that his lady-love is undergoing captivity in his behalf, Aucassin spends his time moping. To induce him to fight, his father finally promises that if he will go forth and drive away the foe he will be allowed to see Nicolette and kiss her. The prospect of such a reward so fires the young hero, that he sallies forth, routs the besiegers, and, seizing the Count of Valence, brings him back a prisoner. On entering the castle, he immediately begins to clamour for Nicolette, but his father now declares he would rather see the maiden burned as a witch than to let his son have anything more to do with her. Hearing this, Aucassin indignantly declares that such being the case, he will free his prisoner, an act of generosity which infuriates his father, who had hoped to be enriched by the Count's ransom. To punish Aucassin, the Count of Biaucaire now thrusts him into prison, but although the lovers are sharing the same fate, they languish apart, and, therefore, spend all their time lamenting.

One night, when the moon is shining bright, Nicolette, who has heard she is likely to be brought to trial and burned, decides to effect her escape. As the old woman who mounts guard over her is fast asleep, she softly ties together her sheets and towels, and, fastening them to a pillar, lets herself down by the window into the garden, whence she timidly steals out into the night.

The poem now artlessly describes Nicolette's beauty as she trips over the dewy grass, her tremors as she slips through the postern gate, and her lingering at the foot of the tower where her lover is imprisoned.

While pausing there, Nicolette overhears his voice lamenting, and, thrusting her head into an aperture in the wall, tells him that she is about to escape and that as soon as she is gone they will set him free. To convince her lover that it is she who is talking, Nicolette cuts off a golden curl, which she drops down into his dungeon, repeating that she must flee. But Aucassin beseeches her not to go, knowing a young maid is exposed to countless dangers out in the world, and vehemently declares he would die were any one to lay a finger upon her. He adds that she alone shall be his wife, and that the mere thought of her belonging to any one else is unendurable. This declaration of love cheers poor Nicolette, who is so entranced by her lover's words that she fails to notice the approach of a patrol. A young sentinel, however, peering down from the walls, touched by Nicolette's beauty and by the plight of these young lovers, warns them of their danger. But not daring to speak openly to Nicolette, he chants a musical warning, which comes just in time to enable her to hide behind a pillar. There she cowers until the guards pass by, then, slipping down into the dry moat—although it is a perilous undertaking—she painfully climbs up its other side and seeks refuge in a neighbouring forest, where, although the poem informs us there are "beasts serpentine," she feels safer than in town.

While wandering in this wilderness Nicolette runs across some shepherds whom she bribes to go and tell Aucassin that a wild beast is ranging through the forest, and to bid him come and slay it as soon as possible. Having thus devised means to entice her lover out of Biaucaire, Nicolette wanders on until she reaches a lovely spot, where she erects a rustic lodge, decking it with the brightest flowers she can find, in hopes that her lover, when weary of hunting, will rest beneath its flowery roof, and guess that it was erected by her fair hands.

Meantime the Count of Biaucaire, hearing that Nicolette has vanished, sets his son free, and, seeing him sunk in melancholy, urges him to go out and hunt, thinking the exercise may make him forget the loss of his beloved. Still, it is only when shepherds come and report that a wild beast is ranging through the forest, that the youth mounts his steed and sallies forth, his father little suspecting that instead of tracking game, he is bent on seeking traces of his beloved.

Ere long Aucassin encounters an old charcoal-burner, to whom he confides his loss, and who assures him such a sorrow is nothing compared to his own. On discovering that the poor man's tears can be stayed with money, Aucassin bestows upon him the small sum he needs, receiving in return the information that a lovely maiden has been seen in the forest. Continuing his quest, Aucassin comes in due time to the flowery bower, and, finding it empty, sings his love and sorrow in tones that reach Nicolette's ear. Then, dismounting from his horse to rest here for the night, Aucassin manages to sprain his shoulder. Thereupon Nicolette steals into the bower and takes immediate measures to mitigate the pain.

The mere fact that Nicolette is beside him helps Aucassin to forget everything else, and it is only after the first raptures are over, that they decide not to linger in the forest, where the Count of Biaucaire will soon find and separate them. To prevent such a calamity, they decide to depart together, and, as there is no extra steed for Nicolette to ride, her lover lifts her up on his horse before him, clasping her tight and kissing her repeatedly as they gallop along.

Aucassin the strong, the fair,
Gentle knight and lover rare,
From the forest forth doth go,
Holding on his saddle-bow
Nicolete that he loves so;
Then to kiss her doth begin,
Eyes and forehead, mouth and chin.
Full of wisdom sayeth she,
" Aucassin, sweet friend to me,
Tell me, whither do we go?"
" Dearest love, how should I know?
Whither go we, nought I care,
Forest, plain, or hillside bare,
So that I be with thee there."
Through the village, through the town,
Up the hill, across the down,
Riding onward through the land,
Thus together forth they passed.
On a day they came at last
Where no town nor houses be,
Lighted down upon the sand
Along the sea.

Thus the lovers travel all night, reach the sea-shore at dawn, and wander along it, arms twined around each other, while their weary steed follows them with drooped head.

At sunrise a vessel nears the shore, upon which they embark to get out of reach of the wrath of the Count of Biaucaire. The vessel, however, is soon overtaken by a terrible tempest, which, after tossing it about for seven days, drives it into the harbour of Torelore. This is the mediaeval 'topsy-turvy land,' for on entering the castle Aucassin learns

The Lovers on the Sea-shore
Main R. Bocher

that the King is lying abed, because a son has been born to him, while the Queen is at the head of the army fighting! This state of affairs so incenses Aucassin, that, armed with a big stick, he enters the King's room, gives him a good beating, and wrings from him a promise that no man in his country will ever lie abed again when a child is born, or send his wife out to do hard work. Having effected this reform in the land of Torelore, Aucassin and Nicolette dwell there peacefully for three years, at the end of which time the castle is taken by some Saracens. They immediately proceed to sack it, carrying off its inmates to sell them as slaves. Bound fast, Aucassin and Nicolette are thrust into separate ships, but, although these are going to the same port, a sudden tempest drives the vessel in which Aucassin lies to the shore of Biaucaire. There the people capture it, and finding their young master, set him free, and invite him to take possession of his castle, for, his father having died during his absence, he is now master of all he surveys.

Meantime Nicolette, landing at Carthage, discovers that this is her native town, and recognizes in her captors—her father and brothers. They are so overjoyed at recovering this long-lost sister that they propose to keep her with them, but Nicolette assures them she will never be happy until she rejoins Aucassin. Meantime she learns to play on the viol, and, when she has attained proficiency on this instrument, sets out in the guise of a wandering minstrel to seek her beloved. Conveyed by her brothers to the land of Biaucaire, Nicolette, soon after landing, hears that Aucassin, who has recently returned, is sorely bewailing the loss of his beloved. Presenting herself before Aucassin—who does not recognize her owing to the disguise—Nicolette plays so charmingly that she draws tears from his eyes. Then she begs to know his sorrows, and, on hearing he has lost his lady-love, suggests he woo the King of Carthage's daughter. Loudly averring he will never woo any one save Nicolette, Aucassin turns sadly away, whereupon the strolling minstrel assures him he shall see his beloved before long. Although it seems impossible to Aucassin that this prediction should be verified, Nicolette has little difficulty in fulfilling her promise, for, hastening back to her old home, she obtains some of her own clothes, and, thus restored to her wonted appearance, presents herself before the delighted Aucassin, who, overjoyed to see her once more, clasps her rapturously to his heart.

The ballad adds that the two lovers, united for good and all, lived happy ever after, and were an example to all faithful lovers in the beautiful land of Biaucaire.

SPANISH EPICS

LITERATURE was born in Spain only when the Christians began to reconquer their country from the Moors. The first literary efforts therefore naturally reflected a warlike spirit, and thus assumed the epic form. Very few of these poems still exist in their original shape save the *Poema del Cid*, the great epic treasure of Spain, as well as the oldest monument of Spanish literature. Besides this poem, there exist fragments of epics on the Infantes of Lara and on Fernan Gónzales, and hints of others of which no traces now remain. These poems were popularized in Spain by the *juglares*, who invented Bernardo del Carpio so as to have a hero worthy to off-set to the Roland of the *jongleurs*, —their French neighbours. But the poems about this hero have all perished, and his fame is preserved only in the prose chronicles. In the *Cronica rimada* of the thirteenth century, we discover an account of the Cid's youth, together with the episode where he slays Ximena's father, which supplied Corneille with the main theme of his tragedy.

The Spaniards also boast of a thirteenth-century poem of some 2500 stanzas on the life of Alexander, a fourteenth-century romance about Tristan, and the chivalric romance of *Amadis de Gaule*, which set the fashion for hosts of similar works, whose popularity had already begun to wane when Cervantes scotched all further attempts of this sort by turning the chivalric romance into ridicule in his *Don Quixote*.

The Spaniards also cultivated the epic ballad, or *romancero*, before the Golden Age of their literature (1550–1700), drawing their subjects from the history or legends of France and Spain, and treating mainly of questions of chivalry and love. Arthur, the Round Table, and the Quest for the Holy Grail, were their stock subjects, previous to the appearance of *Amadis de Gaule*, a work of original fiction remodelled and extended in the fifteenth century by Garcia Ordonez de Montalvo. During the Golden Age, Spain boasts more than two hundred artificial epics, treating of religious, political, and historical matters. Among these the *Auracana* of Erzilla, the *Argentina* of Centenera, and the *Austriada* of Rufo can be mentioned. Then Velasco revived the *Aeneid* for his countrymen's benefit, and religious themes such as Azevedo's *Creacion del Munde* became popular.

The latest of the Spanish epics is that of Saavedra, who, in his *El Moro Exposito*, has cleverly revived the old Spanish legend of the Infantes of Lara. It is, however, *The Cid* which is always quoted as Spain's representative epic.

THE CID

This poem, of some 3700 lines, is divided into two cantos, and was written about 1200. It is a compilation from extant ballads in regard to the great Spanish hero Rodrigo Diaz de Bivar, born between 1030 and 1040, whose heroic deeds were performed at the time when the Christian kings were making special efforts to eject the Moors who had invaded Spain 300 years before.

The first feat mentioned relates that Rodrigo's father, having been insulted by Don Gomez, pined at the thought of leaving this affront unavenged, until his son, who had never fought before, volunteered to defend him. Not only did Rodrigo challenge and slay Don Gomez, but, cutting off his head, bore it to his father as a proof that his enemy was dead, a feat which so pleased the old gentleman that he declared Rodrigo should henceforth be head of the family.

After thus signalizing himself, Rodrigo was suddenly called up to face five Moorish kings who had been making sallies into Castile. Not only did he defeat them, but took them prisoner, thereby winning from them the title by which he is commonly known, of 'the Cid' or 'The Lord.'

Shortly after this Donna Ximena, daughter of Don Gomez, appeared before King Ferrando demanding satisfaction for her father's death, and consenting to forego revenge only on condition that Rodrigo would marry her. The young hero having assented, the couple were united in the presence of the King, after which Rodrigo took his beautiful bride to his mother, with whom he left her until he had earned the right to claim her by distinguishing himself in some way.

It seems that Ferrando of Castile was then disputing from the King of Aragon the possession of Calahorra, a frontier town. The monarchs decided to settle their difference by a duel, stipulating that the town should belong to the party whose champion triumphed.

Ferrando having selected Rodrigo as his champion, our hero set out to meet his opponent, delaying on the way long enough to rescue a leper from a bog. Then, placing this unfortunate on his horse before him, Rodrigo bore him to an inn, where, in spite of the remonstrances of his followers, he allowed the leper to share his bed and board. That night, while lying beside his loathsome bed-fellow, Rodrigo suddenly felt a cold breath pass through him, and discovered that his companion was gone. He beheld in his stead St Lazarus, who proclaimed that, since Rodrigo had been so charitable, he would meet with prosperity, and might know whenever he felt a cold shiver run down his spine that it was an omen of success. Thus encouraged, Rodrigo rode on to take part in the duel, but he had been so delayed that the battle call had already sounded, and Alvar Fanez, his cousin, was preparing to fight in his stead. Bidding his cousin step aside, Rodrigo entered the lists, and soon won Calahorra for Ferrando.

Pleased with what Rodrigo had accomplished, the King now showered honours upon him, which so aroused the jealousy of the courtiers that they began to conspire with the Moors to ruin him. It happened, however, that they addressed their first proposals to the very kings whom Rodrigo had conquered, and who proved loyal enough to send him word of the plot. On discovering the treachery of the courtiers, the King banished them, but the wife of Don Garcia pleaded so eloquently with the Cid, that he furnished the banished man with letters of introduction to one of the Moorish kings, who, to please his conqueror, bestowed the city of Cabra upon him.

Although treated with such generosity, Don Garcia proved ungrateful, and even tried to cheat the Moors. Hearing this, the Cid, siding with his former enemies, came into their country to take away from Don Garcia the city which had been allotted for his use.

During one of Ferrando's absences from home, the Moors invaded one of his provinces, whereupon Rodrigo, in retaliation, besieged the city of Coimbra. While he was thus engaged his army suffered so much from lack of provisions that it finally seemed as if he would have to give up his undertaking. But the monks, who had advised the Cid to besiege the city, now came to his rescue, and by feeding his army from their own stores enabled Rodrigo to recover another town from the pagans.

Delighted with this new accession of territory, Ferrando knighted Rodrigo, who meantime had added to his title of the Cid that of Campeador, 'the champion,' and hereafter was often mentioned as 'the one born in a fortunate hour.' In addition, the King bestowed upon Rodrigo the governorship of the cities of Coimbra and Zamorra, which were to be reoccupied by Christians.

Shortly after this, the Pope demanded that Ferrando should do homage to the empire, but the King rejoined that Spain was independent and therefore refused to obey. Hearing that large forces were marching against him to compel him to submit, Ferrando placed the Cid at the head of an army, and our hero not only defeated the enemy at Tobosa, but won so brilliant a victory that the Pope never ventured to renew his demands.

Feeling death draw near, Ferrando divided his realm between his sons, who became Kings of Castile, Leon, and Galicia, and bestowed upon his daughters the cities of Zamorra and Toro. Although disappointed not to inherit the whole realm, the eldest prince, Don Sancho, dared not oppose his father's will until one of his brothers proceeded to dispossess one of their sisters. Under the plea that the promise made to their father had already been broken, Don Sancho now set out to conquer the whole realm, but proved so unfortunate in his first battle as to fall into his brother's hands. There he would have remained for the rest of his life, had not the Cid delivered him, taken his captor, and confiscated his realm in Sancho's behalf. Hearing this, the third king, Alfonso, clamoured for his share of his brother's spoil, and, as none was allotted him, declared war in his turn. In this campaign Sancho proved victorious only when the Cid fought in his behalf, and the struggle resulted in the imprisonment of Alfonso, who would have been slain had not his sister asked that he should be allowed to enter a monastery. From there Alfonso soon effected his escape, and hastened to seek refuge among the Moors at Toledo.

Don Sancho, having meantime assumed all three crowns, became anxious to dispossess his sister of Zamorra. But the Cid refused to take part in so unchivalrous a deed, and thereby so angered the King that he vowed he would exile him. When the Cid promptly rejoined that in that case he would hasten to Toledo and offer his services to Alfonso to help him recover all he had lost, Sancho repented and apologized. He did not, however, relinquish his project of despoiling his sister of Zamorra, but merely dispensed the Cid from accompanying him.

As Zamorra was well defended by Vellido Dolfos, the Princess's captain, King Sancho was not able to take the town. He so sorely beset the inhabitants, however, that Vellido Dolfos resolved to get the better of him by strategy. Feigning to be driven out of the city, he secretly joined Don Sancho, and offered to deliver the city into his hands if the King would only accompany him to a side gate. Notwithstanding adverse omens, the credulous Sancho, believing him, rode off, only to meet his death at the postern gate, inside which his murderer immediately took refuge.

On learning that his master had been slain, the Cid hastened to avenge him, and, as Sancho had left no heir, proclaimed Alfonso his successor. We are told that this young Prince had already heard of his brother's death through a message from his sister, and, fearing the Moors would not allow him to depart for good, had merely asked permission to visit his kin. The wary Moorish king consented, but only on condition Alfonso would promise never to attack him or his sons, should he become king.

When Alfonso arrived at Zamorra, all the Spaniards readily did homage to him save the Cid, who refused his allegiance until the King had solemnly sworn he had no share in his brother's death. To satisfy the Cid, therefore, Alfonso and twelve of his men took a threefold oath in the church of Burgos; but it is said Alfonso never forgave the humiliation which the Cid thus inflicted upon him.

The new monarch proved to be a wise ruler for the kingdoms of Leon, Castile, Galicia, and Portugal. He was not without his troubles, however, for shortly after his succession the Cid quarrelled with one of his nobles. Next the Moorish kings became disunited, and Alfonso's former host summoned him to his aid. Not only did Alfonso assist this King of Toledo, but invited him into his camp, where he forced him to release him from his promise made on leaving his city. Not daring to refuse while in the power of the Christians, the Moorish king reluctantly consented, and was surprised and delighted to hear Alfonso immediately renew the oath, for, while not willing to be friends with the Moors under compulsion, he had no objection to enter into an alliance with them of his own free will.

Not long after this the King of Navarre sent forth his champion to challenge one of Alfonso's, the stake this time being three castles which the Cid won. But the Moors, taking advantage of an illness of the Cid which followed this battle, rose up against Alfonso, who was compelled to wage war against them. In this campaign he would have fallen into the enemy's hands had not the Cid risen from his sick-bed to extricate him from peril!

By this time the renown of the Cid was so great, that people in speaking of him invariably termed him 'the Perfect One,' thereby arousing such jealousy among the courtiers, that they persuaded Alfonso his subject was trying to outshine him! In anger the King decreed Rodrigo's immediate banishment, and, instead of allowing him the customary thirty days to prepare for departure, threatened to put him to death were he found within the land nine days later! As soon as the Cid informed his friends that he was banished, one and all promised to follow wherever he went, as did his devoted cousin Alvar Fanez.

It is at this point that the present poem of the Cid begins, for the ballads covering the foregoing part of the Cid's life exist only in a fragmentary state. We are told that the decree of banishment proved a signal for the courtiers to plunder the hero's house, and that the Cid, gazing sadly upon its ruins, exclaimed, "My enemies have done this!" Then, seeing a poor woman stand by, he bade her secure her share, adding that for his part he would henceforth live by pillaging the Moors, but that the day would come when he would return home laden with honours.

On his way to Burgos the Cid was somewhat cheered

by good omens, and was joined by so many knights in quest of adventure that no less than sixty banners fluttered behind him. A royal messenger had, however, preceded him to this city, to forbid the people to show him hospitality and to close his own house against him. The only person who dared inform the Cid of this fact was a little maid, who tremblingly reported that he was to be debarred from all assistance.

> "O thou that in a happy hour didst gird thee with the sword,
> It is the order of the King; we dare not, O my lord!
> Sealed with his royal seal hath come his letter to forbid
> The Burgos folk to open door, or shelter thee, my Cid.
> Our goods, our homes, our very eyes, in this are all at stake;
> And small the gain to thee, though we meet ruin for thy sake.
> Go, and God prosper thee in all that thou dost undertake."[1]

Pausing at the church only long enough to say a prayer, the Cid rode out of the gates of Burgos and camped on a neighbouring hill, where his nephew Martin Antolinez brought him bread and wine, declaring he would henceforth share the Cid's fortunes in defiance of the King. It was to this relative that the Cid confided the fact that he was without funds and must raise enough money to defray present expenses. Putting their heads together, these two then decided to fill two huge chests with sand, and offer them to a couple of Jews in Burgos for 600 marks, stating that the chests contained treasures too heavy and valuable to be taken into exile, and assuring them that, if they solemnly pledged themselves not to open the chests for a year, they could then claim them, provided the Cid had not redeemed them in the meanwhile. Trusting to the Cid's word

[1] All the quotations from *The Cid* are taken from the translation by Ormsby.

and hoping to enrich themselves by this transaction, the Jews gladly lent the 600 marks and bore away the heavy chests.

Having thus secured the required supplies, the Cid proceeded to San Pedro de Cardena, where he entrusted his wife Ximena and two daughters to the care of the prior, leaving behind him funds enough to meet all their expenses. Then, although parting with his family was as hard as "when a finger-nail is torn from the flesh," the Cid rode away, crossing the frontier just as the nine days ended. He was there greatly cheered by a vision of the angel Gabriel, who assured him all would be well with him.

The prayer was said, the mass was sung, they mounted to depart;
My Cid a moment stayed to press Ximena to his heart:
Ximena kissed his hand, as one distraught with grief was she:
He looked upon his daughters: "These to God I leave," said he;
"Unto our Lady and to God, Father of all below;
He knows if we shall meet again:—and now, sirs, let us go."

As when the finger-nail from out the flesh is torn away,
Even so sharp to him and them the parting pang that day.
Then to his saddle sprang my Cid, and forth his vassals led;
But ever as he rode, to those behind he turned his head.

Entering the land of the Moors with a force of 300 men, the Cid immediately proceeded to take a castle and to besiege the city of Alcocer. But this town resisted so bravely, that after fifteen weeks the Cid decided to effect by strategy the entrance denied by force. Feigning discouragement, he, therefore, left his camp, whereupon the inhabitants immediately poured out of the city to visit it, leaving the gates wide open behind them. The Cid, who was merely hiding near by, now cleverly cut off their retreat and thus entered Alcocer through wide-open gates.

No sooner did the Moors learn that the Cid had conquered this important place, than they hastened to besiege it, cutting off the water supply, to compel the Christians to come out. To save his men from perishing of thirst, the Cid made so vigorous a sortie that he not only drove the enemy away, but captured their baggage, thus winning so much booty that he was able to send thirty caparisoned steeds to Alfonso, as well as rich gifts in money to his wife. In return, the bearer of these welcome tokens was informed by King Alfonso that Rodrigo would shortly be pardoned and recalled.

Meanwhile the Cid, leaving Alcocer, had taken up his abode on the hill near Medina, which still bears his name. Thence he proceeded to the forest of Tebar, where he again fought so successfully against the Moors that he compelled the city of Saragossa to pay tribute to him. Rumours of these triumphs enticed hundreds of Castilian knights to join him, and with their aid he outwitted all the attempts the Moors made to regain their lost possessions. We are also told that in one of these battles the Cid took prisoner Don Ramon, who refused to eat until free. Seeing this, the Cid took his sword, Colada, and promised to set him and his kinsmen free if they would only eat enough to have strength to depart. Although doubtful whether this promise would be kept, Don Ramon and his followers partook of food and rode away, constantly turning their heads to make sure that they were not pursued.

He spurred his steed, but, as he rode, a backward glance he bent,
Still fearing to the last my Cid his promise would repent:
A thing, the world itself to win, my Cid would not have done:
No perfidy was ever found in him, the Perfect One.

As some of his subjects were sorely persecuted

by the Moors, Alfonso now sent word to the Cid to punish them, a task the hero promised to perform, provided the King would pledge himself never again to banish a man without giving him thirty days' notice, and to make sundry other wise reforms in his laws. Having thus secured inestimable boons for his fellow-countrymen, the Cid proceeded to besiege sundry Moorish castles, all of which he took, winning thereby much booty. Having thus served his monarch, the Cid was recalled in triumph to Castile, where he was told to keep all he had won from the Moors. In return the Cid helped Alfonso to secure Toledo, seeing the King with whom this King had sworn alliance was now dead. It was while the siege of this city was taking place that Bishop Jerome was favoured by a vision of St Isidro, who predicted they would take the city, a promise verified in 1085, when the Cid's was the first Christian banner to float above its walls. Our hero now became governor of this town, but, although he continued to wage war against the Moors, his successes had made the courtiers so jealous that they induced the King to imprison Ximena and her daughters.

Perceiving he was no longer in favour at court, the Cid haughtily withdrew, and, when Alfonso came down into Valencia, demanding that the cities which had hitherto paid tribute to his subject should now do so to him, the Cid retaliated by invading Alfonso's realm. None of the courtiers daring to oppose him, Alfonso had cause bitterly to repent of what he had done, and humbly assured his powerful subject he would never molest him again. Ever ready to forgive an ungrateful master, the Cid withdrew, and for a time King and subject lived in peace.

Although the Cid had permitted the Moors to remain in the cities he had conquered, they proved rather restive under the Christian yoke, and guided by Abeniaf finally told the Moors in Northern Africa that if they would only cross the sea they would deliver Valencia into their hands. But this conspiracy soon became known to the Moors who favoured the Cid, and they immediately notified him, holding their town, which was in dire peril, for twelve days.

To keep his promise, Abeniaf finally hauled some of the Moors up over the walls by means of ropes, and the presence of these foes in their midst compelled the Moors who favoured the Cid to leave the city in disguise, thus allowing Abeniaf and his allies to plunder right and left and even to murder the Moorish king. This done, Abeniaf himself assumed the regal authority, and began to govern the city in such an arbitrary way that he soon managed to offend even his own friends.

Meantime the Moors who had fled rejoined the Cid, and, when they reported what had occurred, Rodrigo wrote to Abeniaf, reproaching him for his treachery and demanding the surrender of the property he had left in the town. As Abeniaf replied that his allies had taken possession of it, the Cid termed him a traitor and swore he would secure revenge. Thereupon our hero set out with an army, and, finding himself unable to take the city by assault, began to besiege it, pulling down the houses in the suburbs to secure necessary materials to construct his camp. Then he began a systematic attack on the city, mastering one of its defences after another and carrying on the siege with such vigour that he thereby won additional glory. All the Moorish captives taken were sent out through his lines into the open country, where they were invited to pursue their agricultural avocations, and assured protection, provided they would pay tribute of one-tenth of the produce of their lands.

Meantime the people in the besieged city suffered so sorely from hunger, that they finally sent word they would treat with the Cid if he would allow Abeniaf and his followers to leave the country unharmed. The Cid having consented to this proposal, the invading Moors withdrew to Morocco, whence, however, they soon returned in increased numbers to recapture Valencia and take their revenge upon Abeniaf, who had proved treacherous to them also. To check the advance of this foe, the Cid flooded the country by opening the sluices in the irrigation canals, and the invaders, fancying themselves in danger of drowning, beat a hasty retreat. Because Abeniaf took advantage of these circumstances to turn traitor again, the Cid besieged him in Valencia for nine months, during which the famine became so intense that the inhabitants resorted to all manner of expedients to satisfy their hunger.

Throughout this campaign the Cid ate his meals in public, sitting by himself at a high table, and assigning the one next him to the warriors who won the most distinction in battle. This table was headed by Alvar Fanez, surrounded by the most famous knights. A notorious coward, pretending to have done great deeds, advanced one day to claim a seat among the heroes. Perceiving his intention, the Cid called him to come and sit with him, whereupon the knight became so elated that when he again found himself on the field of battle he actually did wonders! Witnessing his efforts, the Cid generously encouraged him and, after he had shown himself brave indeed, publicly bade him sit with the distinguished knights.

The city of Valencia having finally opened its gates, the Cid marched in with a train of provision-wagons, for he longed to relieve the starving. Then, sending for the principal magistrates, he expressed commiseration for their sufferings, adding that he would treat the people fairly, provided they proved loyal in their turn. But, instead of occupying the city itself, he and the Christians returned to the suburbs, enjoining upon the Moorish governor to maintain order among his people, and slay none but Abeniaf, who had proved traitor to all.

Soon after, realising that the Moors and Christians would never be able to live in peace within the same enclosure, the Cid appointed another place of abode for the Moors. Then he and his followers marched into Valencia, which they proceeded to hold, in spite of sundry attempts on the part of the Moors to recover possession of so important a stronghold.

When the Moorish King of Seville ventured to attack the Cid, he and his 30,000 men experienced defeat, and many of his force were drowned in the river while trying to escape. Such was the amount of spoil obtained in this and other battles, that the Cid was able to make his soldiers rich beyond their dreams, although by this time he had a very large force, for new recruits constantly joined him during his wars with the Moors.

As the Cid had vowed on leaving home never to cut his beard until recalled, he was now a most venerable-looking man, with a beard of such length that it had to be bound out of his way by silken cords whenever he wanted to fight. Among those who now fought in the Cid's ranks was Hieronymo

(Jerome), who became Bishop of Valencia, and who, in his anxiety to restore the whole land to Christian rule, fought by the Cid's side, and invariably advised him to transform all captured mosques into Christian churches.

> But lo ! all armed from head to heel the Bishop Jerome shows ;
> He ever brings good fortune to my Cid where'er he goes.
> " Mass have I said, and now I come to join you in the fray ;
> To strike a blow against the Moor in battle if I may,
> And in the field win honour for my order and my hand.
> It is for this that I am here, far from my native land.
> Unto Valencia did I come to cast my lot with you,
> All for the longing that I had to slay a Moor or two.
> And so, in warlike guise I come, with blazoned shield, and lance,
> That I may flesh my blade to-day, if God but give the chance.
> Then send me to the front to do the bidding of my heart :
> Grant me this favour that I ask, or else, my Cid, we part ! "

Now that he had a fixed abiding place, the Cid bade Alvar Fanez and Martin Antolinoz carry a rich present to Don Alfonso, and obtain his permission to bring his wife and daughters to Valencia. The same messengers were also laden with a reward for the Abbot of San Pedro, under whose protection the Cid's family had taken refuge, and with funds to redeem the chests of sand from the Jews at Burgos, begging their pardon for the deception practised upon them and allowing them higher interest than they could ever have claimed. Not only did the messengers gallantly acquit themselves of this embassy, but boasted everywhere of the five pitched battles the Cid had won and of the eight towns now under his sway.

On learning that the Cid had conquered Valencia, Alfonso expressed keen delight, although his jealous courtiers did not hesitate to murmur that they could have done as well ! The monarch also granted permission to Doña Ximena and her daughters to join the Cid, and the three ladies set out with their escorts for Valencia. Nine miles outside this city, the Cid met them, mounted on his steed Bavieca, which he had won from the Moors, and, joyfully embracing wife and daughters, welcomed them to Valencia, where from the top of the Alcazar he bade them view the fertile country which paid tribute to him.

But, three months after the ladies' arrival, 50,000 Moors crossed over from Africa to recover their lost territory. Hearing this, the Cid immediately laid in a stock of provisions, renewed his supplies of ammunition, and inspected the walls and engines of his towns to make sure they could resist. These preparations concluded, he told his wife and daughters they should now see with their own eyes how well he could fight! Soon after the Moors began the siege of the city (1102), the Cid arranged that some of his troops should slip out and attack them from behind while he faced them. By this stratagem the Moors were caught between opposing forces, and overestimating the numbers of their enemies, fled in terror, allowing the Cid to triumph once more, although he had only 4000 men to oppose to their 50,000! Thanks to this panic of the Moors, the Cid collected such huge quantities of booty, that he was able to send 100 fully equipped horses to King Alfonso, as well as the tent which he had captured from the Moorish monarch. These gifts not only pleased Alfonso, but awed and silenced the courtiers, among whom were the Infantes of Carrion, who deemed it might be well to sue for the Cid's daughters, since the father was able to bestow such rich gifts. Having reached this decision, these scheming youths approached the King, who, counting upon his vassals' implicit obedience to his commands promised they should marry as they wished.

When the bearers of the Cid's present, therefore, returned to Valencia, they bore a letter wherein Alfonso bade the Cid give his daughters in marriage to the Infantes of Carrion. Although this marriage suited neither the old hero nor his wife, both were far too loyal to oppose the King's wishes, and humbly sent word they would obey.

Then the Cid graciously went to meet his future sons-in-law. They were escorted to the banks of the Tagus by Alfonso himself, who there expressed surprise at the length of the Cid's beard, and seemed awed by the pomp with which he was surrounded, for at the banquet all the chief men ate out of dishes of gold, and no one was asked to use anything less precious than silver. Not only did the Cid assure his future sons-in-law that his daughters should have rich dowries, but, the banquet ended, escorted them back to Valencia, where he entertained them royally.

The wedding festivities lasted fifteen days, but even after they were over the Infantes of Carrion tarried in Valencia, thus giving the Cid more than one opportunity to regret having bestowed his daughters' hands upon youths who possessed neither courage nor nobility of character. While the young men were still lingering in Valencia, it happened one afternoon—while the Cid lay sleeping in the hall—that a huge lion, kept in the court-yard for his amusement, escaped from its keepers. While those present immediately rushed forward to protect the sleeper, the Cid's sons-in-law, terrified at the sight of the monster, crept one beneath the hero's couch and the other over a wine-press, thus soiling his garments so that he was not fit to be seen. At the

The Cid and the Lion
Willy Pogany

lion's roar the Cid awoke. Seeing at a glance what had occurred, he sprang forward, then, laying a powerful hand on the animal's mane, compelled him to follow him out of the hall, and thrust him ignominiously back into his cage.

The Infantes having so plainly revealed their cowardice, people made fun of them and roused their resentment to such an extent that, when the Moors again threatened Valencia, they offered to go forth and defend the Cid. This show of courage delighted the old hero, who sallied forth accompanied by both sons-in-law and by the Bishop, who was a mighty fighter. Although most of the warriors present did wonders on this occasion, the Infantes of Carrion were careful not to run any risk, although one of them purchased a horse which a soldier had won from the Moors, and shamelessly passed it off as his own trophy. Pleased to think this son-in-law had so distinguished himself, the Cid complimented him after the battle, where he himself had slain so many Moors and won so much booty that he was able to send another princely present to Alfonso. Perceiving they were still objects of mockery among the followers of the Cid, the Infantes now begged permission to take their wives home, although their real intention was to make these helpless girls pay for the insults they had received. Little suspecting this fact, the Cid regretfully allowed his daughters to depart, and tried to please his sons-in-law by bestowing upon them the choice swords, Tizona and Colada, won in the course of his battles against the Moors.

Two days' journey from Valencia the Infantes prepared to carry out the revenge they had planned, but while conferring in regard to its details were overheard by a Moor, who, vowing he would have nothing to do with such cowards, left them unceremoniously. Sending on their main troops with a cousin of the girls, Felez Munoz, who served as their escort, the Infantes led their wives into a neighbouring forest, where, after stripping them, they beat them cruelly, kicked them with their spurs, and abandoned them grievously wounded and trembling for their lives. When the Infantes rejoined their suite without their wives, Felez Munoz, suspecting something was wrong, rode back hastily, and found his cousins in such a pitiful plight that they were too weak to speak. Casting his own cloak about the nearly naked women, he tenderly bore them into a thicket, where they could lie in safety while he watched over them all night, for he did not dare leave them to go in quest of aid. At dawn he hurried off to a neighbouring village and secured help. There, in the house of a kind man, the poor ladies were cared for, while their cousin hastened on to apprise the Cid of what had occurred.

Meantime the Infantes had met Alvar Fanez conveying to the King another present, and, on being asked where were their wives, carelessly rejoined they had left them behind. Ill pleased with such a report, Alvar Fanez and his troops hurried back in quest of the ladies, but found nothing save traces of blood, which made them suspect foul play. On discovering what had really happened to the Cid's daughters, Alvar Fanez hurried on to deliver the present to the King, and indignantly reported what treatment the Cid's daughters had undergone at the hands of the bridegrooms the King had chosen for them, informing him that since he had made the marriage it behoved him to see justice done.

Horrified on hearing what had occurred, Alfonso summoned the Cortes, sending word to the Cid and to the Infantes to appear before it at Toledo three months hence.

Meantime the Cid, learning what had befallen his poor girls, hastened to them, took them home, and, hearing that the King himself would judge his case, decided to abide by the decision of the Cortes. At the end of the third month, therefore, the Cid's followers—who had preceded him—erected in the royal hall at Toledo the ivory seat he had won at Valencia, and Alfonso himself openly declared the Cid quite worthy to occupy a throne by his side, seeing no one had ever served him so well as the man whom the courtiers were always trying to belittle. The day for the solemn session having dawned, the Cid entered the hall, followed by 100 knights, while the Infantes of Carrion appeared there with equal numbers, being afraid of an attack. When summoned to state his wrongs, the Cid quietly rose from his ivory throne, declaring that, having bestowed upon the Infantes two swords of great price, he demanded their return, since, as they refused to have anything more to do with his daughters, he could no longer consider them his sons. All present were amazed at the mildness of the Cid's speech and at his demanding merely the return of his swords, and the Infantes, glad to be let off so easily, promptly resigned both weapons into the Cid's hand. With his precious swords lying across his lap, the Cid now declared that having also given the Infantes large sums of money he wished those returned also, and, although the young men objected, the court sentenced them to pay the sum the Cid claimed. Both these demands having been granted, the Cid next required satisfaction for the treatment the Infantes had inflicted upon his daughters, eloquently describing to the Cortes the cruelty and treachery used.

"So please your Grace! once more upon your clemency I call;
A grievance yet remains untold, the greatest grief of all.
And let the court give ear, and weigh the wrong that hath been done.
I hold myself dishonoured by the Lords of Carrion.
Redress by combat they must yield; none other will I take.
How now, Infantes! what excuse, what answer do ye make?
Why have ye laid my heartstrings bare? In jest or earnest, say,
Have I offended you? and I will make amends to-day.

"My daughters in your hands I placed the day that forth ye went,
And rich in wealth and honours from Valencia were ye sent.
Why did ye carry with you brides ye loved not, treacherous curs?
Why tear their flesh in Corpes wood with saddle-girths and spurs,
And leave them to the beasts of prey? Villains throughout were ye!
What answer ye can make to this 'tis for the court to see."

When the Cid added that Alfonso was responsible for these unfortunate marriages, the monarch admitted the fact, and asked what the Infantes of Carrion could say in their own defence. Insolently they declared the Cid's daughters not worthy to mate with them, stating they had, on the whole, treated them better than they deserved by honouring them for a time with their attentions.

Had not the Cid forbidden his followers to speak until he granted permission, these words would have been avenged almost as soon as uttered. But, forgetting his previous orders, the aged Cid now demanded of Pero Mudo (the 'dumb man') why he did not speak, whereupon this hero boldly struck one of the Infantes' party and challenged them all to fight.

Thus compelled to settle the difficulty by a judicial duel, the King bade the Infantes and their uncle be ready to meet the Cid's champions in the lists on the morrow. The poem describes the encounter thus:

The marshals leave them face to face and from the lists are gone;
Here stand the champions of my Cid, there those of Carrion;
Each with his gaze intent and fixed upon his chosen foe,
Their bucklers braced before their breasts, their lances pointing low,
Their heads bent down, as each man leans above his saddle-bow.
Then with one impulse every spur is in the charger's side,
And earth itself is felt to shake beneath their furious stride;
Till, midway meeting, three with three, in struggle fierce they lock,
While all account them dead who hear the echo of the shock.

The cowardly Infantes, having been defeated, publicly confessed themselves in the wrong, and were ever after abhorred, while the Cid returned to Valencia with the spoils wrung from his adversaries and proudly presented to his wife and daughters the three champions who had upheld their cause.

He who a noble lady wrongs and casts aside—may he
Meet like requital for his deeds, or worse, if worse there be.
But let us leave them where they lie—their meed is all men's scorn.
Turn we to speak of him that in a happy hour was born.
Valencia the Great was glad, rejoiced at heart to see
The honoured champions of her lord return in victory.

Shortly after this the Cid's pride was further salved by proposals of marriage from the princes of Aragon and Navarre, and thus his descendants in due time sat upon the thrones of these realms.

And he that in a good hour was born, behold how he hath sped!
His daughters now to higher rank and greater honour wed:
Sought by Navarre and Aragon for queens his daughters twain;
And monarchs of his blood to-day upon the thrones of Spain.

Five years now elapsed during which the Cid lived happy, honoured by all and visited by embassies even from distant Persia. But the Cid was now old and felt his end near, for St Peter visited him one night and warned him that, although he would die in thirty days, he would triumph over the Moors even after life had departed.

This assurance was most comforting, for hosts of Moors had suddenly crossed the seas and were about to besiege Valencia. Trusting in St Peter's warning, the Cid made all his preparations for death, and, knowing his followers would never be able to hold the city after he was gone, bade them keep his demise secret, embalm his body, bind it firmly on his steed Bavieca, and boldly cut their way out of the city with him in their van.

Just as had been predicted, the Cid died on the thirtieth day after his vision, and, his corpse having been embalmed as he directed, his followers prepared to leave Valencia. To the amazement of the Moors, the gates of the city they were besieging were suddenly flung open wide, and out sallied the Christians with the Cid in their midst. The mere sight of this heroic leader caused such a panic, that the little troop of 600 Christian knights safely conveyed their dead chief and his family through the enemy's serried ranks to Castile. Other detachments led by the Bishop and Gil Diaz then drove these Moors back to Africa after securing immense spoil.

Seeing Valencia abandoned, the Moors whom the Cid had established without the city returned to take possession of their former houses, on one of which they discovered an inscription stating that the Cid Campeador was dead and would no longer dispute possession of the city.

Meantime the funeral procession had gone on to the Monastery of San Pedro de Cardena, where the Cid was buried, as he requested, and where his marvellously preserved body sat in his ivory throne ten years, before it was placed in its present tomb.

For two years and a half the steed Bavieca was reverently tended by the Cid's followers, none of whom, however, ever presumed to bestride him. As for Ximena, having mounted guard over her husband's remains four years, she finally died, leaving grandchildren to rule over Navarre and Aragon.

And so his honour in the land grows greater day by day.
Upon the feast of Pentecost from life he passed away.
For him and all of us the Grace of Christ let us implore.
And here ye have the story of my Cid Campeador.

PORTUGUESE EPICS

PORTUGUESE literature, owing to its late birth, shows little originality. Besides, its earliest poems are of a purely lyrical and not of an epical type. Then, too, its reigning family being of Burgundian extraction, it borrowed its main ideas and literary material from France. In that way Charlemagne, the Arthurian romances, and the story of the Holy Grail became popular in Portugal, where it is even claimed that *Amadis de Gaule* originated, although it received its finished form in Spain.

The national epic of Portugal is the work of Luis de Camoëns, who, inspired by patriotic fervour, sang in *Os Lusiades* of the discovery of the eagerly sought maritime road to India. Of course, Vasco da Gama is the hero of this epic, which is described *in extenso* further on.

In imitation of Camoëns, sundry other Portuguese poets attempted epics on historical themes, but none of their works possess sufficient merits to keep their memory green.

During the sixteenth century, many versions of the prose epics or romances of chivalry were rife, *Amadis de Gaule* and its sequel, *Palmerina d'Inglaterra*, being the most popular of all.

Later on Meneses composed, according to strict classic rules, a tedious epic entitled *Henriqueida* in praise of the monarch Henry, and de Macedo left *O Oriente*, an epical composition which enjoyed a passing popularity.

THE LUSIAD

Introduction

The author of the Portuguese epic, Luis de Camoëns, was born at Lisbon in 1524. Although his father, commander of a warship, was lost at sea during his infancy, his mother contrived to give him a good education, and even sent him to the University at Coimbra, where he began to write poetry.

After graduating Camoëns served at court, and there incurred royal displeasure by falling in love with a lady his Majesty chose to honour with his attentions. During a period of banishment at Santarem, Camoëns began *The Lusiad* (*Os Lusiades*), an epic poem celebrating Vasco da Gama's journey to India in 1497 and rehearsing with patriotic enthusiasm the glories of Portuguese history. Owing to its theme, this epic, which a great authority claims should be termed " the Portugade," is also known as the Epic of Commerce or the Epic of Patriotism.

After his banishment Camoëns obtained permission to join the forces directed against the Moors, and shortly after lost an eye in an engagement in the Strait of Gibraltar. Although he distinguished himself as a warrior, Camoëns did not even then neglect the Muse, for he reports he wielded the pen with one hand and the sword with the other.

After this campaign Camoëns returned to court, but, incensed by the treatment he received at the hands of jealous courtiers, he soon vowed his ungrateful country should not even possess his bones, and sailed for India, in 1553, in a fleet of four vessels, only one of which was to arrive at its destination, Goa.

While in India Camoëns sided with one of the

native kings, whose wrath he excited by imprudently revealing his political tendencies. He was, therefore, exiled to Macao, where for five years he served as 'administrator of the effects of deceased persons,' and managed to amass a considerable fortune while continuing his epic. It was on his way back to Goa that Camoëns suffered shipwreck, and lost all he possessed, except his poem, with which he swam ashore.

Sixteen years after his departure from Lisbon, Camoëns returned to his native city, bringing nothing save his completed epic, which, owing to the pestilence then raging in Europe, could be published only in 1572. Even then *The Lusiad* attracted little attention, and won for him only a small royal pension, which, however, the next king rescinded. Thus, poor Camoëns, being sixty-two years old, died in an almshouse, having been partly supported since his return by a Javanese servant, who begged for his master in the streets of Lisbon.

Camoëns' poem *Os Lusiades*, or 'The Lusitanians' (*i.e.* Portuguese), comprises ten books, containing 1102 stanzas in heroic iambics, and is replete with mythological allusions. Its outline is as follows :

Book I

After invoking the Muses and making a ceremonious address to King Sebastian, the poet describes how Jupiter, having assembled the gods on Mount Olympus, directs their glances upon Vasco da Gama's ships plying the waves of an unknown sea, and announces to them that the Portuguese, who have already made such notable maritime discoveries, are about to achieve the conquest of India.

Bacchus, who has long been master of this land,

thereupon wrathfully vows Portugal shall not rob him of his domain, while Venus and Mars implore Jupiter to favour the Lusitanians, whom they consider descendants of the Romans. The king of the gods is so ready to grant this prayer, that he immediately dispatches Mercury to guide the voyagers safely to Madagascar. Here the Portuguese, mistaken for Moors on account of their swarthy complexions, are at first made welcome. But when the islanders discover the strangers are Christians, they determine to annihilate them if possible. So, instigated by one of their priests—Bacchus in disguise—the islanders attack the Portuguese when they next land to get water. Seeing his men in danger, da Gama discharges his artillery, and the terrified natives fall upon their knees and not only beg for mercy, but offer to provide him with a pilot capable of guiding him safely to India.

This offer is accepted by da Gama, who does not suspect that this pilot has instructions to take him to Quiloa, where all Christians are slain. To delude the unsuspecting Portuguese navigator into that port, the pilot avers the Quiloans are Christians; but all his evil plans miscarry, thanks to the interference of Mars and Venus, who by contrary winds hinder the vessels from entering this port.

Book II

The traitor pilot now steers toward Mombasa, where meanwhile Bacchus has been plotting to secure the death of the Portuguese. But here Venus and her nymphs block the entrance of the harbour with huge rocks, and the pilot, realizing the Christians are receiving supernatural aid, jumps overboard and is drowned!

Venus, having thus twice rescued her *protégés* from imminent death, now visits Olympus, and by the exercise of all her coquettish wiles obtains from Jupiter a promise to favour the Portuguese. In accordance with this pledge, Mercury himself is dispatched to guide the fleet safely to Melinda, whose harbour the Portuguese finally enter, decked with flags and accompanied by triumphant music.

> Now Gama's bands the quiv'ring trumpet blow,
> Thick o'er the wave the crowding barges row,
> The Moorish flags the curling waters sweep,
> The Lusian mortars thunder o'er the deep;
> Again the fiery roar heaven's concave tears,
> The Moors astonished stop their wounded ears;
> Again loud thunders rattle o'er the bay,
> And clouds of smoke wide-rolling blot the day;
> The captain's barge the gen'rous king ascends,
> His arms the chief enfold, the captain bends
> (A rev'rence to the scepter'd grandeur due):
> In silent awe the monarch's wond'ring view
> Is fix'd on Vasco's noble mien; the while
> His thoughts with wonder weigh the hero's toil.
> Esteem and friendship with his wonder rise,
> And free to Gama all his kingdom lies.[1]

Book III

As Vasco da Gama has solemnly vowed not to leave his ship until he can set foot upon Indian soil he refuses to land at Melinda, although cordially invited to do so by the native king. Seeing the foreign commander will not come ashore, the King visits the Portuguese vessel, where he is sumptuously entertained and hears from da Gama's own lips an enthusiastic outline of the history of Portugal.

After touching upon events which occurred there in mythological ages, Vasco relates how Portugal,

[1] All the quotations from *The Lusiad* are from Mickle's translation.

under Viriagus, resisted the Roman conquerors, and what a long conflict his country later sustained against the Moors. He also explains by what means Portugal became an independent kingdom, and enthusiastically describes the patriotism of his countryman Egas Moniz, who, when his King was captured at the battle of Guimaraens, advised this Prince to purchase his liberty by pledging himself to do homage to Castile. But, his master once free, Egas Moniz bade him retract this promise, saying that, since he and his family were pledged for its execution, they would rather lose their lives than see Portugal subjected to Castile.

"'And now, O king,' the kneeling Egas cries,
'Behold my perjured honour's sacrifice:
If such mean victims can atone thine ire,
Here let my wife, my babes, myself expire.
If gen'rous bosoms such revenge can take,
Here let them perish for the father's sake:
The guilty tongue, the guilty hands are these,
Nor let a common death thy wrath appease;
For us let all the rage of torture burn,
But to my prince, thy son, in friendship turn.'"

Touched by the patriotism and devotion of Moniz, the foe not only spared his life, but showered favours upon him and even allowed him to go home.

The King, thus saved from vassalage by the devotion of Moniz, is considered the first independent ruler of Portugal. Shortly after this occurrence, he defeated five Moorish rulers in the battle of Ourique, where the Portuguese claim he was favoured with the appearance of a cross in the sky. Because of this miracle, the Portuguese monarch incorporated a cross on his shield, surrounding it with five coins, said to represent the five kings he defeated.

Later on, being made a prisoner at Badajoz, he abdicated in favour of his son.

After proudly enumerating the heroic deeds of various Alphonsos and Sanchos of Portugal, Da Gama related the touching tale of Fair Inez de Castro (retold by Mrs Hemans), to whom Don Pedro, although she was below him in station, was united by a secret marriage. For several years their happiness was unbroken, and several children had been born to them before the King, Don Pedro's father, discovered this alliance. Taking advantage of a temporary absence of his son, Alfonso the Brave sent for Inez and her children and sentenced them all to death, although his daughter-in-law fell at his feet and implored him to have mercy upon her little ones, even if he would not spare her. The King, however, would not relent, and signalled to the courtiers to stab Inez and her children.

> "In tears she utter'd—as the frozen snow
> Touch'd by the spring's mild ray, begins to flow,
> So just began to melt his stubborn soul,
> As mild-ray'd Pity o'er the tyrant stole;
> But destiny forbade: with eager zeal
> (Again pretended for the public weal),
> Her fierce accusers urg'd her speedy doom;
> Again dark rage diffus'd its horrid gloom
> O'er stern Alonzo's brow: swift at the sign,
> Their swords, unsheath'd, around her brandish'd shine.
> O foul disgrace, of knighthood lasting stain,
> By men of arms a helpless lady slain!"

On returning home and discovering what his father had done, Don Pedro was ready to rebel, but was restrained from doing so by the intervention of the Queen. But, on ascending the throne when his father died, Don Pedro had the body of his murdered wife lifted out of the grave, decked in regal apparel, seated on the throne beside him, and he compelled all the courtiers to do homage to her and kiss her dead hand, vowing as much honour should be shown her as if she had lived to be queen. This ceremony ended, the lady's corpse was laid in a tomb, over which her mourning husband erected a beautiful monument. Then, hearing his wife's slayers had taken refuge with Pedro the Cruel, Don Pedro waged fierce war against this monarch until he surrendered the culprits, who, after being tortured, were put to death.

Vasco da Gama also related how another king, Fernando, stole fair Eleanora from her husband, and vainly tried to force the Portuguese to accept their illegitimate daughter Beatrice as his successor.

Book IV

Rather than accept as queen a lady who had married a Spanish prince, who would probably unite their country with Spain, the Portuguese fought the battle of Eljubarota in favour of Don John, and succeeded in dictating terms of peace to the Spanish at Seville. Some time after this the King of Portugal and his brother were captured by the Moors, and told they could recover their freedom only by surrendering Ceuta. Pretending acquiescence, the King returned to Portugal, where, as he had settled with his brother, who remained as hostage with the Moors, he refused to surrender the city.

After describing the victories of Alfonso V, Vasco da Gama related how John II, thirteenth King of Portugal, first began to seek a maritime road to India, and how his successor, Emmanuel, was invited in a vision, by the gods of the Indus and Ganges, to come and conquer their country.

"Here as the monarch fix'd his wond'ring eyes,
Two hoary fathers from the streams arise;
Their aspect rustic, yet, a reverend grace
Appear'd majestic on their wrinkled face:
Their tawny beards uncomb'd, and sweepy long,
Adown their knees in shaggy ringlets hung;
From every lock the crystal drops distil,
And bathe their limbs, as in a trickling rill;
Gay wreaths of flowers, of fruitage and of boughs
(Nameless in Europe), crown'd their furrow'd brows."

Book V

Such was the enthusiasm caused by this vision that many mariners dedicated their lives to the discovery of this road to India. Among these Gama modestly claims his rank, declaring that, when he called for volunteers to accompany him, more men than he could take were ready to follow him. [History reports, however, that, such was the terror inspired by a voyage in unknown seas, Vasco da Gama had to empty the prisons to secure a crew!] Then the narrator added that he had—as was customary—taken ten prisoners with him, whose death sentence was to be commuted provided they faithfully carried out any difficult task he appointed.

After describing his parting with his father, Vasco da Gama relates how they sailed past Mauritania and Madeira, crossed the line, and losing sight of the polar star took the Southern Cross as their guide.

"O'er the wild waves, as southward thus we stray,
Our port unknown, unknown the wat'ry way,
Each night we see, impress'd with solemn awe,
Our guiding stars and native skies withdraw,
In the wide void we lose their cheering beams,
Lower and lower still the pole-star gleams.

. . . .

Another pole-star rises o'er the wave:
Full to the south a shining cross appears,
Our heaving breasts the blissful omen cheers:
Seven radiant stars compose the hallow'd sign
That rose still higher o'er the wavy brine.

A journey of five months, diversified by tempests, electrical phenomena, and occasional landings, brought them to the Cape of Tempests, which since Diaz had rounded it was called the Cape of Good Hope. While battling with the tempestuous seas of this region, Vasco da Gama beheld, in the midst of sudden darkness, Adamastor, the Spirit of the Cape, who foretold all manner of dangers from which it would be difficult for them to escape.

"We saw a hideous phantom glare;
High and enormous o'er the flood he tower'd,
And 'thwart our way with sullen aspect lower'd:
An earthy paleness o'er his cheeks was spread,
Erect uprose his hairs of wither'd red;
Writhing to speak, his sable lips disclose,
Sharp and disjoin'd, his gnashing teeth's blue rows:
His haggard beard flow'd quiv'ring on the wind,
Revenge and horror in his mien combin'd;
His clouded front, by with'ring lightnings scarr'd,
The inward anguish of his soul declar'd.
His red eyes, glowing from their dusky caves,
Shot livid fires: far echoing o'er the waves
His voice resounded, as the cavern'd shore
With hollow groan repeats the tempest's roar."

The King of Melinda here interrupts Vasco da Gama's tale to explain he has often heard of that Adamastor, a Titan transformed into a rock but still possessing supernatural powers.

Resuming his narrative, da Gama next describes their landing to clean their foul ships, their sufferings from scurvy, their treacherous welcome at Mozambique, their narrow escape at Quiloa and Mombasa, and ends his account with his joy at arriving at last at Melinda.

Book VI

In return for the hospitality enjoyed on board the Portuguese ships, the King of Melinda supplies da Gama with an able pilot, who, steering straight for India, brings the Portuguese safely to their goal, in spite of the fact that Bacchus induces Neptune to stir up sundry tempests to check them. But, the prayers of the Christian crew and the aid of Venus counteract Bacchus' spells, so da Gama's fleet enters Calicut in 1497, and the Lusitanians thus achieve the glory of discovering a maritime road to India!

Book VII

We now hear how a Moor, Monçaide, detained a prisoner in Calicut, serves as interpreter for da Gama, explaining to him how this port is governed by the Zamorin, or monarch, and by his prime minister. The interpreter, at da Gama's request, then procures an audience from the Zamorin for his new master.

Book VIII

The poet describes how on the way to the palace da Gama passes a heathen temple, where he and his companions are shocked to behold countless idols, but where they can but admire the wonderful carvings adorning the walls on three sides. In reply to their query why the fourth wall is bare, they learn it has been predicted that India shall be conquered by strangers, whose doings are to be depicted on the fourth side of their temple.

After hearing da Gama boast about his country, the Zamorin dismisses him, promising to consider a trade treaty with Portugal. But, during the next night, Bacchus, disguised as Mahomet, appears to the Moors in Calicut, and bids them inform the Zamorin that da Gama is a pirate, whose rich goods he can secure if he will only follow their advice.

This suggestion, duly carried out, results in da Gama's detention as a prisoner when he lands with his goods on the next day. But, although the prime minister fancies the Portuguese fleet will soon be in his power, da Gama has prudently given orders that, should any hostile demonstration occur before his return, his men are to man the guns and threaten to bombard the town. When the Indian vessels therefore approach the Portuguese fleet, they are riddled with shot.

Book IX

As the Portuguese next threaten to attack the town, the Zamorin promptly sends da Gama back with a cargo of spices and gems and promises of fair treatment hereafter. The Portuguese thereupon sail home, taking with them the faithful Monçaide, who is converted on the way and baptized as soon as they land at Lisbon.

Book X

On the homeward journey Venus, wishing to reward the brave Lusitanians for all their pains and indemnify them for their past hardships, leads them to her "Isle of Joy." Here she and her nymphs entertain them in the most approved mythological style, and a siren foretells in song all that will befall their native country between Vasco da Gama's journey and Camoën's time. Venus herself guides the navigator to the top of a hill, whence she vouchsafes him a panoramic view of all the kingdoms of the earth and of the spheres which compose the universe.

In this canto we also have a synopsis of the life of St Thomas, the Apostle of India, and see the Portuguese sail happily off with the beauteous brides they have won in Venus' Isle of Joy. The return home is safely effected, and our bold sailors are welcomed in Lisbon with delirious joy, for their journey has crowned Portugal with glory. The poem concludes, as it began, with an apostrophe from the poet to the King.

The Lusiad is so smoothly written, so harmonious, and so full of similes that ever since Camoën's day it has served as a model for Portuguese poetry and is even yet an accepted and highly prized classic in Portuguese literature.

ITALIAN EPICS

THE fact that Latin remained so long the chief literary language of Europe prevented an early development of literature in the Italian language. All the popular European epics and romances current in Italy were written in Latin, but many of them were also known in Provençal in the northern part of the peninsula. It was, therefore, chiefly imitations of the Provencal bards' work which first appeared in Italian, in the thirteenth century, one of the best poets of that time being the Sordello with whom Dante converses in Purgatory.

Stories relating to the Charlemagne cycle found particular favour in Northern Italy, and especially at Venice. In consequence there were many Italian versions of these old epics, as well as of the allegorical *Roman de la Rose*.

It was at the court of Frederick II, in Sicily, that the first real school of Italian poetry developed, and from there the custom of composing exclusively in the vernacular spread over the remainder of the country. These early poets chose love as their main topic, and closely imitated the Provençal style. Then the *dolce stil nuovo*, or sweet new style, was introduced by Guinicelli, who is rightly considered the first true Italian poet of any note. The earliest Italian epic, the *Buovo d'Antona*, and an adaptation of *Reynard the Fox*, were current in the first half of the thirteenth century at Venice and elsewhere. In the second half appeared prose romances, such as tales about Arthur and his knights, the journey of Marco Polo, and new renderings of the old story of Troy.

Professional story-tellers now began to wander from

place to place in Northern and Central Italy, entertaining auditors of all classes and ages with stories derived from every attainable source. But the first great epic poet in Italy was Dante (1265–1321), whose *Divina Commedia*, begun in 1300, is treated separately in this volume.

Although Petrarch was prouder of his Latin than of his Italian verses, he too greatly perfected Italian poetry, thus enabling his personal friend Boccaccio to handle the language with lasting success in the tales which compose his *Decameron*. These are the Italian equivalents of the *Canterbury Tales*, and in several cases both writers have used the same themes.

By the fifteenth century, and almost simultaneously with the introduction of printing, came the Renaissance, when a number of old epics were reworked. Roland—or, as he is known in Italy, Orlando—is the stock hero of this new school of poets, several of whom undertook to relate his love adventures. Hence we have *Orlando Innamorato*, by Boiardo and Berni, as well as *Morgante Maggiore* by Pulci, where Roland also figures. In style and tone these works are charming, but the length of the poems and the involved adventures of their numerous characters prove very wearisome to modern readers. Next to Dante, as a poet, the Italians rank Ariosto, whose *Orlando Furioso*, or Roland Insane, is a continuation of Boiardo's *Orlando Innamorato*. Drawing much of his material from the French romances of the Middle Ages, Ariosto breathes new life into the old subject and graces his tale with a most charming style. His subject was parodied by Folengo in his *Orlandino* when Roland began to pall upon the Italian public.

The next epic of note in Italian literature is Torquato Tasso's *Gerusalemme Liberata*, composed in the second half of the sixteenth century, and still immensely popular owing to its exquisite style. Besides this poem, of which Godfrey of Bouillon is the hero and which is *par excellence* the epic of the crusades, Tasso composed epics on *Rinaldo*, on *Gerusalemme Conquistata*, and *Sette Giornate del Mundo Creato*.

Some of Ariosto's contemporaries also attempted the epic style, including Trissino, who in his *Italia Liberata* relates the victories of Belisarius over the Goths in blank verse. His fame, however, rests on *Sofonisba*, the first Italian tragedy, in fact "the first regular tragedy in all modern literature."

Although no epics of great note were written thereafter, Alamanni composed *Girone il Cortese* and the *Avarichde*, which are intolerably long and wearisome.

"The poet who set the fashion of fantastic ingenuity" was Marinus, whose epic *Adone*, in twenty cantos, dilates on the tale of Venus and Adonis. He also wrote *Gerusalemme Distrutta* and *La Strage degl' Innocenti*, and his poetry is said to have much of the charm of Spenser's.

The last Italian poet to produce a long epic poem was Fortiguerra, whose *Ricciardetto* has many merits, although we are told the poet wagered to complete it in as many days as it has cantos, and won his bet.

The greatest of the Italian prose epics is Manzoni's novel *I Promessi Sposi*, which appeared in 1830. Since then Italian poets have not written in the epic vein, save to give their contemporaries excellent metrical translations of Milton's *Paradise Lost*, of the *Iliad*, the *Odyssey*, the *Argonautica*, the *Lusiad*, etc.

THE DIVINE COMEDY

THE INFERNO

Introduction

In the Middle Ages it was popularly believed that Lucifer, falling from Heaven, punched a deep hole in the earth, stopping only when he reached its centre. This funnel-shaped hole, directly under Jerusalem, is divided by Dante into nine independent circular ledges, communicating only by means of occasional rocky stairways or bridges. In each of these nine circles are punished sinners of a certain kind.

Canto I

In 1300, when thirty-five years of age, Dante claims to have strayed from the straight path in the "journey of life," only to encounter experiences bitter as death, which he relates in allegorical form to serve as warning to other sinners. Rousing from a stupor not unlike sleep, the poet finds himself in a strange forest at the foot of a sun-kissed mountain. On trying to climb it, he is turned aside by a spotted panther, an emblem of luxury or pleasure (Florence), a fierce lion, personifying ambition or anger (France), and a ravening wolf, the emblem of avarice (Rome). Fleeing in terror from these monsters, Dante beseeches aid from the only fellow-creature he sees, only to learn he is Virgil, the poet and master from whom he learned "that style which for its beauty into fame exalts me."

The Entrance to Hell

Evelyn Paul

Then Virgil reveals that he has been sent to save Dante from the ravening wolf (which also personifies the papal or Guelf party), only to guide him through the horrors of the Inferno, and the sufferings of Purgatory, up to Paradise, where a "worthier" spirit will attend him.

Canto II

The length of the journey proposed daunts Dante, until Virgil reminds him that cowardice has often made men relinquish honourable enterprises, and encourages him by stating that Beatrice, moved by love, forsook her place in Heaven to bid him serve as Dante's guide. He adds that when he wondered how she could leave, even for a moment, the heavenly abode, she explained that the Virgin Mary sent Lucia, to bid her rescue the man who had loved her ever since she was a child. Like a flower revived after a chilly night by the warmth of the sun, Dante, invigorated by these words, intimates his readiness to follow Virgil.

Canto III

The two travellers, passing through a wood, reach a gate, above which Dante perceives this inscription:

> "Through me you pass into the city of woe:
> Through me you pass into eternal pain:
> Through me among the people lost for aye.
> Justice the founder of my fabric moved:
> To rear me was the task of power divine,
> Supremest wisdom, and primeval love.
> Before me things create were none, save things
> Eternal, and eternal I endure.
> All hope abandon, ye who enter here." [1]

Unable to grasp its meaning, Dante begs Virgil

[1] All the quotations are taken from Cary's translation.

to interpret, and learns they are about to descend into Hades. Having visited this place before, Virgil boldly leads Dante through this portal into an ante-hell region, where sighs, lamentations, and groans pulse through the starless air. Shuddering with horror, Dante inquires what it all means, only to be told that the souls "who lived without praise or blame," as well as the angels who remained neutral during the war in Heaven, are confined in this place, since Paradise, Purgatory, and Inferno equally refuse to harbour them and death never visits them.

While he is speaking, a long train of these unfortunate spirits, stung by gadflies, sweeps past them, and in their ranks Dante recognizes the shade of Pope Celestine V, who, "through cowardice made the grand renunciation,"—*i.e.* abdicated his office at the end of five months, simply because he lacked courage to face the task intrusted to him.

Passing through these spirits with downcast eyes, Dante reaches Acheron, the river of death, where he sees, steering toward them, the ferry-man Charon, whose eyes are like fiery wheels and who marvels at beholding a living man among the shades. When Charon grimly orders Dante back to earth, Virgil silences him with the brief statement: "so 'tis will'd where will and power are one." So, without further objection, Charon allows them to enter his skiff and hurries the rest of his freight aboard, beating the laggards with the flat of his oar. Because Dante wonders at such ill-treatment, Virgil explains that good souls are never forced to cross this stream, and that the present passengers have richly deserved their punishment. Just then an earthquake shakes the whole region, and Dante swoons in terror.

Canto IV

When he recovers his senses, Dante finds himself no longer in Charon's bark, but on the brink of a huge circular pit, whence arise, like emanations, moans and wails, but wherein, owing to the dense gloom, he can descry nothing. Warning him they are about to descend into the "blind world," and that his sorrowful expression—which Dante ascribes to fear—is caused by pity, Virgil conducts his disciple into the first circle of Hell. Instead of lamentations, only sighs are heard, while Virgil explains that this semi-dark limbo is reserved for unbaptized children, and for those who, having lived before Christ, must "live desiring without hope." Full of compassion for these sufferers, Dante inquires whether no one from above ever visited them, and is told that One, bearing trophies of victory, once arrived there to ransom the patriarchs Adam, Abel, Noah, and others, but that until then none had ever been saved.

Talking busily, the two wend their way through a forest of sighing spirits, until they approach a fire, around which dignified shades have gathered. Informing Dante that these are men of honoured reputations, Virgil points out among them four mighty figures coming to meet them, and whispers they are Homer, Horace, Ovid, and Lucan. After conversing for a while with Virgil, these bards graciously welcome Dante as sixth in their poetic galaxy. Talking of things which cannot be mentioned save in such exalted company, Dante walks on with them until he nears a castle girdled with sevenfold ramparts and moat. Through seven consecutive portals the six poets pass on to a meadow, where Dante beholds all the creations of their brains, and meets Hector, Aeneas, Camilla, and Lucretia, as well as the philosophers, historians, and mathematicians who from time to time have appeared upon our globe. Although Dante would fain have lingered here, his guide leads him on, and, as their four companions vanish, they two enter a place "where no light shines."

Canto V

Stepping down from this circle to a lower one, Dante and Virgil reach the second circle of the Inferno, where all who lived unchaste lives are duly punished. Smaller in circumference than the preceding circle—for Dante's Hell is shaped like a graduated funnel—this place is guarded by the judge Minos, who examines all newly arrived souls, and consigns them to their appointed circles by an equal number of convolutions in his tail.

> For when before him comes the ill-fated soul,
> It all confesses; and that judge severe
> Of sins, considering what place in hell
> Suits the transgression, with his tail so oft
> Himself encircles, as degrees beneath
> He dooms it to descend.

On beholding Dante, Minos speaks threateningly, but, when Virgil again explains they have been sent hither by a higher power Minos too allows them to pass. Increasing sounds of woe now strike Dante's ear, until presently they attain the intensity of a deafening roar. Next he perceives that the whirlwind, sweeping violently round this abyss, holds in its grasp innumerable spirits which are allowed no rest. Like birds in a tempest they swirl past Dante, to whom Virgil hastily points out Semiramis, Dido, Cleopatra, Helen, Achilles, Paris, and Tristan, together with many others.

Obtaining permission to address two shades floating toward him, Dante learns that the man is the Paolo who fell in love with his sister-in-law, Francesca da Rimini. Asked how she fell, the female spirit, moaning there is no greater woe than to recall happy times in the midst of misery, adds that while she and Paolo read together the tale of Launcelot they suddenly realized they loved in the same way, and thus fell into the very sin described in this work, for "book and writer both were love's purveyors." Scarcely has she confessed this when the wind, seizing Francesca and Paolo, again sweeps them on, and Dante, hearing their pitiful moans, swoons from compassion.

Canto VI

Recovering his senses, Dante finds Virgil has meantime transferred him to the third circle, a region where chill rains ever fall, accompanied by hail, sleet, and snow. Here all guilty of gluttony are rent and torn by Cerberus, main ruler of this circle. Flinging a huge fistful of dirt into the dog's gaping jaws to prevent his snapping at them, Virgil leads Dante quickly past this three-headed monster, to a place where they tread on the shades which pave the muddy ground. One of these, sitting up, suddenly inquires of Dante whether he does not recognize him, adding that he is the notorious Florentine glutton Ciacco. Fancying this shade may possess some insight into the future, Dante inquires what is to become of his native city, and learns that one political party will drive out the other, only to fall in its turn three years later. The glutton adds that only two just men are left in Florence, and, when Dante asks what has become of his friends, tells him he will doubtless meet them in the various circles of Hades, should he continue his downward course.

Then the spirit begs that, on returning to the "pleasant world," Dante will recall him to his friends' memory, and, closing his eyes, sinks back among the other victims, all of whom are more or less blind. Vouchsafing the information that this sinner will not rise again "ere the last angel-trumpet blow," Virgil leads Dante over the foul mixture of shades and mud, explaining that, although the accursed can never hope to attain perfection, they are not entirely debarred from improvement.

Canto VII

Talking thus, the two travellers descend to the fourth circle, ruled by Plutus, god of wealth, who allows them to proceed only after Virgil has informed him their journey is ordained, and is to be pursued to the very spot where Michael confined Satan. The mere mention of his master, the ex-archangel, causes Plutus to grovel; and Dante and Virgil, proceeding on their journey, discover that the fourth circle is occupied by all whom avarice mastered, as well as by prodigals, who are here condemned to roll heavy rocks, because their lives on earth were spent scuffling for money or because they failed to make good use of their gold. Dante descries among the victims tonsured polls, proving that monks themselves are not exempt from these sins. Meanwhile Virgil expounds how the Creator decreed nations should wield the mastery in turn, adding that these people are victims of Fortune, whose proverbial fickleness he ably describes.

After passing a well, whose boiling waters overflow and form a stream, they follow the latter's downward course to the marsh called Styx, where hundreds of naked creatures wallow in the mire, madly clutching and striking each other. Virgil explains that these are those "whom anger overcame," and adds that the sullen are buried beneath the slimy waters, where their presence is betrayed by bubbles caused by their breath which continually rise to the surface. Edging around this loathsome pool, the two poets finally arrive at the door of a tall tower.

Canto VIII

From the lofty turret flash flaming signals, evidently designed to summon some bark or ferry, since a vessel soon appears. Once more Virgil has to silence a snarling boatman (Phlegyas) ere he can enter his skiff, where he invites Dante to follow him. Then they row across the mire, whence heads keep emerging from time to time. One of the sufferers confined here suddenly asks Dante "Who art thou that camest ere thine hour?" only to be hastily assured the poet does not intend to stay. Just as Dante expresses the wish to know whom he is addressing, he recognizes this sinner (Argenti) and turns from him in loathing, an act which wins Virgil's approval. When Dante further mutters he wishes this monster were stifled in the mud, Virgil suddenly points to a squad of avenging spirits who, sweeping downward, are about to fulfil this cruel wish, when the culprit rends himself with his own teeth and plunges back into the Styx.

Sailing along, Virgil tries to prepare Dante for their arrival at the city of Dis, whose minarets, coloured by a fiery glow from within, now shine in the distance. Steered into the moat surrounding this city, the travellers slowly circle its iron walls, from which hosts of lost souls lean clamouring, "Who is this that without death first felt goes through the region of the dead?" When Virgil signals he will explain, the demons disappear as if to admit them; but, when the travellers reach the gates, they find them still tightly closed. Virgil then explains that these very demons tried to oppose even Christ's entrance to Hades, and adds that their power was broken on the first Easter Day.

Canto IX

Quailing with terror, Dante hears Virgil admit that few have undertaken to tread these paths, although they are familiar to him, seeing that guided by a witch (the Sibyl of Cumaea), he came here with Aeneas. While Virgil is talking, the three Furies appear at the top of the tower, and, noting the intruders, clamour for Medusa to come and turn them into stone! Bidding Dante avoid the Gorgon's petrifying glance, Virgil further assures the safety of his charge by holding his hands over Dante's eyes. While thus blinded, the author of the poem hears waves splash against the shore, and, when Virgil's hands are removed, perceives an angel walking dry-shod over the Styx. At a touch from his hand, the gates of Dis open wide, and, without paying heed to the poets, who have instinctively assumed the humblest attitude, their divine rescuer recrosses the bog, leaving them free to enter into the iron fortress. There they find countless sinners cased in red-hot coffins sunk in burning marl. On questioning his guide, Dante learns that each open sepulchre contains an arch-heretic, or leader of some religious sect, and that each tomb is heated to a degree corresponding to the extent of the harm done by its occupant's teachings.

Canto X

Gingerly treading between burning tombs and fortress wall, Virgil conducts Dante to an open sepulchre, where lies the Ghibelline leader Farinata. Partly rising out of his glowing tomb, this warrior informs Dante that the Guelfs—twice driven out of Florence—have returned thither. At that moment another victim, peering over the edge of his coffin, anxiously begs for news of his son Guido, thus proving that, while these unfortunates know both past and future, the present remains a mystery to them. Too amazed at first to speak, Dante mentions Guido in the past tense, whereupon the unhappy father, rashly inferring his son is dead, plunges back into his sepulchre with a desperate cry. Not being able to correct his involuntary mistake and thus comfort this sufferer, Dante begs Farinata to inform his neighbour, as soon as possible, that his son is still alive. Then, perplexed by all he has seen and heard, Dante passes thoughtfully on, noting the victims punished in this place, until, seeing his dismay, Virgil comforts him with the assurance that Beatrice will explain all he wishes to know at the end of his journey.

Canto XI

The poets now approach a depression, whence arises a stench so nauseating that they are compelled to take refuge behind a stone tomb to avoid choking. While they pause there, Dante perceives that this sepulchre bears the name of Pope Anastasius, who has been led astray. Tarrying there to become acclimated to the smell, Virgil informs his companion they are about to pass through three gradations of the seventh circle, where are punished the violent, or those who by force worked injury to God, to themselves, or to their fellow-men.

Canto XII

His charge sufficiently prepared for what awaits him, Virgil leads the way down a steep path to the next rim, where they are confronted by the Minotaur, before whom Dante quails, but whom Virgil defies by mentioning Theseus. Taking advantage of the moment when the furious, bull-like monster charges at him with lowered head, Virgil runs with Dante down a declivity, where the stones, unaccustomed to the weight of mortal feet, slip and roll in ominous fashion. This passage, Virgil declares, was less dangerous when he last descended into Hades, for it has since been riven by the earthquake which shook this region when Christ descended into hell.

Pointing to a boiling river of blood (Phlegethon) beneath them, Virgil shows Dante sinners immersed in it at different depths, because while on earth they offered violence to their neighbours. Although anxious to escape from these bloody waters, the wicked are kept within their appointed bounds by troops of centaurs, who, armed with bows and arrows, continually patrol the banks. When these guards threateningly challenge Virgil, he calmly rejoins he wishes to see their leader, Chiron, and, while awaiting the arrival of this worthy, shows

The Seventh Circle
Evelyn Paul

Dante the monster Nessus, who tried to kidnap the wife of Hercules.

On drawing near to them, Chiron is amazed to perceive that one of the intruders is alive, as is proved by the fact that he casts a shadow and that stones roll beneath his tread! Noticing his amazement, Virgil explains he has been sent here to guide his mortal companion through the Inferno, and beseeches Chiron to detail a centaur to carry Dante across the river of blood, since he cannot, spirit-like, tread air. Selecting Nessus for this duty, Chiron bids him convey the poet safely across the bloody stream, and, while performing this office, the centaur explains that the victims more or less deeply immersed in blood are tyrants who delighted in bloodshed, such as Alexander, Dionysius, and others. Borne by Nessus and escorted by Virgil, Dante reaches the other shore, and, taking leave of them, the centaur "alone repass'd the ford."

Canto XIII

The travellers now enter a wild forest, which occupies the second division of the seventh circle, where Virgil declares each barren thorn-tree is inhabited by the soul of a suicide. In the gnarly branches perch the Harpies, whose uncouth lamentations echo through the air, and who greedily devour every leaf that sprouts. Appalled by the sighs and wailings around him, Dante questions Virgil, who directs him to break off a twig. No sooner has he done so than he sees blood trickle from the break and hears a voice reproach him for his cruelty. Thus Dante learns that the inmate of this tree was once private secretary to Frederick II, and that, having fallen into unmerited disgrace, he basely took refuge in suicide. This victim's words have barely died away when the blast of a horn is heard, and two naked forms are seen fleeing madly before a huntsman and a pack of mastiffs. The latter, pouncing upon one victim, tears him to pieces, while Dante shudders at this sight. Meantime Virgil explains that the culprit was a young spendthrift, and that huntsman and hounds represent the creditors whose pursuit he tried to escape by killing himself.

Canto XIV

Leaving this ghastly forest, Dante is led to the third division of this circle, a region of burning sands, where hosts of naked souls lie on the ground, blistered and scathed by the rain of fire and vainly trying to lessen their pain by thrashing themselves with their hands. One figure, the mightiest among them, alone seems indifferent to the burning rain, and, when Dante inquires who this may be, Virgil replies that it is Capaneus (one of the seven kings who besieged Thebes), who, in his indomitable pride, taunted Jupiter and was slain by his thunderbolt.

Treading warily to avoid the burning sands, Virgil and his disciple cross a ruddy brook which flows straight down from Mount Ida in Crete, where it rises at the foot of a statue whose face is turned toward Rome. Virgil explains that the waters of this stream are formed by the tears of the unhappy, which are plentiful enough to feed the four mighty rivers of Hades! While following the banks of this torrent, Dante questions why they have not yet encountered the other two rivers which fall into the pit; and discovers that, although they have been travelling in a circle, they have not by far completed one whole round of the gigantic funnel, but have stepped down from one ledge to the other after walking only a short distance around each circumference.

Canto XV

The high banks of the stream of tears protect our travellers from the burning sand and the rain of fire, until they encounter a procession of souls, each one of which stares fixedly at them. One of these recognizes Dante, who in his turn is amazed to find there his old schoolmaster Ser Brunetto, whom he accompanies on his way, after he learns that he and his fellow-sufferers are not allowed to stop, under penalty of lying 100 years without fanning themselves beneath the rain of fire. Walking by his former pupil's side, Brunetto in his turn questions Dante and learns how and why he has come down here, ere he predicts that in spite of persecutions the poet will ultimately attain great fame.

Canto XVI

Reaching a spot where the stream they are following suddenly thunders down into the eighth circle, Dante beholds three spirits running toward him, whirling round one another "in one restless wheel," while loudly exclaiming his garb denotes he is their fellow-countryman! Gazing into their fire-scarred faces, Dante learns these are three powerful Guelfs; and when they crave tidings of their native city, he tells them all that has recently occurred there. Before vanishing these spirits piteously implore him to speak of them to mortals on his return to earth, and leave Dante and Virgil to follow the stream to the verge of the abyss. There Virgil loosens the rope knotted around Dante's waist, and, casting one end of it down into the abyss, intimates that what he is awaiting will soon appear. A moment later a monster rises from the depths, climbing hand over hand up the rope.

Canto XVII

This monster is Geryon, the personification of fraud, and therefore a mixture of man, beast, and serpent. When he reaches the upper ledge, Virgil bargains with him to carry them down, while Dante converses with neighbouring sorrowful souls, who are perched on the top of the cliff and hide their faces in their hands. All these spirits wear purses around their necks, because as usurers while on earth they lived on ill-gotten gains. Not daring to keep his guide waiting, Dante leaves these sinners, and hurries back just as Virgil is taking his seat on the monster's back. Grasping the hand stretched out to him, Dante then timorously mounts beside his guide.

> As one, who hath an ague fit so near,
> His nails already are turn'd blue, and he
> Quivers all o'er, if he but eye the shade;
> Such was my cheer at hearing of his words.
> But shame soon interposed her threat, who makes
> The servant bold in presence of his lord.
> I settled me upon those shoulders huge,
> And would have said, but that the words to aid
> My purpose came not, "Look thou clasp me firm."

Then, bidding Dante hold fast so as not to fall, Virgil gives the signal for departure. Wheeling slowly, Geryon flies downward, moderating his speed so as not to unseat his passengers. Comparing his sensations to those of Phaeton falling from the sun-chariot, or to Icarus' horror when he dropped into the sea, Dante describes how, as they circled down on the beast's back, he caught fleeting glimpses of fiery pools and was almost deafened by the rising chorus of wails. With a falcon-like swoop Geryon finally alights on the next level, and, having deposited his passengers at the foot of a splintered rock, darts away like an arrow from a taut bow-string.

Canto XVIII

The eighth circle, called Malebolge (Evil Pits), is divided into ten gulfs, between which rocky arches form bridge-like passages. This whole region is of stone and ice, and from the pit in the centre continually rise horrid exhalations. Among the unfortunates, incessantly lashed by horned demons in the first gulf, Dante perceives one who was a notorious pander on earth and who is justly suffering the penalty of his crimes. Later on, watching a train of culprits driven by other demons, Dante recognizes among them Jason, who secured the Golden Fleece, thanks to Medea, but proved faithless to her in the end.

Crossing to the second division, Dante beholds sinners buried in dung, in punishment for having led astray their fellow-creatures by flattery. One of them, whom the poet recognizes, emerging from his filthy bath, sadly confesses, "Me thus low down my flatteries have sank, wherewith I ne'er enough could glut my tongue." In this place Dante also notes the harlot Thais, expiating her sins, with other notorious seducers and flatterers.

Canto XIX

By means of another rocky bridge the travellers reach the third gulf, where are punished all who have been guilty of simony. These are sunk, head first, in a series of burning pits, whence emerge only the red-hot soles of their convulsively agitated feet. Seeing a ruddier flame hover over one pair of soles, Dante timidly inquires to whom they belong, whereupon Virgil, carrying him down to this spot, bids him seek his answer from the culprit himself. Peering down into the stone-pit, Dante then timidly proffers his request, only to be hotly reviled by Pope Nicholas III, who first mistakes his interlocutor for Pope Boniface, and confesses he was brought to this state by nepotism. But, when he predicts a worse pope will ultimately follow him down into this region, Dante sternly rebukes him.

Canto XX

Virgil is so pleased with Dante's speech to Pope Nicholas that, seizing him in his arms, he carries him swiftly over the bridge which leads to the fourth division. Here Dante beholds a procession of chanting criminals whose heads are turned to face their backs. This sight proves so awful that Dante weeps, until Virgil bids him note the different culprits. Among them is the witch Manto, to whom Mantua, his native city, owes its name, and Dante soon learns that all these culprits are the famous soothsayers, diviners, magicians, and witches of the world, who thus are punished for having presumed to predict the future.

Canto XXI

From the top of the next bridge they gaze into a dark pit, where public peculators are plunged into boiling pitch, as Dante discovers by the odour, which keenly reminds him of the shipyards at Venice.

Virgil there directs Dante's attention toward a demon, who hurls a sinner headlong into the boiling tar, and, without watching to see what becomes of him, departs in quest of some other victim. The poet also perceives that, whenever a sinner's head emerges from the pitchy waves, demons thrust him down again by means of long forks. To prevent his charge falling a prey to these active evil spirits, Virgil directs Dante to hide behind a pillar of the bridge and from there to watch all that is going on.

While Dante lurks there, a demon, descrying him, is about to attack him, but Virgil so vehemently proclaims they are here by Heaven's will that the evil spirit drops his fork and becomes powerless to harm them. Perceiving the effect he has produced, Virgil then summons Dante from his hiding-place, and sternly orders the demon to guide them safely through the ranks of his grimacing fellows, all of whom make obscene gestures as they pass.

Canto XXII

Dante, having taken part in battles, is familiar with military manœuvres, but he declares he never beheld such ably marshalled troops as the demon hosts through which they pass. From time to time he sees a devil emerge from the ranks to plunge sinners back into the lake of pitch, or to spear one with his fork and, after letting him writhe aloft for a while, hurl him back into the asphalt lake. One of these victims, questioned by Virgil, acknowledges he once held office in Navarre, but, rather than suffer at the hands of the demon tormentors, this peculator voluntarily plunges back into the pitch. Seeing this, the baffled demons fight each other, until two actually fall into the lake, whence they are fished in sorry plight by fellow-fiends.

Canto XXIII

By a passage-way so narrow that they are obliged to proceed in single file, Dante and Virgil reach the next division, the former continually glancing behind him lest the demons pursue him. His fears are only too justified, and Virgil, seeing his peril, catches him up in his arms and runs with him to the next gulf, knowing demons never pass beyond their beat.

> Never ran water with such hurrying pace
> Adown the tube to turn a land-mill's wheel,
> When nearest it approaches to the spokes,
> As then along that edge my master ran,
> Carrying me in his bosom, as a child,
> Not a companion.

In the sixth division where they now arrive, they behold a procession of victims, weighed down by gilded leaden cowls, creeping along so slowly that Dante and Virgil pass all along their line although they are not walking fast. Hearing one of these bowed figures address him, Dante learns that, because he and his companions were hypocrites on earth, they are doomed to travel constantly around this circle of the Inferno, fainting beneath heavy loads.

A moment later Dante notices that the narrow path ahead of them is blocked by a writhing figure pinned to the ground by three stakes. This is Caiaphas, who insisted it was fitting that one man should suffer for the people, and who, having thus sentenced Christ to the cross, must suffer the whole procession to tramp over his prostrate form. The cowled figure with whom Dante is conversing informs him, besides, that in other parts of the circle are Ananias and the other members of the Sanhedrim who condemned Christ. Deeming Dante has now seen enough of this region, Virgil inquires where they can find an exit from this gulf, and is shown by a spirit a steep ascent.

Canto XXIV

So precipitous is this passage that Virgil half carries his charge, and, panting hard, both scramble to a ledge overhanging the seventh gulf of Malebolge, where innumerable serpents prey upon naked robbers, whose hands are bound behind them by writhing snakes. Beneath the constant bites of these reptiles, the robber-victims turn to ashes, only to rise phœnix-like a moment later and undergo renewed torments. Dante converses with one of these spirits, who, after describing his own misdeeds, prophesies in regard to the future of Florence.

Canto XXV

The blasphemous speeches and gestures of this speaker are silenced by an onslaught of snakes, before whose attack he attempts to flee, only to be overtaken and tortured by a serpent-ridden centaur, whom Virgil designates as Cacus. Further on, the travellers behold three culprits who are alternately men and writhing snakes, always, however, revealing more of the reptile than of the human nature and form.

The other two
Look'd on, exclaiming, "Ah! How dost thou change,
Agnello! See! thou art nor double now
Nor only one." The two heads now became
One, and two figures blended in one form

Appear'd, where both were lost. Of the four lengths
Two arms were made: the belly and the chest,
The thighs and legs, into such members changed
As never eye hath seen.

Canto XXVI

From another bridge Dante gazes down into the eighth gulf, where, in the midst of the flames, are those who gave evil advice to their fellow-creatures. Here Dante recognizes Diomedes, Ulysses, and other heroes of the *Iliad*—with whom his guide speaks—and learns that Ulysses, after his return to Ithaca, resumed his explorations, ventured beyond the pillars of Hercules, and, while sailing in the track of the sun, was drowned in sight of a high mountain.

Canto XXVII

In the midst of another bed of flames, Dante next discovers another culprit, to whom he gives the history of the Romagna, and whose life-story he hears before following his leader down to the ninth gulf of Malebolge.

Canto XXVIII

In this place Dante discovers the sowers of scandal, schism, and heresy, who exhibit more wounds than all the Italian wars occasioned. Watching them, Dante perceives that each victim is ripped open by a demon's sword, but that his wounds heal so rapidly that every time the spirit passes a demon again his torture is renewed. Among these victims Dante recognizes Mahomet, who, wondering that a living man should visit Hell, points out Dante to his fellow-shades. Passing by the travellers, several victims mention their names, and Dante thus discovers among them the leaders of strife between the Italian states, and shudders when Bertrand de Born, a fellow-minstrel, appears bearing his own head like a lantern, in punishment for persuading the son of Henry II of England to rebel.

Canto XXIX

Gazing in a dazed way at the awful sights of this circle, Dante learns it is twenty-one miles in circumference, ere he passes on to the next bridge, where lamentations such as assail one's ears in a hospital constantly arise. In the depths of the tenth pit, into which he now peers, Dante distinguishes victims of all manners of diseases, and learns these are the alchemists and forgers undergoing the penalty of their sins. Among them Dante perceives a man who was burned alive on earth for offering to teach mortals to fly! So preposterous did such a claim appear to Minos—judge of the dead—that he ruthlessly condemned its originator to undergo the punishment awarded to magicians, alchemists, and other pretenders.

Canto XXX

Virgil now points out to Dante many impostors, perpetrators of fraud, and false-coiners, among whom we note the woman who falsely accused Joseph, and Sinon, who persuaded the Trojans to convey the wooden horse into their city. Not content with the tortures inflicted upon them, these criminals further increase each others' sufferings by cruel taunts, and Dante, fascinated by what he sees, lingers beside this pit, until Virgil cuttingly observes that "to hear such wrangling is a joy for vulgar minds."

Canto XXXI

Touched by the remorseful shame which Dante now shows, Virgil draws him on until they are almost deafened by a louder blast than was uttered by Roland's horn at Roncevaux. Peering in the direction of the sound, Dante descries what he takes for lofty towers, until Virgil informs him that when they draw nearer still he will discover they are giants standing in the lowest pit but looming far above it in the mist. Ere long Dante stares in wonder at chained giants seventy feet tall, whom Virgil designates as Nimrod, Ephialtes, and Antaeus.

As with circling round
Of turrets Montereggion crowns his walls,
E'en thus the shore, encompassing the abyss,
Was turreted with giants, half their length
Uprearing, horrible, whom Jove from heaven
Yet threatens, when his muttering thunder rolls.

Antaeus being unchained, Virgil persuades him to lift them both down in the hollow of his hands to the next level, "where guilt is at its depth." Although Dante's terror in the giant's grip is almost overwhelming, he is relieved when his feet touch the ground once more, and he watches with awe as the giant straightens up again like the mast of a huge ship.

Yet in the abyss,
That Lucifer with Judas low ingulfs,
Lightly he placed us; nor, there leaning, stay'd;
But rose, as in a barque the stately mast.

Canto XXXII

Confessing that it is no easy task to describe the bottom of the universe which he has now reached,

Dante relates how perpendicular rocks rose up on all sides as far as he could see. He is gazing upward in silent wonder, when Virgil suddenly cautions him to beware lest he tread upon some unfortunate. Gazing down at his feet, Dante then becomes aware that he is standing on a frozen lake, wherein stick fast innumerable sinners, whose heads alone emerge, cased in ice owing to the tears constantly flowing down their cheeks.

Seeing two so close together that their very hair seems to mingle, Dante, on inquiring, learns they are two brothers who slew each other in an inheritance quarrel, for this is Caina, the region where the worst murderers are punished, and, like every other part of the Inferno, it is crowded with figures.

> A thousand visages
> Then mark'd I, which the keen and eager cold
> Had shaped into a doggish grin; whence creeps
> A shivering horror o'er me, at the thought
> Of those frore shallows.

It happens that, while following his guide over the ice, Dante's foot strikes a projecting head. Permission being granted him to question its owner, Dante, because he at first refuses to speak, threatens to pull every hair out of his head, and actually gives him a few hard tugs. Then the man admits he is a traitor and that there are many others of his kind in Antenora, the second division of the lowest circle.

Canto XXXIII

Beholding another culprit greedily gnawing the head of a companion, Dante learns that while on earth this culprit was Count Ugolino de' Gherardeschi, whom his political opponents, headed by the Archbishop Ruggiero, seized by treachery and locked up in the Famine-tower at Pisa, with two sons and two grandsons. Ugolino feelingly describes his horror when one morning he heard them nail up the door of the prison, and realized he and his were doomed to starve! Not a word did the prisoners exchange regarding their fate, although all were aware of the suffering awaiting them. At the end of twenty-four hours, beholding traces of hunger in the beloved faces of his children, Ugolino gnawed his fists in pain. One of his grandsons, interpreting this as a sign of unbearable hunger, then suggested that he should eat one of them, whereupon he realized how needful it was to exercise self-control if he did not wish to increase the sufferings of the rest. Ugolino then describes how they daily grew weaker, until his grandsons died at the end of the fourth day, vainly begging him to help them. Then his sons passed away, and, groping blindly among the dead, he lingered on, until, famine becoming more potent than anything else, he yielded to its demands. Having finished this gruesome tale, Ugolino continued his feast upon the head of his foe!

> Thus having spoke,
> Once more upon the wretched skull his teeth
> He fasten'd like a mastiff's 'gainst the bone,
> Firm and unyielding.

Dante, passing on, discovers many other victims encased in the ice, and is so chilled by a glacial breeze that his face muscles stiffen. He is about to ask Virgil whence this wind proceeds, when one of the ice-encrusted victims implores him to remove its hard mask from his face. Promising to do so in return for the man's story, Dante learns he is a friar who, in order to rid himself of inconvenient kinsmen, invited them all to dinner, where he suddenly uttered the fatal words which served as a signal for hidden assassins to despatch them. When Dante indignantly exclaims the perpetrator of this heinous deed is on earth, the criminal admits that, although his shadow still lingers above ground, his soul is down here in Ptolomea, undergoing the penalty for his sins. Hearing this, Dante refuses to clear away the ice, and excuses himself to his readers by stating "ill manners were best courtesy to him."

Canto XXXIV

Virgil now directs Dante's glance ahead, until our poet dimly descries what looks like an immense windmill. Placing Dante behind him to shield him a little from the cruel blast, Virgil leads him past countless culprits, declaring they have reached Judecca, a place where it behoves him to arm his heart with strength. So stiff with cold that he is hovering between life and death, Dante now beholds Dis or Satan, Emperor of the Infernal Regions, sunk in ice down to his waist, and discovers that the wind is caused by the constant flutter of his bat-like wings. He also perceives that Satan is as much larger than the giants just seen, as they surpass mankind, and states that, were the father of evil as fair as he is foul, one might understand his daring to defy God.

> If he were beautiful
> As he is hideous now, and yet did dare
> To scowl upon his Maker, well from him
> May all our misery flow.

Then Dante describes Satan's three heads, one red, one yellow and white, and one green, declaring that the arch-fiend munches in each mouth the sinners Judas, Cassius, and Brutus. After allowing Dante to gaze a while at this appalling sight, Virgil informs his charge that, having seen all, it behoves them to depart. With a brief order to Dante to cling tightly round his neck, Virgil, seizing a moment when Satan's wings are raised, darts beneath them, and clutching the demon's shaggy sides painfully descends toward the centre of the earth. Down, down they go until they reach the evil spirit's thighs, where, the centre of earth's gravity being reached, Virgil suddenly turns round and begins an upward climb with his burden. Although Dante fully expects soon to behold Satan's head once more, he is amazed to discover they are climbing up his leg. Then, through a chimney-like ascent, where the climbing demands all their strength, Dante and Virgil ascend toward the upper air.

Explaining they are about to emerge at the antipodes of the spot where they entered Hades, where they will behold the great Western Sea, Virgil adds they will find in its centre the Mount of Purgatory, constructed of the earth displaced by Satan's fall. Thus, Dante and his leader return to the bright world, and, issuing from the dark passage in which they have been travelling, once more behold the stars!

By that hidden way
My guide and I did enter, to return
To the fair world; and heedless of repose
We climb'd, he first, I following his steps,
Till on our view the beautiful lights of heaven
Dawn'd through a circular opening in the cave:
Thence issuing we again beheld the stars.

THE DIVINE COMEDY

THE PURGATORIO

Canto I

About to sing of a region where human spirits are purged of their sins and prepared to enter heaven, Dante invokes the aid of the Muses. Then, gazing about him, he discovers he is in an atmosphere of sapphire hue, all the more lovely because of the contrast with the infernal gloom whence he has just emerged. It is just before dawn, and he beholds with awe four bright stars—the Southern Cross—which symbolize the four cardinal virtues.

After contemplating these stars awhile, Dante, turning to the north to get his bearings, perceives that Virgil has been joined in this ante-purgatorial region by Cato, who wonderingly inquires how they escaped " the eternal prison-house."

Virgil's gesture and example have meantime forced Dante to his knees, so it is in this position that the Latin poet explains how a lady in Heaven bade him rescue Dante—before it was too late—by guiding him through Hell and showing him how sinners are cleansed in Purgatory. The latter part of Virgil's task can, however, be accomplished only if Cato will allow them to enter the realm which he guards. Moved by so eloquent a plea, Cato directs Virgil to wash all traces of tears and of infernal mirk from Dante's face, girdle him with a reed in token of humility, and then ascend the Mount of Purgatory—formed of the earthy core ejected from Hades—which he points out in the middle of a lake with reedy shores.

Leading his charge in the early dawn across a meadow, Virgil draws his hands first through the dewy grass and then over Dante's face, and, having thus removed all visible traces of the passage through Hades, takes him down to the shore to girdle him with a pliant reed, the emblem of humility.

Canto II

Against the whitening east they now behold a ghostly vessel advancing toward them, and when it approaches near enough they descry an angel standing at its prow, his outspread wings serving as sails. While Dante again sinks upon his knees, he hears, faintly at first, the passengers in the boat singing the psalm "When Israel went out of Egypt."

Making the sign of the cross upon each passenger's brow, the angel allows his charges to land, and vanishes at sunrise, just as the new-comers, turning to Virgil, humbly inquire the way to the mountain. Virgil rejoins that he too is a recent arrival, although he and his companion travelled a far harder road than theirs. His words making them aware of the fact that Dante is a living man, the spirits crowd around him, eager to touch him. Among them he recognizes the musician Casella, his friend. Unable to embrace a spirit—although he tries to do so—Dante, after explaining his own presence here, begs Casella to comfort all present by singing of love. Just as this strain ends, Cato reappears, urging them to hasten to the mountain and there cast aside the scales which conceal God from their eyes. At these words all the souls present scatter like a covey of pigeons, and begin ascending the mountain, whither Virgil and Dante slowly follow them.

As a wild flock of pigeons, to their food
Collected, blade or tares, without their pride
Accustom'd, and in still and quiet sort,
If aught alarm them, suddenly desert

Their meal, assail'd by more important care;
So I that new-come troop beheld, the song
Deserting, hasten to the mountain's side,
As one who goes, yet, where he tends, knows not.

Canto III

While painfully ascending the steep slope, Dante, seeing only his own shadow lengthening out before him, fears his guide has abandoned him, and is relieved to see Virgil close behind him and to hear him explain that disembodied spirits cast no shadow. While they are talking, they reach the foot of the mountain and are daunted by its steep and rocky sides. They are vainly searching for some crevice whereby they may hope to ascend, when they behold a slowly advancing procession of white-robed figures, from whom Virgil humbly inquires the way.

As sheep, that step from forth their fold, by one,
Or pairs, or three at once; meanwhile the rest
Stand fearfully, bending the eye and nose
To ground, and what the foremost does, that do
The others, gathering round her if she stops,
Simple and quiet, nor the cause discern;
So saw I moving to advance the first,
Who of that fortunate crew were at the head,
Of modest mien, and graceful in their gait.
When they before me had beheld the light
From my right side fall broken on the ground,
So that the shadow reach'd the cave; they stopp'd,
And somewhat back retired: the same did all
Who follow'd, though unweeting of the cause.

These spirits too are startled at the sight of a living being, but, when Virgil assures them Dante is not here without warrant, they obligingly point out "the straight and narrow way" which serves as entrance to Purgatory. This done, one spirit, detaching itself from the rest, inquires whether Dante does not remember Manfred, King of Naples and Sicily, and whether he will not, on his return to earth, inform the Princess that her father repented of his sins at the moment of death and now bespeaks her prayers to shorten his time of probation.

Canto IV

Dazed by what he has just seen and heard, Dante becomes conscious of his surroundings once more, only when the sun stands considerably higher, and when he has arrived at the foot of a rocky pathway up which he painfully follows Virgil, helping himself with his hands as well as his feet. Arrived at its top, both gaze wonderingly around them, and perceive by the position of the sun that they must be at the antipodes of Florence, where their journey began. Panting with the exertions he has just made, Dante expresses some fear lest his strength may fail him, whereupon Virgil kindly assures him the way, so arduous at first, will become easier and easier the higher they ascend.

Just then a voice, addressing them, advises them to rest, and Dante, turning, perceives, among other spirits, a sitting figure, in whom he recognizes a friend noted for his laziness. On questioning this spirit, Dante learns that this friend, Belacqua, instead of exerting himself to climb the mount of Purgatory, is idly waiting in hopes of being wafted upward by the prayers of some "heart which lives in grace." Such slothfulness irritates Virgil, who hurries Dante on, warning him the sun has already reached its meridian and night will all too soon overtake them.

Canto V

Heedless of the whispered comments behind him because he is opaque and not transparent like the other spirits, Dante follows Virgil, until they overtake a band of spirits chanting the *Miserere.* These too seem surprised at Dante's density, and, when assured he is alive, eagerly inquire whether he can give them any tidings of friends and families left on earth. Although all present are sinners who died violent deaths, as they repented at the last minute they are not wholly excluded from hope of bliss. Unable to recognize any of these, Dante nevertheless listens to their descriptions of their violent ends, and promises to enlighten their friends and kinsmen in regard to their fate.

Canto VI

Virgil moves on, and Dante feels constrained to follow, although the spirits continue to pluck at his mantle, imploring him to hear what they have to say. Touched by the sorrows of men of his own time or famous in history, Dante wistfully asks his guide whether prayers can ever change Heaven's decrees, and learns that true love can work miracles, as he will perceive when he beholds Beatrice. The hope of meeting his beloved face to face causes Dante to urge his guide to greater speed and almost gives wings to his feet. Presently Virgil directs his companion's attention to a spirit standing apart, in whom Dante recognizes the poet Sordello, who mourns because Mantua—his native city as well as Virgil's—drifts in these political upheavals like a pilotless vessel in the midst of a storm.

Canto VII

Virgil now informs Sordello that he, Virgil, is debarred from all hope of heaven through lack of faith. Thereupon Sordello reverently approaches him, calling him "Glory of Latium," and inquiring whence he comes. Virgil explains how, led by heavenly influence, he left the dim limbo of ante-hell, passed through all the stages of the Inferno, and is now seeking the place "Where Purgatory its true beginning takes." Sordello rejoins that, while he will gladly serve as guide, the day is already so far gone that they had better spend the night in a neighbouring dell. He then leads Virgil and Dante to a hollow, where, resting upon fragrant flowers, they prepare to spend the night, with a company of spirits who chant "*Salve Regina*." Among these the new-comers recognize with surprise several renowned monarchs, whose doings are briefly described.

Canto VIII

Meantime the hour of rest has come:

> Now was the hour that wakens fond desire
> In men at sea, and melts their thoughtful heart
> Who in the morn have bid sweet friends farewell,
> And pilgrim newly on his road with love
> Thrills, if he hear the vesper bell from far
> That seems to mourn for the expiring day.

Dante and Virgil witness the evening devotions of these spirits, which conclude with a hymn so soft, so devout, that their senses are lost in ravishment. When it has ended, the spirits all gaze expectantly upward, and soon behold two green-clad angels, with flaming swords, who alight on eminences at either end of the glade. These heavenly warriors are sent by Mary to mount guard during the hours of darkness, and to prevent the serpent from gliding unseen into their miniature Eden. Still led by Sordello, the poets withdraw to a leafy recess, where Dante discovers a friend whom he had cause to believe detained in Hell. This spirit explains that if he is not indeed languishing there he owes this blessing to the prayers of his daughter Giovanna, who has not forgotten him although his wife has married again.

Dante is gazing with admiration at three stars (symbols of Faith, Hope, and Charity), when Sordello points out the serpent, who is no sooner descried by the angels than they swoop down and put him to flight.

> I saw not, nor can tell,
> How those celestial falcons from their seat
> Moved, but in motion each one well descried.
> Hearing the air cut by their verdant plumes,
> The serpent fled; and, to their stations, back
> The angels up return'd with equal flight.

Canto IX

Dante falls asleep in this valley, but, just as the first gleams of light appear, he is favoured by a vision, wherein—like Ganymede—he is borne by a golden-feathered eagle into a glowing fire where both are consumed. Wakening with a start from this disquieting dream, Dante finds himself in a different spot, with no companion save Virgil, and notes that the sun is at least two hours high.

Virgil now assures him that, thanks to Santa Lucia (type of God's grace), he has in sleep been conveyed to the very entrance of Purgatory. Gazing at the high cliffs which encircle the mountain, Dante now perceives a deep cleft, through which he and Virgil arrive at a vast portal (the gate of penitence), to which three huge steps of varying colour and size afford access. At the top of these steps, on a diamond threshold, sits the Angel of Absolution with his flashing sword. Challenged by this warder, Virgil explains that they have been guided hither by Santa Lucia, at whose name the angel bids them draw near. Up a polished step of white marble (which typifies sincerity), a dark step of cracked stone (symbol of contrition), and one of red porphyry (emblem of self-sacrifice), Dante arrives at the angel's feet and humbly begs him to unbar the door. In reply the angel inscribes upon the poet's brow, by means of his sword, seven *P's*, to represent the seven deadly sins (in Italian, *peccata*), of which mortals must be purged ere they can enter Paradise.

After bidding Dante have these signs properly effaced, the angel draws from beneath his ash-hued mantle the golden key of authority and the silver key of discernment, stating that when St Peter entrusted them to his keeping he bade him err "rather in opening than in keeping fast." Then, the gate open, the angel bids them enter, adding the solemn warning "he forth again departs who looks behind."

Canto X

Mindful of this caution, Dante does not turn, although the gates close with a clash behind him, but follows his guide along a steep pathway. It is only after painful exertions that they reach the first terrace of Purgatory, or place where the sin of pride is punished. They now pass along a white marble cornice,—some eighteen feet wide,—whose walls are decorated with sculptures which would not have shamed the best masters of Greek art. Here are represented such subjects as the Annunciation, David dancing before the Ark, and Trajan granting the petition of the unfortunate widow. Proceeding along this path, they soon see a procession of spirits approaching, all bent almost double beneath huge burdens. As they creep along, one or another gasps from time to time, "I can endure no more."

Canto XI

The oppressed spirits fervently pray for aid and forgiveness, while continuing their weary tramp around this cornice, where they do penance for undue pride. Praying that they may soon be delivered, Virgil inquires of them where he can find means to ascend to the next circle, and is told to accompany the procession which will soon pass the place. The speaker, although unable to raise his head, confesses that his arrogance while on earth so incensed his fellow-creatures that they finally rose up against him and murdered him. Stooping so as to catch a glimpse of the bent face, Dante realizes he is talking to a miniature painter who claimed to be without equal, and therefore has to do penance.

> The noise
> Of worldly fame is but a blast of wind,
> That blows from diverse points, and shifts its name,
> Shifting the point it blows from.

Canto XII

Journeying beside the bowed painter (who names some of his fellow-sufferers), Dante's attention is directed by Virgil to the pavement beneath his feet, where he sees carved Briareus, Nimrod, Niobe, Arachne, Saul, etc.,—in short, all those who dared measure themselves with the gods or who cherished overweening opinions of their attainments. So absorbed is Dante in contemplation of these subjects that he starts when told an angel is coming to meet them, who, if entreated with sufficient humility, will doubtless help them to reach the next level.

The radiant-faced angel, robed in dazzling white, instead of waiting to be implored to help the travellers, graciously points out steps where the rocks are sundered by a cleft, and, when Dante obediently climbs past him, a soft touch from his wings brushes away the *P.* which stands for pride, and thus frees our poet of all trace of this heinous sin. But it is only on reaching the top of the stairway that Dante becomes aware of this fact.

Canto XIII

The second ledge of Purgatory, which they have now reached, is faced with plain grey stone, and Virgil leads his companion a full mile along it ere they become aware of a flight of invisible spirits, some of whom chant "They have no wine!" while the others respond "Love ye those who have wrong'd you." These are those who, having sinned through envy, can be freed only by the exercise of charity. Then, bidding Dante gaze fixedly, Virgil points out this shadowy host, clothed in sackcloth, sitting back against the rocks, and Dante takes particular note of two figures supporting each other. He next discovers that one and all of these victims have their eyelids sewn so tightly together with wire that passage is left only for streams of penitential tears.

When allowed to address them, Dante, hoping to comfort them, offers to bear back to earth any message they wish to send. It is then that one of these spirits informs Dante that on earth she was Sapia, a learned Siennese, who, having rejoiced when her country was defeated, is obliged to do penance for heartlessness. Marvelling that any one should wander among them with eyes unclosed, she inquires by what means Dante has come here, bespeaks his prayers, and implores him to warn her countrymen not to cherish vain hopes of greatness or to sin through envy.

Canto XIV

The two spirits leaning close together, in their turn question who Virgil and Dante may be ? When they hear mention of Rome and Florence, they hotly inveigh against the degeneracy of dwellers on the banks of the Tiber and Arno.

Shortly after leaving this place with his guide, Dante hears the wail : "Whosoever finds will slay me," a cry followed by a deafening crash.

Canto XV

Circling round the mountain, always in the same direction, Dante notes the sun is about to set, when another dazzling angel invites them up to the next level—where anger is punished—by means of a stairway less steep than any of the preceding. As they climb, the angel softly chants " Blessed the merciful " and " Happy thou that conquer'st," while he brushes aside the second *P.*, and thus cleanses Dante from envy. But, when Dante craves an explanation of what he has heard and seen, Virgil assures him that only when the five remaining " scars " have vanished from his brow, can Beatrice herself satisfy his curiosity.

On reaching the third level, they find themselves enveloped in a dense fog, through which Dante dimly beholds the twelve-year-old Christ in the Temple and overhears His mother chiding Him. Next he sees a woman weeping, and lastly Stephen stoned to death.

Canto XVI

Urged by his guide to hasten through this bitter blinding fog—a symbol of anger which is punished here—Dante stumbles along, mindful of Virgil's caution, " Look that from me thou part not." Meanwhile voices on all sides invoke " the Lamb of God that taketh away the sins of the world." Then, all at once, a voice addresses Dante, who, prompted by Virgil, inquires where the next stairway may be ? His interlocutor, after bespeaking Dante's prayers, holds forth against Rome, which, boasting of two suns—the Pope and the Emperor—has seen the one quench the other. But the arrival of an angel, sent to guide our travellers to the next level, soon ends this conversation.

Canto XVII

Out of the vapours of anger—as dense as any Alpine fog—Dante, who has caught glimpses of famous victims of anger, such as Haman and Lavinia, emerges with Virgil, only to be dazzled by the glorious light of the sun. Then, climbing the ladder which the angel points out, Dante feels him brush away the third obnoxious *P.*, while chanting, " Blessed are the peacemakers." They now reach the fourth ledge, where the sin of indifference or sloth is punished, and, as they trudge along it, Virgil explains that all indifference is due to a lack of love, a virtue on which he eloquently discourses.

Canto XVIII

A multitude of spirits now interrupt Virgil, and, when he questions them, two, who lead the rest, volubly quote examples of fervent affection and zealous haste. They are closely followed by other spirits, the backsliders, who, not having had the strength or patience to endure, preferred inglorious ease to adventurous life and are now consumed with regret.

Canto XIX

In the midst of a trance which overtakes him, Dante next has a vision of the Siren which beguiled Ulysses and of Philosophy or Truth. Then, morning having dawned, Virgil leads him to the next stairway, up which an angel wafts them, chanting " Blessed are they that mourn, for they shall be comforted," while he brushes away another sin scar from our poet's forehead.

In this fifth circle those guilty of avarice undergo punishment by being chained fast to the earth to which they clung, and which they bedew with penitent tears. One of these, questioned by Dante, reveals himself as Pope Adrian V, who, dying a month after his elevation to the papal chair, repented in time of his grasping past. When Dante kneels compassionately beside this august sufferer, he is implored to warn the Pope's kinswoman to eschew the besetting sin of their house.

Canto XX

A little farther on, among the grovelling figures which closely pave this fifth cornice, Dante beholds

Hugues Capet, founder of the third dynasty of French kings, and stigmatized as "root of that ill plant," because this poem was composed only a few years after Philip IV's criminal attempt against Pope Boniface at Agnani. The poets also recognize there Pygmalion (brother of Dido), Midas, Achan, Heliodorus, and Crassus, ere they are startled by feeling the whole mountain tremble beneath them and by hearing the spirits exultantly cry "Glory to God!"

Canto XXI

Clinging to Virgil in speechless terror, Dante hears his guide assure the spirit which suddenly appears before them that the Fates have not yet finished spinning the thread of his companion's life. When questioned by the travellers in regard to the noise and earthquake, this spirit informs them that the mountain quivers with joy whenever a sinner is released, and that, after undergoing a punishment of five hundred years, he—Statius—is now free to go in quest of his master Virgil, whom he has always longed to meet. Dante's smile at these words, together with his meaning glance at Virgil, suddenly reveal to the spirit that his dearest wish is granted, and Statius reverently does obeisance to the poet from whose fount he drew his inspiration.

Canto XXII

The three bards are next led by an angel up another staircase, to the sixth cornice (Dante losing another *P.* on the way), where the sins of gluttony and drunkenness are punished. As they circle this ledge, Dante questions how Statius became guilty of the sin of covetousness, for which he was doomed to journey round the fifth circle? In reply Statius rejoins that it was not because of covetousness, but of its counterpart, over-lavishness, that he suffered so long, and principally because he was not brave enough to own himself a Christian. Then he inquires of Virgil what has become of their fellow-countrymen Terence, Caecilius, Plautus, and Varro, only to learn that they too linger in the dark regions of ante-hell, where they hold sweet converse with other pagan poets.

Reverently listening to the conversation of his companions, Dante drinks in "mysterious lessons of sweet poesy" and silently follows them until they draw near a tree laden with fruit and growing beside a crystal stream. Issuing from this tree a voice warns them against the sin of gluttony—which is punished in this circle—and quotes such marked examples of abstinence as Daniel feeding on pulse and John the Baptist living on locusts and wild honey.

Canto XXIII

Dante is still dumbly staring at the mysterious tree when Virgil bids him follow, for they still have far to go. They next meet weeping, hollow-eyed spirits, so emaciated that their bones start through their skin. One of these recognizes Dante, who is aghast that his friend Forese should be in such a state and escorted by two skeleton spirits. Forese replies that he and his companions are consumed by endless hunger and thirst, although they eat and drink without ever being satisfied. When Dante expresses surprise because a man only five years dead should already be so high up the mount of Purgatory, Forese explains that his wife's constant prayers have successively freed him from detention in the other circles. In return Dante states why he is here and names his companions.

Canto XXIV

Escorting the three travellers on their way, Forese inquires what has become of his sister, Piccarda, ere he points out various spirits, with whom Dante converses, and who predict the coming downfall of his political foes. But these spirits suddenly leave Dante to dart toward trees, which tantalizingly withhold their fruit from their eager hands, while hidden voices loudly extol temperance.

Canto XXV

In single file the three poets proceed on their way, commenting on what they have seen, and Statius expounds his theories of life. Then they ascend to the seventh ledge, where glowing fires purge mortals of all sensuality. Even as they toil toward this level, an angel voice extols chastity, and Dante once more feels the light touch which he now associates with the removal of one of the scars made by the angel at the entrance of Purgatory. Arrived above, the poets have to tread a narrow path between the roaring fires and the abyss. So narrow is the way, that Virgil bids Dante beware or he will be lost!

> Behoved us, one by one, along the side,
> That border'd on the void, to pass; and I
> Fear'd on one hand the fire, on the other fear'd
> Headlong to fall: when thus the instructor warn'd:
> "Strict rein must in this place direct the eyes.
> A little swerving and the way is lost."

As all three warily proceed, Dante hears voices in

the fiery furnace alternately imploring the mercy of God and quoting examples of chastity, such as Mary and Diana, and couples who proved chaste though married.

Canto XXVI

As the poets move along the rim, Dante's shadow, cast upon the roaring flames, causes such wonder to the victims undergoing purification that one of them inquires who he may be. Just as Dante is about to answer, his attention is attracted by hosts of shadows, who, after exchanging hasty kisses, dash on, mentioning such famous examples of dissoluteness as Pasiphae, and the men who caused the destruction of Sodom and Gomorrah. Turning to his interlocutor, Dante then explains how he came hither and expresses a hope he may soon be received in bliss. The grateful spirit then gives his name, admits he sang too freely of carnal love, and adds that Dante would surely recognize many of his fellow-sufferers were he to point them out. Then, bespeaking Dante's prayers, he plunges back into the fiery element which is to make him fit for Paradise

Canto XXVII

Just as the sun is about to set, an angel approaches them, chanting " Blessed are the pure in heart," and bids them fearlessly pass through the wall of fire which alone stands between them and Paradise. Seeing Dante hang back timorously, Virgil reminds him that he will find Beatrice on the other side, whereupon our poet plunges recklessly into the glowing furnace, whither both his companions precede him, and whence all three issue on an upward path.

There they make their couch on separate steps, and Dante gazes up at the stars until he falls asleep and dreams of a lovely lady, culling flowers in a meadow, singing she is Lea (the mediaeval type of active life), and stating that her sister Rachel (the emblem of contemplative life) spends the day gazing at herself in a mirror.

At dawn the pilgrims awake, and Virgil assures Dante that before this day ends his hunger for a sight of Beatrice will be appeased. This prospect so lightens Dante's heart that he almost soars to the top of the stairway. There Virgil, who has led him through temporal and eternal fires, bids him follow his pleasure until he meets the fair lady who bade him undertake this journey.

> Till those bright eyes
> With gladness come, which, weeping, made me haste
> To succour thee, thou mayst or seat thee down
> Or wander where thou wilt. Expect no more
> Sanction of warning voice or sign from me,
> Free of thine own arbitrement to choose,
> Discreet, judicious. To distrust thy sense
> Were henceforth error. I invest thee then
> With crown and mitre, sovereign o'er thyself.

Canto XXVIII

Through the Garden of Eden Dante now wanders with Statius and Virgil, until he beholds, on the other side of a pellucid stream (whose waters have the "power to take away remembrance of offence"), a beautiful lady (the Countess Matilda), who smiles upon him. Then she informs Dante she has come to "answer every doubt" he cherishes, and, as they wander along on opposite sides of the stream, she expounds for his benefit the creation of man, the

Fall and its consequences, and informs him how all the plants that grow on earth originate here. The water at his feet issues from an unquenchable fountain, and divides into two streams, the first of which, Lethe, " chases from the mind the memory of sin," while the waters of the second, Eunoe, have the power to recall "good deeds to one's mind."

Canto XXIX

Suddenly the lady bids Dante pause, look, and hearken. Then he sees a great light on the opposite shore, hears a wonderful music, and soon beholds a procession of spirits, so bright that they leave behind them a trail of rainbow-coloured light. First among them march the four and twenty elders of the Book of Revelation ; they are followed by four beasts (the Evangelists), and a gryphon, drawing a chariot (the Christian Church or papal chair), far grander than any that ever graced imperial triumph at Rome. Personifications of the three evangelical virtues (Charity, Faith, and Hope) and of the four moral virtues (Prudence, etc.), together with St Luke and St Paul, the four great Doctors of the Church, and the apostle St John, serve as body-guard for this chariot, which stops opposite Dante with a noise like thunder.

Canto XXX

The wonderful light, our poet now perceives, emanates from a seven-branched candlestick, and illuminates all the heavens like an aurora borealis. Then, amid the chanting, and while angels shower flowers down upon her, he beholds in the chariot a lady veiled in white, in whom, although transfigured, he instinctively recognizes Beatrice (a personification of Heavenly Wisdom). In his surprise Dante impulsively turns toward Virgil, only to discover that he has vanished !

Beatrice comforts him, however, by promising to be his guide hereafter, and gently reproaches him for the past until he casts shamefaced glances at his feet. There, in the stream (which serves as nature's mirror), he catches a reflection of his utter loathsomeness, and becomes so penitent, that Beatrice explains she purposely brought him hither by the awful road he has travelled to induce him to lead a changed life hereafter.

Canto XXXI

Beatrice then accuses him of yielding to the world's deceitful pleasures after she left him, and explains how he should, on the contrary, have striven to be virtuous so as to rejoin her. When she finally forgives him and bids him gaze into her face once more, he sees she surpasses her former self in loveliness as greatly as on earth she outshone all other women. Dante is so overcome by a sense of his utter unworthiness that he falls down unconscious, and on recovering his senses finds himself in the stream, upheld by the hand of a nymph (Matilda), who sweeps him along, "swift as a shuttle bounding o'er the wave," while angels chant, "Thou shalt wash me" and "I shall be whiter than snow."

Freed from all haunting memories of past sins by Lethe's waters, Dante finally lands on the "blessed shore." There Beatrice's hand-maidens welcome him, and beseech her to complete her work by revealing her inner beauty to this mortal, that he may portray it for mankind. But, although Dante gazes at her

Beatrice

Dante Gabriel Rossetti

in breathless admiration, words fail him to render what he sees.

O splendour!
O sacred light eternal! who is he,
So pale with musing in Pierian shades,
Or with that fount so lavishly imbued,
Whose spirit should not fail him in the essay
To represent thee such as thou didst seem,
When under cope of the still-chiming heaven
Thou gavest to open air thy charms reveal'd?

Canto XXXII

Dante is still quenching a "ten-years' thirst" by staring at his beloved, when her attendants admonish him to desist. But, although he obediently turns aside his eyes, like a man who has gazed too long at the sun, he sees her image stamped on all he looks at. He and Statius now humbly follow the glorious procession, which enters a forest and circles gravely round a barren tree-trunk, to which the chariot is tethered. Immediately the dry branches burst into bud and leaf, and, soothed by angelic music, Dante falls asleep, only to be favoured by a vision so startling, that on awakening he eagerly looks around for Beatrice. The nymph who bore him safely through the waters then points her out, resting beneath the mystic tree, and Beatrice, rousing too, bids Dante note the fate of her chariot. The poet then sees an eagle (the Empire) swoop down from heaven, tear the tree asunder, and attack the chariot (the Church), into which a fox (heresy) has sprung as if in quest of prey. Although the fox is soon routed by Beatrice, the eagle makes its nest in the chariot, beneath which arises a seven-headed monster (the seven capital sins), bearing on its back a giant, who alternately caresses and chastises a whore.

Canto XXXIII

The seven Virtues having chanted a hymn, Beatrice motions to Statius and Dante to follow her, asking the latter why he is so mute? Rejoining she best knows what he needs, Dante receives from her lips an explanation of what he has just seen, which he is bidden reveal to mankind. Conversing thus, they reach the second stream, of whose waters Beatrice bids her friend drink, and after that renovating draught Dante realizes he has now been made pure and "apt for mounting to the stars."

THE PARADISO

Introduction

The Paradise of Dante consists of nine crystalline spheres of different sizes, the Moon, Mercury, Venus, the Sun, Mars, Jupiter, Saturn, the Fixed Stars, and the Empyrean, enclosed one within the other, and revolved by the Angels, Archangels, Princedoms, Powers, Virtues, Dominations, Thrones, Cherubim, and Seraphim. Beyond these orbs, whose whirling motions cause "the music of the spheres," lies a tenth circle, the real Heaven (a Rose), where "peace divine inhabits," and of which the Divine Essence or Trinity forms the very core.

Canto I

Paradise opens with Dante's statement that in Heaven he was "witness of things, which to relate again, surpasseth the power of him who comes from thence." He therefore invokes the help of Apollo to describe that part of the universe upon which is lavished the greatest share of light. Then, while gazing up into Beatrice's eyes, Dante, freed from earth's trammels, suddenly feels himself soar upward, and is transferred with indescribable swiftness into a totally different medium.

Canto II

Perceiving his bewilderment, Beatrice reassures him in a motherly strain, and, gazing around him, Dante realizes they have entered the translucent circle of the Moon (revolved by angels). After warning his fellow-men "the way I pass ne'er yet was run," Dante goes on to relate what Beatrice teaches him in regard to the heavenly spheres and spiritual evolution, and how she promises to reveal to him "the truth thou lovest."

Canto III

In the pearl-hued atmosphere of the moon, Dante beholds, "as through a glass, darkly," shadowy, nun-like forms, and is told by Beatrice to communicate with them. Addressing the form nearest him, Dante learns she is Piccarda (sister of Forese), who was kidnapped by her husband after she had taken the veil. Although she would fain have kept her religious vows, Piccarda proved a faithful wife, and declares she and her fellow-spirits are content to remain in their appointed sphere until called higher by the Almighty.

> She with those other spirits gently smiled;
> Then answer'd with such gladness, that she seem'd
> With love's first flame to glow: "Brother! our will
> Is, in composure, settled by the power
> Of charity, who makes us will alone
> What we possess, and nought beyond desire."

All her companions also wished to be brides of Christ, but patiently did their duty, and, knowing that "in His will is our tranquillity," they now spend all their time singing *Ave Maria.* When these nun-like forms vanish, Dante gazes at Beátrice in hopes of learning more.

Canto IV

In reply to Dante's inquiring glance, Beatrice explains that those compelled to sin against their desire are ever held blameless in Heaven. Then, stating:

> "Not seldom, brother, it hath chanced for men
> To do what they had gladly left undone;"

she adds that "the will that wills not, still survives unquenched," and that by will power only St Lawrence and Mucius Scævola were enabled to brave fire. Then she makes him see how truth alone can satisfy a mind athirst for knowledge.

Canto V

Beatrice asserts that the most precious gift bestowed upon mankind was freedom of will, and that "knowledge comes of learning well retain'd." She concludes that when man makes a vow he offers his will in sacrifice to God, and that for that reason no vow should be thoughtlessly made, but all should be rigidly kept. Still, she admits it is better to break a promise than, like Jephthah and Agamemnon, to subscribe to a heinous crime, and states that either Testament can serve as guide for Jews or Christians. Again drawing Dante upward by the very intensity of her gaze, she conveys him to the second circle, the heaven of Mercury (revolved by Archangels). Here, in an atmosphere as pellucid as water, Dante perceives thousands of angels coming toward him, singing " Lo! one arrived to multiply our loves!" These spirits assure Dante he was born in a happy hour, since he is allowed, ere the " close of fleshly warfare," to view the glories of Heaven—and express a desire to share their lights with him. So Dante questions the spirit nearest him, which immediately glows with loving eagerness to serve him, until it becomes a dazzling point of light.

Canto VI

This spirit announces he is Justinian, chosen to clear " from vain excess the encumbered laws," 500 years after the Christian era began, and that it was in order to devote all his time to this task that he consigned the military power to Belisarius. He proceeds to give Dante a *résumé* of Roman history, from the kidnapping of the Sabines to his own day, laying stress on the triumphs won by great generals. He also specially mentions the hour " When Heaven was minded that o'er all the world His own deep calm should brood," the troublous days of the empire, and the feud of the Guelfs and Ghilbellines, the two principal political factions of Dante's time. Next he explains that Mercury is inhabited by " good spirits whose mortal lives were busied to that end that honour and renown might wait on them," and quotes in particular Raymond Bérenger, whose four daughters became queens.

Canto VII

After this speech Justinian vanishes with his angelic companions, and Dante, duly encouraged, inquires of Beatrice how " just revenge could be with justice punished?" She informs him that, as in Adam all die through the power of sin, so all can by faith live again through Christ, thanks to God's goodness.

Canto VIII

Although unaware of the fact, Dante, whose eyes have been fixed on Beatrice, has during her exposition been wafted up to the third heaven, that of Venus (revolved by Princedoms). In the planet of love—where Beatrice glows with increased beauty—are innumerable souls "imperfect through excess of love," which are grouped in constantly revolving circles. All at once one of these luminous spirits approaches Dante, and, after expressing great readiness to serve him, introduces himself as Charles Martel, King of Hungary, brother of Robert of Naples. Thirsting for information, Dante inquires of him "how bitter can spring when sweet is sown?" In a lengthy disquisition in reply, this spirit mentions how children often differ from their parents, quotes Esau and Jacob as marked examples thereof, and adds that nature, guided by Providence, produces at will a Solon, Xerxes, Melchisedec, or Daedalus.

Canto IX

The next spirit with whom Beatrice converses is the fair Cunizza, who like the Magdalen "loved much," and therefore obtained pardon for her sins. Before vanishing, she foretells coming political events, and introduces the Provençal bard Folco, whose poems on love were to be republished after 500 years of oblivion. After relating his life, this poet informs Dante that the harlot Rahab was admitted to this heaven in reward for saving Joshua's spies.

This spirit concludes his interview by censuring the present papal policy, declaring it far too worldly, avaricious, and time-serving to find favour in Heaven.

Canto X

Drawn upward this time by the attraction of the sun, Dante finds himself in a dazzling sphere (revolved by Powers), where he and Beatrice behold consecutive moving wreaths, each composed of twelve blessed spirits who while on earth were noted as teachers of divinity and philosophy. One of these singing, revolving wreaths encompasses our travellers, until one of its members, St Thomas Aquinas, ceases his ineffable song long enough to present his companions and explain their titles to immortal glory.

Canto XI

St Thomas Aquinas, in his conversation with Dante, relates the life of St Francis of Assisi, dwelling particularly upon his noble character, and describing how, after becoming wedded to Poverty, he founded the order of the Franciscans, received the stigmata, and died in odour of sanctity, leaving worthy disciples and emulators, such as St Dominic, to continue and further the good work he had begun. He adds that many of the saint's followers are represented in the innumerable glowing wreaths which people the heaven of the Sun.

Canto XII

Still encompassed by one rainbow circle after another, Dante is told by St Buonaventura of

Dominic's inestimable services to mankind, and hears about his fervent zeal and deep faith.

Canto XIII

While Dante and Beatrice gaze with awe and admiration upon the circles of light which revolve through all the signs of the zodiac, St Thomas Aquinas solves several of Dante's doubts, and cautions him never to accede to any proposition without having duly weighed it.

> "Let not the people be too swift to judge;
> As one who reckons on the blades in field,
> Or e'er the crop be ripe. For I have seen
> The thorn frown rudely all the winter long,
> And after bear the rose upon its top;
> And bark, that all her way across the sea
> Ran straight and speedy, perish at the last
> E'en in the haven's mouth."

Canto XIV

Proceeding from circle to circle, Dante and Beatrice reach the innermost ring, where the latter bids Solomon solve Dante's doubts by describing the appearance of the blest after the resurrection of the body. In words almost as eloquent as those wherewith St Gabriel transmitted his message to Mary, Solomon's complies.

> "Long as the joy of Paradise shall last,
> Our love shall shine around that raiment, bright
> As fervent; fervent as, in vision, blest;
> And that as far, in blessedness, exceeding,
> As it hath grace, beyond its virtue, great.
> Our shape, regarmented with glorious weeds
> Of saintly flesh, must, being thus entire,
> Show yet more gracious. Therefore shall increase
> Whate'er, of light, gratuitous imparts
> The Supreme Good; light, ministering aid,

The better to disclose his glory: whence,
The vision needs increasing, must increase
The fervour which it kindles; and that too
The ray, that comes from it."

As he concludes his explanation a chorus of spiritual voices chant "Amen," and Solomon, directing Dante's glance upward, shows him how the bright spirits of this sphere group themselves in the form of a cross, —glowing with light and pulsing with music,— whereon "Christ beamed," a sight none can hope to see save those who "take up their cross and follow Him."

Cantos XV, XVI

In the midst of the rapture caused by these sights and sounds, Dante is amazed to recognize, in one of the angels which continually shift places in the glowing cross, his ancestor Cacciaguida, who assures him Florence proved happy as long as its inhabitants led simple and virtuous lives, but rapidly degenerated and became corrupt when covetousness, luxury, and pleasure took up their abode within its walls.

Canto XVII

Encouraged by Beatrice, who stands at a short distance to leave him more freedom, Dante begs his great ancestor to reveal what is about to befall him, so that, forewarned, he may most wisely meet his fate. In reply Cacciaguida tells him he will be exiled from Florence, and compelled to associate with people who will turn against him, only to rue this fact with shame later on. He adds Dante will learn how bitter is the savour of other's bread and how hard to climb another's stairs.

> " Thou shalt leave each thing
> Beloved most dearly: this is the first shaft
> Shot from the bow of exile. Thou shalt prove
> How salt the savour is of other's bread;
> How hard the passage, to descend and climb
> By other's stairs."

Then Cacciaguida goes on to state that Dante shall finally find refuge in Lombardy, with Can Grande, and while there will compose the poems depicting his memorable journey down through sin to the lowest pit and upward through repentance to the realm of bliss.

> " For this, there only have been shown to thee,
> Throughout these orbs, the mountain, and the deep,
> Spirit, whom fame hath note of. For the mind
> Of him who hears is loath to acquiesce
> And fix its faith, unless the instance brought
> Be palpable, and proof apparent urge."

Seeing Dante's dismay at this prediction, Beatrice comforts him by a smile, and, seeing he is again wrapped in contemplation of her, warns him that " these eyes are not thy only Paradise."

Canto XVIII

Beatrice leads her charge into the fifth heaven, that of Mars, revolved by Virtues and inhabited by transfigured martyrs, confessors, and holy warriors, such as Joshua, the Maccabees, Charlemagne, Orlando, Godfrey of Bouillon, and other men of note. These worthies form a part of the mystic cross, and each glows with transcendent light as Beatrice points them out one after another. Then Beatrice wafts her charge into the sixth heaven, that of Jupiter (revolved by Dominations). Here the spirits of rulers famous for justice, moving with kaleidoscopic tints and rapidity, alternately form mystic letters spelling "Love righteousness, ye that be judges of the earth," or settle silently into the shape of a gigantic eagle. This sight proves so impressive that Dante sinks to his knees, fervently praying justice may indeed reign on earth as in Heaven.

Canto XIX

To his intense surprise Dante now hears the mystic eagle proclaim in trumpet tones that justice and pity shall be exacted, and that no man shall be saved without them. He adds that eternal judgment is incomprehensible to mortal ken, that mere professions are vain, and that many so-called Christian potentates (some of whom he names) will present a sorry figure on Judgment Day.

Canto XX

After a period of silence, the same Eagle (an emblem of the Empire) proceeds to exalt certain rulers, especially those glorified spirits which form the pupil of his eye (David), and his eyelids (Trajan, Hezekiah, Constantine). As he mentions their names they glow like priceless rubies, and he explains that, although some of them lived before Christ was made flesh, all have been redeemed because Faith, Hope, and Charity are their sponsors.

> "The three nymphs,
> Whom at the right wheel thou beheld'st advancing,
> Were sponsors for him, more than thousand years
> Before baptizing. O how far removed,
> Predestination! is thy root from such
> As see not the First Cause entire: and ye,
> O mortal men! be wary how ye judge:

For we, who see our Maker, know not yet
The number of the chosen; and esteem
Such scantiness of knowledge our delight:
For all our good is, in that primal good,
Concentrate; and God's will and ours are one."

Canto XXI

Meantime Beatrice, who has grown more and more beautiful as they rise, explains, when Dante again gazes upon her, that she no longer dares smile, lest he be consumed like Semele when she beheld Jove. The magnetic power of her glance suffices again, however, to transfer him to the seventh heaven, that of Saturn (revolved by Thrones). This sphere is the abiding place of contemplative and abstinent hermits and monks. There our poet beholds a ladder, up whose steps silently ascend those whose lives were spent in retirement and holy contemplation. Amazed by all he sees, and conscious he no longer hears the music of the spheres, Dante wonders until informed by one of the spirits, coming down the steps to meet him, that at this stage the heavenly music is too loud and intense for human ears. Seeing his interlocutor suddenly become a whirling wheel of light, Dante inquires what this may mean, only to be told spirits obscured on earth by fleshly garments shine brighter in Heaven. The spirit then gives his name (St Peter Damian), vividly describes the place where he built his hermitage, and declares many modern prelates have sinned so grievously through lechery or avarice that they are now detained in Inferno or Purgatory. As he speaks, spirit after spirit flits down the stairs, each bound on some errand of charity to the spheres below.

Canto XXII

Startled by a loud cry, Dante is reassured by St Damian's statement that no harm can befall him in Heaven. Next Beatrice directs his attention to some descending spirits, the most radiant of which is St Benedict, who explains how blissful spirits often leave the heavenly abode " to execute the counsel of the Highest." He adds that Dante has been selected to warn mortals, none of whom will ever be allowed to venture hither again. Then St Benedict describes his life on earth and inveighs against the corruption of the monks of Dante's time.

His speech ended, St Benedict vanishes, and Beatrice wafts Dante up the mystic stairs, through the constellation of the Gemini, to the eighth heaven, that of the Fixed Stars (revolved by the Cherubim). Declaring he is so near " the last salvation " that his eyes should be unclouded, Beatrice removes the last veil from his sight, and bids him gaze down at the spheres through which they have passed, and " see how vast a world thou hast already put beneath thy feet." Smiling at the smallness of the earth left behind him, Dante, undazzled by the mild light of the moon or the glow of the sun, gazes at the seven revolving spheres until all the scheme of creation is " made apparent to him."

Canto XXIII

Beatrice, who is still standing beside him, finally tears him away from his contemplation of what is beneath him, and directs his glance aloft, where he catches his first glimpse of Christ, escorted by His Mother and by the Church triumphant. Too dazzled and awed at first to grasp what he sees, Dante feels heart and mind expand, as he listens enraptured to sweeter music than was ever made by the nine muses. Meantime the spirits escorting Christ crown the Virgin with lilies, and all sing the praises of the Queen of Heaven.

Canto XXIV

Beatrice and Dante are now joined by the spirit of St Peter, who examines Dante on faith, receiving the famous reply: " Faith is the substance of the things we hope for, and evidence of those that are not seen." Not only does St Peter approve Dante's definition, but he discusses theological questions with him, leading him meanwhile further into this sphere.

Canto XXV

Presently a spirit approaches them which is designated by Beatrice as St James. After greeting St Peter and smiling upon Beatrice, St James reveals he has been sent hither by Christ to examine Dante upon hope, whereupon our poet, lifting his eyes " to the hills," gains courage enough to answer thus: " Hope is the certain expectation of future glory, which is the effect of grace divine and merit precedent." St James is so pleased with this answer that he glows even more brightly, as St John, " who lay upon the breast of Him, our Pelican," appeared shining so brightly that Dante, turning to ask Beatrice who he is, discovers he can no longer see her although she is close beside him.

> I turn'd, but ah! how trembled in my thought,
> When, looking at my side again to see
> Beatrice, I descried her not; although,
> Not distant, on the happy coast she stood.

Canto XXVI

Dante now ascertains he has merely been temporarily blinded by the excess of light which emanates from St John, who proceeds to examine him in regard to Charity. His answers are greeted by the heavenly chorus with the chant "Holy, holy, holy," in which Beatrice joins, ere she clears the last mote away from Dante's eyes and thus enables him to see more plainly than ever. Our poet now perceives a fourth spirit, in whom he recognizes Adam, father of mankind, who retells the story of Eden, adding that, 4232 years after Creation, Christ delivered him from Hell, and enabled him to view the changes which had taken place in the fortunes of his descendants during that long space of time.

Canto XXVII

After listening enraptured to the melody of the heavenly choir chanting "Glory be to the Father, to the Son, and to the Holy Ghost," Dante gazes upon the four worthies near him, who glow and shine like torches, while "silence reigns in heaven." Then St Peter, changing colour, holds forth against covetousness, and expounds the doctrine of apostolic succession. Since the early popes died as martyrs, he considers it a disgrace that their successors should be guilty of misgovernment. He adds that the keys bestowed upon him should never figure on banners used in waging unrighteous wars, and that his effigy on the papal seal should never appear on worldly documents.

Then Beatrice affords Dante a glimpse of the earth from the Straits of Gibraltar to the Bosphorus, and, when this vision ends, wafts him up into the ninth heaven, the *Primum Mobile*, or spot whence all motion starts, although itself remains immovable.

> Here is the goal, whence motion on his race
> Starts : motionless the centre, and the rest
> All moved around.

Canto XXVIII

From this point Dante watches the universe spin around him, until " she who doth emparadise my soul " draws aside the veil of mortality, and allows him to perceive nine concentric spheres of multitudinous angels constantly revolving round a dazzling point while singing " Hosanna ! " These are the heavenly host, the hierarchy of angels, Seraphim, Cherubim, Thrones, Dominations, Virtues, Powers, Princedoms, Archangels, and Angels, in charge of the various circles which compose Dante's Paradise.

Canto XXIX

Able to read Dante's thoughts, Beatrice explains some of the things he would fain know, and disperses his doubts, cautioning him, if he would be blessed, to rid himself of every atom of pride.

Canto XXX

Once more Dante's eyes are fixed upon Beatrice, whose beauty far transcends his powers of description, and is by her conveyed into the next circle, the Empyrean, or heaven of pure light, into which he is told to plunge as into a river. Eagerly quaffing its ethereal waters to satisfy his ardent thirst for knowledge, Dante beholds the court of Heaven, and descries its myriads of thrones, all occupied by redeemed spirits. These thrones are grouped around a brilliant centre (God) so as to form a dazzling jewelled rose.

Canto XXXI

Robed in snowy white, the redeemed—who form the petals of the Eternal Rose—are visited from time to time by ruby sparks, which are the angels hovering above them, who plunge like bees into the heart of this flower, their glowing faces, golden wings, and white robes adding charms to the scene. After gazing for some time at this sight in speechless wonder, Dante, turning to question Beatrice, discovers she is no longer beside him! At the same time a being robed in glory near him bids him look up at the third row of thrones from the centre, and there behold her in her appointed seat. Eagerly glancing in the direction indicated, Dante perceives Beatrice, who, when he invokes her, smiles radiantly down upon him, ere she again turns her face to the eternal fountain of light.

> So I my suit preferr'd:
> And she, so distant, as appear'd, look'd down,
> And smiled; then towards the eternal fountain turn'd.

The spirit informs Dante he has been sent by Beatrice to assist him to his journey's end, for he is St Bernard, who so longed to behold the Virgin's countenance that that boon was vouchsafed him. Knowing Dante would fain see her too, he bids him find, among the most brilliant lights in the Mystic Rose, the Virgin Mary, Queen of Heaven.

Canto XXXII

The dazzled Dante cannot immediately locate her, so St Bernard points her out, with Eve, Rachel, Beatrice, Sarah, Judith, Rebecca, and Ruth sitting at her feet, and John the Baptist, St Augustine, St Francis, and St Benedict standing close behind her. He also explains that those who believed in "Christ who was to come" are in one part of the rose, while those who "looked to Christ already come" are in another, but that all here are spirits duly assoiled, and adds that, although occupying different ranks, these spirits are perfectly satisfied with the places awarded to them. Told now to look up at the face most closely resembling Christ's, Dante discovers it is that of St Gabriel, angel of the Annunciation, and he descries farther on St Peter, Moses, and St Anna, as well as Santa Lucia, who induced Beatrice to send for him.

Canto XXXIII

This done, St Bernard fervently prays the Virgin, who not only "gives succour to him who asketh it, but oftentimes forerunneth of its own accord the asking," to allow Dante one glimpse of Divine Majesty. Seeing this prayer is graciously received, St Bernard bids Dante look up. Thanks to his recently purified vision, our poet has a glimpse of the Triune Divinity—compounded of love—which so transcends all human expression that he declares "what he saw was not for words to speak."

He concludes his grand poem, however, by assuring us that, although dazed by what he had seen, his

> Will roll'd onward, like a wheel
> In even motion, by the love impell'd,
> That moves the sun in heaven and all the stars.

THE ORLANDOS

Roland, nephew of Charlemagne, hero of the *Song of Roland* and of an endless succession of metrical romances, was as popular a character in Italian literature as in the French. The Italians felt a proprietary interest in Charlemagne because he had been crowned Emperor of the West in Rome in the year 800, and also because he had taken the part of the Pope against the Lombards. Even the names of his twelve great peers were household words in Italy, so tales about Roland—who is known there as Orlando—were sure to find ready hearers.

The adventures of Roland, therefore, naturally became the theme of Italian epics, some of which are of considerable length and of great importance, owing principally to their exquisite versification and diction. Pulci and Boiardo both undertook to depict Roland as a prey to the tender passion in epics entitled *Orlando Innamorato*, while Ariosto, the most accomplished and musical poet of the three, spent more than ten years of his life composing *Orlando Furioso* (1516), wherein he depicts this famous hero driven insane by his passion for an Oriental princess.

Assuming that his auditors are familiar with the characters of Boiardo's unfinished epic, Ariosto, picking up the thread of the narrative at the point where his predecessor dropped it, continues the story in the same vein. It therefore becomes imperative to know the main trend of Boiardo's epic.

It opens with a lengthy description of a tournament at the court of Charlemagne, whither knights from all parts of the globe hasten in order to distinguish themselves in the lists. Chief among these foreign guests are Argalio and Angelica, son and daughter of the King of Cathay, with their escort of four huge giants. The Prince is, moreover, the fortunate possessor of a magic lance, one touch of which suffices to unhorse any opponent, while the Princess, by means of an enchanted ring, can detect and frustrate any spell, or become invisible by putting it in her mouth. On arriving at Charlemagne's court, Argalio stipulates that all the knights he defeats shall belong to his sister, whom in return he offers as prize to any knight able to unhorse him.

Such is the transcendent beauty of Angelica that Argalio is instantly challenged by Astolfo, who is defeated, and then by Ferrau, who, although defeated in the first onset, proves victor in the second, simply because he accidentally seizes the magic lance and directs it against its owner! Since the laws of the tournament award him the prize, Angelica, seeing she cannot otherwise escape, rides hastily away and conceals herself in the forest of Arden. She is, however, pursued thither by many knights who have been captivated by her beauty, among whom are Rinaldo (Renaud de Montauban) and Orlando, who were proposing to challenge her brother next. In the precincts of the forest where Angelica takes refuge are two magic fountains, one whose waters instantly transform love into hate, while the other induces any partaker to love the next person seen.

Prowling around this forest, Rinaldo unsuspectingly quaffs the water which turns love to hate, so he immediately ceases his quest and falls asleep. Meantime Angelica, drinking from the other fountain and coming upon the sleeper, falls madly in love with him and watches for his awakening. But, still under the influence of the magic waters he has imbibed, Rinaldo rides away without heeding her timid wooing, and leaves her to mourn until she too falls asleep.

Orlando, coming up by chance, is gazing in admiration upon this sleeping princess, when Ferrau rides up to claim her as his prize. These knights are fighting for her possession when the clash of their weapons awakens Angelica. Terrified she retreats into the thicket, and, thrusting her ring into her mouth, becomes invisible! Meantime the knights continue their duel until a messenger summons Ferrau to hasten to Spain, where war has broken out.

Angelica, unable to forget Rinaldo since she has partaken of the waters of love, now induces the magician Malgigi to entice her beloved to an island over which she reigns, where she vainly tries to win his affections and to detain him by her side. Still under the influence of the waters of hate, Rinaldo escapes, only to land in a gloomy country, where he is plunged into a loathsome den. There a monster is about to devour him, when Angelica comes to his rescue. But, even though she saves his life, he ungratefully refuses to return her affection, and abruptly leaves her to encounter other untoward adventures. Meantime Orlando, still searching for Angelica, encounters a sorceress who gives him a magic draught which causes him to forget the past, and detains him a captive in the island of Dragontine.

Meanwhile the many knights enamoured with Angelica have gone to besiege her father's capital, but while they are thus employed she escapes from the city—thanks to her magic ring—and goes to deliver Orlando. In return, he pledges himself to drive the besiegers away and save her father's capital, and on the way thither encounters Rinaldo, with whom, not knowing who he is, he fights for two days, so equally are they matched in strength and skill. The moment comes, however, when Orlando is on the point of slaying Rinaldo, and refrains only because Angelica opportunely reveals his opponent's name.

Still urged by Angelica, Orlando next hastens off to destroy the magic island and free its captives, who hurry back to France while their rescuer journeys to Cathay. There Angelica pretends she has fallen in love with him, and accompanies him when he returns to France under pretext of becoming a Christian. Their way again lies through the forest of Arden, where this time Angelica drinks from the fountain of hatred. All her former love for Rinaldo therefore vanishes, and, as the latter has at the same time partaken of the water of love, their parts are reversed, for it is he who now pursues Angelica, whom he previously loathed. His attentions so incense Orlando that he begins a fight, which Charlemagne checks, declaring that Angelica—who is placed in charge of Duke Namus—shall be awarded to the warrior who distinguishes himself most in the coming war.

In the course of this campaign these two knights meet with many adventures, and are accompanied by Bradamant—Rinaldo's sister—who manfully fights by their side. Among their opponents the most formidable are Rogero and the pagan Rodomont, whose boastful language has given rise to the term rodomontade. During one of their encounters, Rogero discovers that his antagonist is Bradamant—a woman—and falls desperately in love with her.

It is at this point that Boiardo's poem ends; and Ariosto, adopting his characters, immediately begins weaving three principal strands of narrative—one relating to the wars of Charlemagne, another to Orlando's madness, and the third to the love of Rogero and Bradamant—Rogero, an ancestor of the Ferrara family (Ariosto's patrons), being the real hero of his poem.

Not satisfied at being placed under the care of Duke Namus of Bavaria, Angelica escapes from his guardianship, only to be pursued by the unwelcome attentions of Rinaldo and Ferrau. While these two fight for her possession, the lady, who spends her time fleeing from unwelcome suitors, escapes, only to fall into the hands of Sacripant, King of Circassia, another admirer, who bears her off in triumph. They meet a knight in white armour (Bradamant in quest of Rogero), ere they are overtaken by Rinaldo. A new duel now ensues, this time between Rinaldo and Sacripant, during which Angelica runs away and seeks refuge with a hermit-magician, who then informs the combatants that Angelica has been carried off to Paris by Orlando. Hearing this, the rivals cease fighting and join forces to rescue the lady, but, when they arrive in Paris, Charlemagne dispatches Rinaldo to England and Scotland, where, among other marvellous adventures, is told the lengthy and fantastic yet beautiful story of Ginevra.

It seems that, although loved by the Duke of Albany, this lady prefers the knight Ariolant. She thereby so enrages her noble suitor that he finally bribes her maid to personate her and admit him by night to her chamber by means of a rope ladder. With fiendish cunning he has advised Ariolant to watch Ginevra, so this true lover, witnessing what he considers irrefutable proof of his lady-love's unchastity, departs in despair to commit suicide. His brother, deeming him already dead, denounces Ginevra, who, brought before the judges, is sentenced to die unless some champion will vindicate her honour. Having meantime discovered the truth, Rinaldo clears the lady by winning a brilliant victory, and leaves only after she is safely married to the man she loves, who after all has not taken his life.

The poet now picks up another thread and shows

us Bradamant seeking Rogero, and discovering, by means of Angelica's magic ring, that he is captive of a magician. After a narrow escape, and a vision of the feats her descendants will perform, Bradamant helps Rogero to recover his freedom. Soon after, this reckless man vaults upon a hippogriff which lands him on an island, where an enchantress changes her visitors into beasts, stones, trees, etc. Instead of becoming one of her permanent victims, Rogero, warned by the myrtle to which he ties his steed, prevails upon her to release her captives, and after many adventures is borne by the same hippogriff to the island of Ebuda, where a maiden is daily sacrificed to a cannibal Orc. When Rogero discovers that the present victim is Angelica, he promptly delivers her and conveys her to Brittany.

Meantime Orlando, mad with love, is vainly seeking Angelica. He too visits Ebuda—but too late to meet her there—and delivers another maiden. Then he returns to France to find Charlemagne so sorely pressed by foes, that he has implored St Michael to interfere in his behalf. This archangel, cleverly enlisting the services of Silence and Discord, brings back Rinaldo and other knights, who drive away the disintegrating pagan force after several bloody encounters. After one of these, Angelica finds a wounded man, whom she nurses back to health, and marries after a romantic courtship in the course of which they carve their names on many a tree.

Still seeking Angelica, Orlando in due time discovers these names, and on learning Angelica is married becomes violently insane. Discarding his armour—which another knight piously collects and hangs on a tree with an inscription warning no one to venture to touch it—Orlando roams hither

Rogero delivering Angelica
F. E. Delacroix
After a carbon print by Braun et Cie.

and thither, performing countless feats of valour, and even swimming across the Strait of Gibraltar to seek adventures in Africa since he cannot get enough in Europe. In the course of his wanderings, Orlando (as well as various other characters in the poem) is favoured by an apparition of Fata Morgana, the water-fairy, who vainly tries to lure him away from his allegiance to his lady-love by offering him untold treasures.

Every once in a while the poem harks back to Rogero, who, having again fallen into a magician's hands, prowls through the labyrinthine rooms of his castle, seeking Bradamant, whom he imagines calling to him for help. Meantime the lady whom he is thus seeking is safe at Marseilles, but, hearing at last of her lover's plight, she too visits the magic castle, and would have been decoyed into its dungeons had not Astolfo appeared with a magic horn, whose first blast makes the castle vanish into thin air! Thus freed, the magician's prisoners gaze around them in wonder, and Rogero and Bradamant embrace with rapture, planning to marry as soon as Rogero has been baptized.

But, on their way to Vallombroso where this sacrament is to take place, the lovers meet with other adventures and are again separated. Under escort of Astolfo, Bradamant sadly returns home, where her mother decrees she shall remain until Rogero can come and claim her. Meantime Rogero has again joined the Saracens, just as Discord has succeeded in kindling a quarrel between Rodomont and Mandricar, who both admire the same lady. They are about to fight for her favour, when the umpire of the lists pertinently suggests that the lady be allowed to express her preference! She frankly does so, and Rodomont, rejected, departs in high dudgeon. In this unhappy frame of mind he attacks everybody he meets, and after many victories is defeated in a battle with the Christians. During this last encounter Rogero is too grievously wounded to be able to join Bradamant, who, hearing a fair lady is nursing her lover, is consumed by jealousy. She therefore—notwithstanding her mother's decree—sets out in the garb of a knight to challenge her recreant lover and defeat him by means of her magic lance.

After unhorsing on the way all those who venture to tilt with her, Bradamant meets Rogero, who, recognizing her in the midst of their duel, flatly refuses to continue the fight, and implores her to accompany him into a neighbouring forest, where he promises to explain all to her satisfaction. They are, however, followed thither by the maiden who has nursed Rogero, who, jealous in her turn, now attacks Bradamant. Rogero, infuriated by Bradamant's imminent peril, is about to slay his nurse remorselessly, when an enchanter's voice proclaims she is his sister, stolen in infancy! All excuse for mutual jealousy being thus removed, the two women agree to join forces and fight in behalf of Charlemagne until Rogero can discharge his obligations to the Saracens, receive baptism, and join the Christian ranks.

Meantime Astolfo has ridden off on the hippogriff to the Earthly Paradise, where he has interviews with many saints and apostles, and whence St John conveys him up to the moon. In that appropriate region the apostle explains that Orlando's insanity is due to his love for an infidel! He further points out where the hero's stray wits are stored, and enables Astolfo to catch them in a vial that he may restore them to their rightful owner. Then, before conveying Astolfo back to earth, St John vouchsafes him a glimpse of the Fates, weaving the web of Destiny, which they cast into the stream of Oblivion, whence only a few shreds are rescued by poets!

On returning from this eventful trip to the moon, Astolfo joins the Saracens. When they finally capture the mad Orlando, he produces his vial, and, making his friend inhale its contents, restores him to his senses. His mad passion for Angelica being now a thing of the past, Orlando concentrates all his efforts to conquer the Saracens and triumphs in many a fight.

Meantime Rogero, on his way to join Bradamant, has been shipwrecked on an island, where a hermit converts him to the Christian faith. While he is here Orlando and Rinaldo arrive with their sorely wounded friend, Oliver, whom they entrust to the hermit's care. Not only is Orlando sane once more, but Rinaldo, having drunk the waters of the contrary fountain, no longer loves Angelica, and willingly promises the hand of his sister Bradamant to the new convert. But, when brother and prospective bridegroom reach court, they learn Charlemagne has promised Bradamant to a Greek prince, to whom the lady has signified that ere he wins her he must fight a duel with her. On hearing that the Greek prince is at present besieging Belgrade, Rogero hastens thither, and performs wonders before he falls into the enemy's hands. But the Greek prince has been so impressed by Rogero's prowess that he promises him freedom if he will only personate him in the dreaded duel with Bradamant. Rogero immediately consents to fight in the prince's armour, and defeats Bradamant, whom Charlemagne thereupon awards to the Greek prince.

In despair at having forfeited his beloved, Rogero rides off to die of grief, but the Greek prince, riding after him to thank him, not only discovers the cause of Rogero's sorrow, but generously relinquishes all claim to Bradamant and volunteers to witness her marriage to Rogero. The courage shown by the bridegroom while at Belgrade has meantime so impressed the Bulgarians, that an embassy arrives to beg him to mount their throne. But before Rogero can assume the Bulgarian crown he is forced to conquer and slay the boastful Rodomont, who envies his exalted position.

Many other characters appear in this poem, complicating the plot until it seems hopelessly involved to most modern readers, but, owing to the many romantic situations, to the picturesque verse, and to the unflagging liveliness of style, this epic is still popular in Italy. It has besides given rise to endless imitations, not only in Italian but in many other languages. It forms part of the great Charlemagne Cycle, of which the last epic is *Ricciardetto*, by Fortiguerra, a priest who wagered he too could compose a string of adventures like those invented by Ariosto. He won his wager, adopting the characters already made famous by Boiardo and Ariosto, and selected as his hero a younger brother of Rinaldo mentioned by his predecessors.

GERUSALEMME LIBERATA, OR JERUSALEM DELIVERED

Torquato Tasso, one of the three great Italian poets, was born at Sorrento in 1544, and, after receiving his education ie various Italian cities, conceived, while at the University of Padua, the idea of writing an epic poem, using an episode in the First Crusade as his theme. In 1572 Tasso became attached to the court of Ferrara, where the Duke and his two sisters delighted in his verses, admired his pastoral *Aminta*, and urged him to finish his projected epic.

During his sojourn at this court Tasso fell in love with Eleonora, sister of the Duke, to whom he read the various parts of his epic as he completed them, and for whose sake he lingered at Ferrara, refusing offers of preferment at Paris and at Florence. Although he completed his epic in 1575, he did not immediately publish it, but sent copies to Rome and Padua for criticism. The learned men to whom he submitted his poem criticised it so freely that the poet's sensitive nature was greatly injured thereby. Almost at the same time the Duke discovered the poet's passion for his sister. Furious to think Tasso should have raised his eyes to a princess, yet afraid lest he should carry his talents elsewhere, the Duke, pretending to deem him insane, placed him under close surveillance. While Tasso was thus a prisoner, false accusations were brought against him, and his poem was published without his consent.

Although Tasso contrived several times to escape from Ferrara, he invariably came back there, hoping to be reconciled to the Duke. It was only in 1586 that he left this place for good and betook himself to Rome and Naples, where he was forced to live on charity. Just as he was about to be publicly crowned in Rome for his epic, he died there, at the age of fifty-two (1595).

The epic *Jerusalem Delivered* contains an account

of the Crusade of 1099 and extends over a period of forty days. It is divided into twenty cantos, written in *ottava rima*, or eight-rhymed stanzas, and, owing to its rhythmic perfection, is still sung by Italian bards to popular audiences.

Canto I

After stating exactly what task he proposes to perform in his poem, the poet describes how the Eternal Father, sitting on His heavenly throne, gazes down upon the plain of Tortosa, where the Crusaders are assembled. Six years have elapsed since they set out from Europe, during which time they have succeeded in taking Nicæa and Antioch, cities now left in charge of influential Crusaders. But Godfrey of Bouillon is pushing on with the bulk of the army, because he is anxious to wrest Jerusalem from the hands of the infidels and restore it to the worship of the true God. While he is camping on this plain, God sends Gabriel to visit him in sleep and inspire him with a resolve to assemble a council, where, by a ringing speech, he will rouse the Christians to immediate action.

On awakening from this vision, Godfrey loses no time in convening such an assembly, and there eloquently urges the Christians to fight, declaring their efforts have failed hitherto mainly because they have lacked purpose and unity. Peter the Hermit thereupon suggests that the Crusaders select one chief, whose orders they will obey, and the warriors present unanimously elect Godfrey of Bouillon as leader. Having secured this exalted post, Godfrey reviews his force, thus giving the poet an occasion to enumerate the leaders of the different corps, or armies, and explain from what countries they come. Among other resounding names, the poet specially mentions Edward and his fair bride Gildippe, who, unwilling to be parted from her spouse, has donned a man's armour and followed him to the Crusade. Among the bravest fighters there, he also quotes Tancred, who, however, seems listless and has accomplished no deed of valour since he fell in love with Clorinda, a fair Amazon whom he met near a fountain.

> To the same warbling of fresh waters drew,
> Arm'd, but unhelm'd and unforeseen, a maid ;
> She was a Pagan, and came thither too,
> To quench her thirst beneath the pleasant shade ;
> Her beautiful fair aspect, thus display'd,
> He sees ; admires ; and, touch'd to transport, glows
> With passion rushing to its fountain head,
> The heart ; 'tis strange how quick the feeling grows ;
> Scarce born, its power in him no cool calm medium knows.

Another hero is Rinaldo (the same as the French Renaud de Montauban), who, although but a boy, escaped from his foster-mother, Queen Mathilda, to go and fight for the deliverance of the Holy Sepulchre. His review completed, Godfrey of Bouillon orders his force to march on toward Jerusalem, whence he wishes to oust the Sultan Aladine (Saladin), who at present is sorely taxing the Christians to obtain funds enough to make war against the advancing Crusaders.

Canto II

Advised by the sorcerer Ismeno, Aladine steals the image of the Virgin from the Christian temple, and sets it up in his mosque, where he resorts to all manner of spells and incantations to destroy her power. During the night, however, the Virgin's image disappears from the mosque and cannot be found, although Aladine offers great rewards for its restoration. Finally, he decrees that, unless the perpetrator of the theft denounces himself, he will slay all the Christians in the town. He is about to carry out this cruel threat when Sophronia, a Christian maid, suddenly decides to sacrifice herself to save her co-religionists. She therefore appears before Aladine, declaring she stole the image from the mosque, whereupon the Sultan in anger orders her to be bound to the stake and burned alive.

> Doomed in tormenting fire to die, they lay
> Hands on the maid ; her arms with rough cords twining,
> Rudely her mantle chaste they tear away,
> And the white veil that o'er her droop'd declining :
> This she endured in silence unrepining,
> Yet her firm breast some virgin tremors shook ;
> And her warm cheek, Aurora's late outshining,
> Waned into whiteness, and a colour took,
> Like that of the pale rose, or lily of the brook.

No sooner has Sophronia been fastened there, praying for God's aid to endure martyrdom without flinching, than Olindo, a young Christian, deeming it impossible to allow a girl to sacrifice her life, rushes forward, declaring he alone committed the crime, but that the maiden, out of love for him, has assumed his guilt to save his life. Only then does he discover that the maiden tied to the stake is the very one he loves, but who hitherto has received his advances coldly ! On hearing the youth accuse himself of having stolen the image, Aladine questions the maiden, who denies it, insisting she alone is to blame. Thereupon the Sultan decrees that both shall perish in the flames, and orders them tied to the stake back to back. It is in this position, and while in imminent peril of death, that the young man deplores the fact he is to die beside the one he hoped to marry and with whom he would fain have spent a long and happy life. The executioners are about to set fire to the pyre where these generous young lovers are to end their days, when a young knight steps forward, loudly proclaiming that none of the Christians are to blame for the disappearance of the image, Allah Himself having removed it from the mosque because He considered it desecration to have such an image within its walls. This young knight turns out to be the warrior maid Clorinda, who not only convinces Aladine that the young people are guiltless, but bribes him to release them, in exchange for her services in the coming war. Touched by each other's devotion, the young couple marry as soon as released.

> Restored to life and liberty, how blest,
> How truly blest was young Olindo's fate!
> For sweet Sophronia's blushes might attest
> That Love at length has touch'd her delicate
> And generous bosom; from the stake in state
> They to the altar pass; severely tried,
> In doom and love already made his mate,
> She now objects not to become his bride,
> And grateful live with him who would for her have died.

Meanwhile two ambassadors have come from Egypt to visit Godfrey in his camp, and try first by persuasion and then by threats to dissuade him from his projected attack upon Jerusalem. In spite of all Alethes and Argantes can say, Godfrey insists upon carrying out his purpose, and, after dismissing these ambassadors with a haughty speech, marches on with his host.

> "Know, then, that we have borne all this distress
> By land and sea—war, want, reverses—all!
> To the sole end that we might gain access
> To sacred Salem's venerable wall;

> That we might free the Faithful from their thrall,
> And win from God His blessing and reward :
> From this no threats our spirit can appal,
> For this no terms will be esteem'd too hard—
> Life, honours, kingdoms lost, or dignity debarr'd."

Canto III

When they come within sight of Jerusalem, the Crusaders, overjoyed, hail the Holy City with cries of rapture, and, falling on their knees, swear to deliver it from the hands of the infidels. Seeing them advance, the pagans make hasty preparations to oppose them, and Clorinda, at the head of a small force, volunteers to make a sortie and boldly attacks the vanguard of the Crusaders.

From the topmost tier of Jerusalem's ramparts, the Sultan Aladine watches their sortie, having beside him Erminia, daughter of the late King of Antioch, whom the Crusaders have sent on to Jerusalem, because they do not care to detain her a prisoner. During her sojourn in her father's town, Erminia has learned to know by sight all the Crusaders, and during her brief captivity she has fallen in love with Tancred, who was detailed to guard her. She can therefore give the Sultan Aladine all the information he wishes, while the battle is going on. From their point of vantage the Sultan and Princess watch Clorinda and Tancred meet, and behold how, after a lively encounter, Tancred strikes off the helmet of his opponent, whose sex is revealed by the streaming of her long golden hair. At sight of the wonderful maiden with whom he has fallen in love, Tancred refuses to continue the fight, although Clorinda urges him to strike. Undaunted by the fact that she is his foe, Tancred not only refuses to strike, but imme-

The Crusaders within sight of Jerusalem
M. Meredith Williams

diately begins to sue the beautiful maiden, who refuses to listen to him, and is soon swept away by Saracen forces, which intervene between her and Tancred.

A battle now rages, in the course of which various knights perform great deeds, but, although Godfrey proves victor on this occasion, he loses Dudon, chief of his Adventurous Band and one of the bravest warriors in his army. While giving her explanations to Aladine in regard to the fight waged beneath their eyes, Erminia is careful to express deadly hatred for Tancred, although the truth is that she loves him dearly and is greatly relieved to see him escape from the fray uninjured.

Many having died in the course of this action, a truce is agreed upon so that both sides may bury their dead, and many funerals are celebrated with all due pomp and ceremony. Next the crusading force decides that siege-engines and towers will be necessary to enable them to scale the high walls of Jerusalem. They therefore send out a force of woodsmen to hew the trees which are to serve for the construction of the required towers.

> The Duke, when thus his piety had paid
> The fun'ral rites, and shed his duteous tears,
> Sent all his skill'd mechanics to invade
> The forest, guarded by a thousand spears;
> Veil'd by low hills it stood, the growth of years,—
> A Syrian shepherd pointed out the vale,
> And thither brought the camp-artificers
> To fabricate the engines doom'd to scale
> The City's sacred towers and turn her people pale.

Canto IV

The scene now changes to the infernal regions, where Satan deems it time to frustrate the Christians' aims, because it would ill-suit diabolical ends to have them recover possession of Jerusalem. Satan stimulates his hosts by reminding them of their forfeited bliss, and encourages them to thwart the Christians by recalling their great deeds in the past. His eloquence is not expended in vain, for the fiends approve of his suggestions, and, when the council is over, flit forth, intent upon fomenting dissension among the leaders of the Crusade, and hindering their attempts in every other way possible.

One demon in particular is dispatched to determine a wizard to send his niece Armida to ensnare the Christians. This enchantress, decked out with all the charms that beauty and toilet can bestow, soon appears in the Christian camp, where, falling at Godfrey's feet, she proceeds to relate a tale of fictitious wrongs, claiming to be heiress to the city of Damascus, whence she has been ejected, and vowing that if she could only secure the aid of a few knights she would soon recover her realm. In return for such aid as she implores from the Christians, she promises to do homage to them for her realm, and even pledges herself to receive baptism. Her artful speeches, the flattery which she lavishes upon Godfrey, and her languishing glances are all calculated to persuade him to grant her request; but the Crusader is so bent upon the capture of Jerusalem that nothing can turn him aside from his purpose.

But, although Godfrey himself is proof against all Armida's blandishments, his knights are not, and among those who succumb to the lady's charms is his own brother Eustace, who begs his permission to take ten knights and accompany the damsel to Damascus. Although Armida professes great gratitude for this help, she entices many other Crusaders to desert the camp, by casting tender glances at them and making each man whom she looks upon believe she loves him only.

> All arts th' enchantress practised to beguile
> Some new admirer in her well-spread snare;
> Nor used with all, nor always the same wile,
> But shaped to every taste her grace and air:
> Here cloister'd is her eye's dark pupil, there
> In full voluptuous languishment is roll'd;
> Now these her kindness, those her anger bear,
> Spurr'd on or check'd by bearing frank or cold,
> As she perceived her slave was scrupulous or bold.

Canto V

Not content with beguiling many knights, Armida further foments a quarrel between Rinaldo and Gernando, Prince of Norway, in regard to the command of the Adventurous Band, which is now without a leader. In the course of this quarrel, Rinaldo is so sorely taunted by his opponent that, although the Crusaders are pledged not to fight each other, he challenges and slays Gernando. Then, afraid to be called to trial and sentenced to death for breaking the rules of the camp, Rinaldo flees to Egypt.

On perceiving how greatly his army is weakened by the desertion of so many brave men, Godfrey is dismayed—all the more so because he hears the Egyptian army is coming to attack him, and because the supplies which he expected have been cut off.

Canto VI

The Egyptian army boasts of no braver warrior than Argantes, who sallies forth to challenge the

Christians, bidding Clorinda follow him at a short distance, and come to his rescue if necessary. Although Argantes has summoned Godfrey to come forth and fight him, it is Tancred who is chosen as champion for the Christians, but as he draws near to his opponent, a glimpse of the fair Clorinda's face makes him forget everything but her.

> He noted not where the Circassian rear'd
> His frightful face to the affronted skies,
> But to the hill-top where his Love appear'd,
> Turn'd, slack'ning his quick pace, his am'rous eyes,
> Till he stood steadfast as a rock, all ice
> Without, all glowing heat within ;—the sight
> To him was as the gates of Paradise ;
> And from his mind the mem'ry of the fight
> Pass'd like a summer cloud, or dream at morning light.

One of the knights in his train, seeing he is not going to fight, spurs forward and meets Argantes, by whom he is defeated. On seeing this knight fall, Tancred, suddenly brought to his senses, starts forward to avenge him, and combats with such fury that Argantes' armour fairly rings with the blows which rain down upon him. Argantes, however, is nearly as brave as Tancred, so the battle rages until nightfall, when the heroes are separated by the heralds, although both vow they will renew the struggle on the morrow. But, when both discover that they have serious wounds, their respective armies decree a six-days' truce and pledge themselves to await the result of the duel.

The wounded Argantes has returned to Jerusalem, where Erminia uses her magic balsams to heal his wounds, secretly wishing meanwhile that she might lavish her care upon Tancred, whom she still loves. So ardent is her desire to behold him that she finally appropriates Clorinda's armour and rides off to the Christian camp, sending a messenger ahead to announce that a lady is coming to heal Tancred if he will give her a safe-conduct to his tent. Tancred immediately sends word the lady will be welcome, but meanwhile the Christians, catching a glimpse of the waiting Erminia, and mistaking her for Clorinda owing to her armour, endeavour to capture her.

Canto VII

To escape from her pursuers, Erminia flees into a trackless forest, where, after wandering for some time, she meets a shepherd, who shelters her in his hut. There she turns shepherdess, but does not forget Tancred, whose name she carves in many a tree. Meantime the news spreads through the camp that Clorinda has been seen and is even now closely pursued by a troop of Christians. On hearing this Tancred, disregarding his wounds, sets out to find her. While wandering thus in the forest, weakened by loss of blood, he is captured by Armida, the enchantress, who detains him in a dungeon, where he eats his heart out for shame because he will not be able to respond when the trumpets sound for the renewal of his duel with Argantes.

The moment having come for this battle and the Crusaders' champion being absent, old Count Raymond volunteers to meet Argantes, and is about to get the better of him, when an archer from the wall suddenly discharges a shaft at him. Such treachery exasperates the Christians, who, exclaiming the truce has been broken, rush upon their foes, and in the general battle which ensues many deeds of valour are performed.

Canto VIII

During this battle a great storm arises, and the Christians, who, notwithstanding their courage, have been worsted, beat a retreat, and find on their return to camp that one of their companions, defeated and mortally wounded, has dispatched a messenger to carry his sword to Rinaldo. The Italian force thereupon accuses Godfrey of having done away with Rinaldo, but he not only succeeds in refuting such an accusation, but sentences his chief detractor to death.

Canto IX

Sultan Solyman of Nicaea who has joined Sultan Aladine of Jerusalem, now comes to attack the Christians by night, assisted by many fiends, but the archangel Michael warns the crusaders of the coming onset and enables them to get the better of their foes by bringing back the troops which followed Armida to Damascus. In this encounter a Christian knight slays a page of the Sultan, who, seeing this child dead, experiences such grief that, after avenging his death, he wishes to withdraw temporarily from the battle.

> " Let Godfrey view once more, and smile to view
> My second exile ;—soon shall he again
> See me in arms return'd, to vex anew
> His haunted peace and never stable reign :
> Yield I do not ; eternal my disdain
> Shall be as are my wrongs ; though fires consume
> My dust, immortal shall my hate remain ;
> And aye my naked ghost fresh wrath assume,
> Through life a foe most fierce, but fiercer from the tomb ! "

Canto X

The Sultan, after journeying part of the way back to Egypt, pauses to rest, and is visited by a wizard, who spirits him over the battle-field and back to Jerusalem in a magic chariot. This vehicle pauses at a hidden cave, the entrance to an underground passage, by which they secretly enter the Sultan's council chamber.

> Ismeno shot the lock; and to the right
> They climb'd a staircase, long untrod, to which
> A feeble, glimm'ring, and malignant light
> Stream'd from the ceiling through a window'd niche;
> At length by corridors of loftier pitch
> They sallied into day, and access had
> To an illumined hall, large, round, and rich;
> Where, sceptred, crown'd, and in dark purple clad,
> Sad sat the pensive King amid his nobles sad.

Solyman, overhearing as he enters some of the nobles propose a disgraceful peace and the surrender of Jerusalem, hotly opposes such a measure, and thus infuses new courage into their breasts.

Canto XI

Meantime Godfrey of Bouillon, having buried his dead, questions the knights who were lured away by Armida, and they relate that, on arriving near the Dead Sea, they were entertained at a sumptuous banquet, where they were given a magic draught, which transformed them for a time into sportive fishes. Armida, having thus demonstrated her power over them, threatened to use it to keep them prisoners forever unless they would promise to abjure their faith. One alone yielded, but the rest, delivered as prisoners to an emissary from Egypt, were met and freed from their bonds by the brave Rinaldo, who, instead of accompanying them back to camp, rode off toward Antioch.

The Christians now prepare for their final assault,

and, advised by Peter the Hermit, walk in solemn procession to the Mount of Olives, where, after singing hymns, all devoutly receive Communion. Thus prepared for anything that may betide, they set out on the morrow to scale the city walls, rolling ahead of them their mighty engines of war, by means of which they hope to seize the city.

Most of the Crusaders have laid aside their heavy armour and assumed the light gear of foot-soldiers the better to scale the walls, upon which Clorinda is posted, and whence she shoots arrow after arrow at the assailants. Wounded by one of the missiles flung from the wall, Godfrey seeks his tent, where, the physician failing to extract the barb, an angel brings a remedy from heaven which instantly cures the wound.

Canto XII

After a while, seeing she does not do as much execution as she would like, Clorinda proposes to Argantes that they steal out of the city by night, and by chemical means set fire to the engines with which the Christians are threatening to capture the city. Willingly Argantes promises to accompany her in this perilous venture, but her slave, hoping to dissuade her, now reveals to her for the first time the story of her birth, and informs her she is the daughter of a Christian. He adds that her dying mother besought him to have her child baptized, a duty he had failed to perform, although repeatedly warned by visions to repair his neglect. But, although similar visions have frequently haunted the dreams of Clorinda herself, she persists in her undertaking to set fire to the war machines.

She has no sooner done so, however, than the Christians, aroused, set out in pursuit of her and of her companions. Bravely covering their retreat, thus enabling them to re-enter the city safely, Clorinda delays her own until the gates are closed. But with great presence of mind, the warrior-maid, who is wearing black armour, mingles in the darkness with the Crusaders. None of these suspects that she does not belong to their ranks, save Tancred, who follows her to a remote place beneath the walls, where he challenges her to a deadly fight, little divining who she is. The battle proves fierce, and both combatants strike until Tancred runs his sword through his opponent. Dying, Clorinda reveals her name and faintly begs Tancred to baptize her before life leaves her body.

> "Friend! thou hast won; I pardon thee, and O
> Forgive thou me! I fear not for this clay,
> But my dark soul—pray for it, and bestow
> The sacred rite that laves all stains away:"
> Like dying hymns heard far at close of day,
> Sounding I know not what in the sooth'd ear
> Of sweetest sadness, the faint words make way
> To his fierce heart, and, touch'd with grief sincere,
> Streams from his pitying eye th' involuntary tear.

Such a request cannot be disregarded, so, although Tancred is frantic with grief at the thought of having slain his beloved, he hurries to a neighbouring stream, draws water in his helmet, and, after baptizing his dying sweetheart, swoons over her body. His companions, finding him there, convey him and Clorinda's body to his tent, where they vainly try to rouse him, but he is so overcome with melancholy that he thinks of nothing but joining Clorinda in her tomb.

Canto XIII

Meantime the foe, having heard of Clorinda's death, vow to avenge her, while the Crusaders seek materials to reconstruct their towers. Hastening to a forest near by, they discover that a wizard has cast such a spell upon it that all who try to enter are frightened away. Finally Tancred enters this place, and, although he is met by earthquakes and other portents, he disregards them all, and starts to cut down a tree. But, when blood gushes from its stem, and when Clorinda's voice informs him he has wounded her again, he flees without having accomplished his purpose. Heat and drought now cause further desertions and discourage the Crusaders, until Godfrey, full of faith in the justice of their cause, prays so fervently that rain is vouchsafed them.

Canto XIV

In a dream Godfrey is now admonished to proceed, and told that if he can only persuade Rinaldo to return, Jerusalem will soon fall into the hands of the Christians. As no one knows whither Rinaldo has gone, Godfrey dispatches two knights in quest of him. After some difficulty they interview a wizard, who, after exhibiting to them his magic palace, tells them that Armida, to punish Rinaldo for rescuing his companions from her clutches, has captured him by magic means and borne him off to her wonderful garden in the Fortunate Isles. The wizard then bestows upon them a golden wand which will defeat all enchantments, and bids them speed to the Fortunate Isles.

Canto XV

Hastening off to the seashore armed with this golden wand, the two knights find a magic vessel, wherein they sail with fabulous speed over the sea, and through the Strait of Gibraltar, out into the western ocean, the nymph at the helm meanwhile informing them that this is the road Columbus is destined to travel. Sailing thus they reach the Fortunate Isles, where, notwithstanding many enchantments and temptations brought to bear to check their advance, they, thanks to the golden wand, force their way into Armida's wonderful garden.

Canto XVI

These windings pass'd, the garden-gates unfold,
And the fair Eden meets their glad survey,—
Still waters, moving crystals, sands of gold,
Herbs, thousand flowers, rare shrubs, and mosses gray;
Sunshiny hillocks, shady vales; woods gay,
And grottoes gloomy, in one view combined,
Presented were; and what increased their play
Of pleasure at the prospect, was, to find
Nowhere the happy Art that had the whole design'd.

So natural seem'd each ornament and site,
So well was neatness mingled with neglect,
As though boon Nature for her own delight
Her mocker mock'd, till fancy's self was check'd;
The air, if nothing else there, is th' effect
Of magic, to the sound of whose soft flute
The blooms are born with which the trees are deck'd;
By flowers eternal lives th' eternal fruit,
This running richly ripe, while those but greenly shoot.

Then, peeping cautiously through the trees, they behold Rinaldo reclining amid the flowers, his head resting in the lap of the enchantress. Biding their time, they watch Armida leave the enamoured knight, then step forward and bid him gaze into the magic mirror they have brought. On beholding in its surface a reflection of himself as he really is, Rinaldo, horrified, is brought to such a sense of his depraved idleness, that he springs to his feet and proposes to leave immediately with his companions. They are about to depart without bidding farewell to the fair enchantress, when she pursues them, and, after vainly pleading with Rinaldo to stay with her, proposes to join him in any capacity. When he abruptly rejects her advances and sails away, Armida, disappointed and infuriated because she has been scorned, hastens off to the Egyptian camp.

Canto XVII

There she joins the Christians' enemies, declaring she dreams of naught save slaying Rinaldo, and takes an important part in the review which the poet describes minutely. To compass her ends the artful Armida, whose charms have been so lavishly displayed that they have fired every breast, promises to belong to the warrior who will bring her Rinaldo's head. Meanwhile this hero has returned to Palestine, and is met by the wizard, who, after reproving him for his dalliance, gives him wonderful armour, and exhibits on the shield the great deeds of ancestors of the Duke of Ferrara.

Canto XVIII

Newly armed, Rinaldo now returns to the Crusaders' camp, apologizes to Godfrey for breaking the rules of the crusade, relates his adventures, and, after humbly confessing his sins, starts forth to brave the spells of the magic forest. Not only does he penetrate within its precincts, but, undeterred by all Armida's enchantments, cuts down a tree, although, in hopes of staying his hand, her voice accuses him of cruelly wounding her! No sooner has this tree fallen than the spell is broken; so other trees are cut down without difficulty, engines built, and all is prepared for a new assault on Jerusalem.

Godfrey is particularly eager to make this new attempt immediately, because a carrier-pigeon has been caught bearing a message from the Egyptians to the Sultan of Jerusalem, apprising him that within five days they will come to his aid. During this assault on Jerusalem, a sorcerer on the walls, working against the Christians, is slain by a rock.

Soon after, thanks to the efforts of the Crusaders, the banner with the Cross floats over the walls of Jerusalem!

> Then raised the Christians all their long loud shout
> Of Victory, joyful, resonant, and high;
> Their words the towers and temples lengthen out;
> To the glad sound the mountains make reply:
>
> . . . .
>
> Then the whole host pours in, not o'er the walls
> Alone, but through the gates, which soon unclose,
> Batter'd or burnt; and in wide ruin falls
> Each strong defence that might their march oppose.
> Rages the sword; and Death, the Slaught'rer, goes
> 'Twixt Woe and Horror with gigantic tread,
> From street to street; the blood in torrents flows,
> And settles in lagoons, on all sides fed,
> And swell'd with heaps on heaps of dying and of dead.

Canto XIX

Tancred, scaling a fortress, meets and slays Argantes, receiving at the same time so grievous a wound that he swoons on the battle-field. Meantime Godfrey has sent a spy to the Egyptian camp to find out whether the army is really coming on to Jerusalem. This spy, meeting Erminia there, induces her not only to reveal all the Egyptians' plans (including a plot to slay Godfrey), but to go back with him. While they journey along together to rejoin the Christian forces, Erminia relates her adventures, saying that while she was playing shepherdess, some freebooters seized her and carried her to the Egyptian camp, where she was placed under Armida's protection. Her story is just finished when they perceive what appears to be a lifeless warrior. By the red cross on his armour the spy recognizes a Christian, and further investigation enables him to identify Tancred. Erminia—who has owned that she loves him—now takes possession of him, binds up his wounds with her hair (!), and vows she will nurse him back to health.

Canto XX

Warned by his spy that the Egyptians mean to send some of their number to mix, during the battle, with his body-guard and kill him, Godfrey changes the ensigns of his men, and thus discovers the conspirators, who are promptly put to death. Seeing the Egyptian army advance, Godfrey, in a stirring speech, urges his men to do their best for the Holy Sepulchre; they fight bravely, and many of them lose their lives. Among the slain are Gildippe and her husband, who, having fought together side by side throughout the campaign, die together and are buried in the same tomb. The other party, however, is far more unfortunate, for the Saracens lose the Sultans Aladine and Solyman, the former slain by Godfrey and the latter by Rinaldo.

Meantime Armida, wavering between love and hate, tries to shoot Rinaldo, then flees; a little later, seeing him slay Solyman, she tries to kill herself. It is at this moment that Rinaldo approaches her, and offers to marry her provided she will be converted. Not only does she now promise conversion and marriage, but accompanies Rinaldo back to the camp.

The Crusaders having completely defeated their foes and secured possession of Jerusalem, march with solemn hymns of praise to the Holy Sepulchre, where all kneel, thanking God for permitting them to deliver it from the hands of the heathen. It is with these thanks that the poem ends.

> Thus conquer'd Godfrey; and as yet there glow'd
> A flush of glory in the fulgent West,
> To the freed City, the once loved abode
> Of Christ, the pious chief and armies press'd:
> Arm'd as he was, and in his sanguine vest,
> With all his knights in solemn cavalcade,
> He reach'd the Temple; there, supremely bless'd,
> Hung up his arms, his banner'd spoils display'd,
> And at the sacred Tomb his vow'd devotions paid.

EPICS OF THE BRITISH ISLES

ALTHOUGH the name 'Celt' was given by the early Greeks to all the people living West of their country, the Romans included under that name only the tribes occupying the countries now known as France, Western Switzerland, Germany west of the Rhine, Belgium, and the British Isles. Blocked together under a generic name, the Celtic race was, however, composed of many tribes, with separate dialects and customs. It has been surmised that two of these tribes, the British and Irish, early took possession of England and Ireland, where they flourished and subdivided until disturbed by further invasions.

The Celts all practised what is termed the Druidic cult, their priests being poets, bards, or gleemen, who could compose in verse and recite ritual, laws, and heroic ballads. During the four hundred years of Roman occupation, the Celts in England became largely Romanized, but the Irish, and their near relatives the Scots, were less influenced by Latin civilization. It is therefore in Ireland, Scotland, and Wales that the oldest traces of Celtic literature are found, for the bards there retained their authority and acted as judges after Christianity had been introduced, and as late as the sixth century. Although St Patrick is reported to have forbidden these Irish bards to continue their pagan incantations, they continued to exert some authority, and it is said that the Irish priests adopted the tonsure which was their distinctive badge. The bards who could recite and compose poems and stories, accompanying themselves on a rudimentary harp, were considered of much higher rank than those who merely recited incantations. They transmitted poems, incantations, and laws, orally only, and no proof exists that the pagan Irish, for instance, committed any works to writing previous to the introduction of Christianity.

The heroic tales of Ireland form a large and well-marked epic cycle, the central tale of the series being the anonymous *Cattle of Cooly*, wherein is related the war waged by the Irish Queen Mab against her husband for the possession of a mystic brown bull. In the course of this war the chief hero, Cuchulain, makes himself famous by defending the country of Ulster single-handed! The still extant tales of this epic cycle number about thirty, and give in detail the lives of hero and heroine from birth to death, besides introducing many legends from Celtic mythology. The oldest MS. version of these tales, in mingled prose and verse, dates back to the twelfth century.

The Fennian or Oisianic poems and tales form another famous Irish cycle, Finn or Fingal, their hero, having acted as commander for a body of mercenaries in the third century. His poet son, Oisin (the Ossian of later romance), is said to have composed at least one of the poems in the famous *Book of Leinster*. Between the twelfth century and the middle of the fifteenth, this Fennian *epos* took on new life, and it continued to grow until the eighteenth century, when a new tale was added to the cycle.

The names of a few of the early Irish poets have been preserved in Irish annals, where we note, for instance, Bishop Fiance, author of a still extant metrical life of St Patrick, and Dallan Frogaell, one of whose poems is to be found in the *Book of the Dun Cow*, compiled before 1106. Up to the thirteenth century most of the poets and harpers used to include Scotland in their circuit, and one of them, Muiredhach, is said to have received the surname of 'the Scotchman,' because he tarried so long in that country.

When, after the fifteenth century, Irish literature began to decline, Irish poems were recast in the native Scotch dialect, thus giving rise to what is known as Gaelic literature, which continued to flourish until the Reformation. Samples of this old Gaelic or Erse poetry were discovered by James Macpherson in the Highlands, taken down from recitation, and used for the English compilation known as the Poems of Ossian. Lacking sufficient talent and learning to remodel these fragments so as to produce a real masterpiece, Macpherson—who ventured to term his work a translation—not only incurred the sharpest criticism, but was branded as a plagiarist.

The Welsh, a poetic race too, boast four great poets—Taliessin, Aneurin, Llywarch Hen, and Myrden (Merlin). These composed poems possessing epic qualities, wherein mention is made of some of the characters of the Arthurian Cycle. One of the five Welsh MSS., which seem of sufficient antiquity and importance to deserve attention, is the *Book of Taliessin*, written probably during the fourteenth century. The Welsh also possess tales in verse, either historical or romantic, which probably antedated the extant prose versions of the same tales. Eleven of these were translated by Lady Charlotte Guest. "The title of this work, the *Mabinogion*, is the plural form of the word *Mabinogi*, which means a story belonging to the equipment of an apprentice-bard, such a story as every bard had necessarily to learn as part of his training."[1]

[1] T. W. Rolleston, *Myths and Legends of the Celtic Race.*

Some of these tales are connected with the great Arthurian Cycle, as Arthur is the hero *par excellence* of Southern Wales, where many places are identified with him or his court.

Although almost as little is known of the historical Arthur as of the historical Roland, both are heroes of important epic cycles. Leader probably of a small band of warriors, Arthur gradually became, in the epics, first general-in-chief, then King, and finally Emperor of all Britain. It is conjectured that the Arthurian legends must have passed from South Wales into Cornwall, and thence into Armorica, "where it is probable the Round Table was invented." Enriched by new accretions from time to time, the Arthurian Cycle finally included the legend of the Holy Grail, which must have originated in Provence and have been carried into Brittany by *jongleurs* or travelling minstrels.

It has been ascertained that the legend of Arthur was familiar among the Normans before Geoffrey of Monmouth wrote his books, and it certainly had an incalculable formative influence on European literature, much of which can be "traced back directly or indirectly to these legends." It was also a vehicle for that element which we call chivalry, which the Church infused into it to fashion and mould the rude soldiers of feudal times into Christian knights, and, as it "expanded the imagination and incited the minds of men to inquiry beyond the conventional notions of things," it materially assisted in creating modern society.

After thus tracing the Celtic germs and influence in English literature, it becomes necessary to hark back to the time of the Teutonic invasions, since English thought and speech, manners and customs are all of Teutonic origin. The invaders brought with them an already formed language and literature, both of which were imposed upon the people. The only complete extant northern epic of Danish-English origin is *Beowulf*, of which a synopsis follows, and which was evidently sung by gleemen in the homes of the great chiefs. Apart from *Beowulf*, some remains of national epic poetry have come down to us in the fine fragments of Finnsburgh and Waldhere, another version of Walter of Aquitaine.

There are also the legends of Havelock the Dane, of King Horn, of Beves of Hamdoun, and of Guy of Warwick, all four of which were later turned into popular prose romances. Intense patriotic feeling also gave birth to *The Battle of Maldon, or Bryhtnoth's Death*, an ancient poem, fortunately printed before it was destroyed by fire. This epic relates how the Viking Anlaf came to England with ninety-three ships, and, after harrying the coast, was defeated and slain in battle.

The earliest Christian poet in England, Caedmon, instead of singing of love or fighting, paraphrased the Scriptures, and depicted the Creation in such eloquent lines that he is said to have inspired some of the passages in Milton's *Paradise Lost.* Chief among the religious poems ascribed to Caedmon, are *Genesis*, *Exodus*, and *Daniel*, but, although in general he strictly conforms with the Bible narrative, he prefixed to *Genesis* an account of the fall of the angels, and thus supplied Milton with the most picturesque feature of his theme.

Next come the epic poems of Cynewulf, *Crist*, *Juliana*, *Elene*, and *Andreas*, also written in alliterative verse. In *Elene* the poet gives us the legend of the finding of the Cross by the Empress Helena, dividing his poem into fourteen cantos or 'fits.'

It is in Gildas and Nennius' *Historia Brittonum* that we find the first mention of the legendary colonization of Britain and Ireland by refugees from Troy, and of the exploits of Arthur and the prophecies of Merlin. This work, therefore, contains some of the "germs of fables which expanded into Geoffrey of Monmouth's *History of Britain*, which was written in Latin some time before 1147," although this historian claims to derive his information from an ancient British book of which no trace can be found.

There is, besides, a very curious yet important legend cycle, in regard to a letter sent from Heaven to teach the proper observation of Sunday. The text of this letter can be found in old English in Wulfstan's homilies. Besides sacred legends, others exist of a worldly nature, such as the supposed letter from Alexander to Aristotle, *The Wonders of the East*, and *The Story of Apollonius of Tyre.* The first two, of course, formed part of the great Alexander cycle, while the latter supplied the theme for *Pericles of Tyre.*

With the Norman Conquest, French became the literary language of England, and modern romance was born. Romance cycles on 'the matter of France' or Legends of Charlemagne, and on 'the matter of Britain' or Legends of Arthur, became popular, and Geoffrey of Monmouth freely made use of his imagination to fill up the early history of Britain, for his so-called history is in reality a prose romance, whence later writers drew themes for many a tale.

Walter Map, born on the border of Wales in 1137,

is credited with the no longer extant Latin prose romance of *Lancelot du Lac*, which included the Quest of the Holy Grail and the Death of Arthur. Besides Wace's *Roman de Brut*, we have that of Layamon, and both poets not only explain how Britain's name is derived from Brut or Brutus—a member of Priam's family and refugee from Troy—but go on to give the history of other early kings of Britain, including Arthur. They often touch the true epic note, as in the wrestling match between Corineus and the giant Goëmagot, use similes drawn from everyday life, and supply us with legends of King Lear and of Cymbeline.

It was toward the end of the twelfth century that Arthur reached the height of his renown as romantic hero, the 'matter of Britain' having become international property, and having been greatly enriched by poets of many climes. By this time Arthur had ceased to be a king of Britain, to become king of a fairyland and chief exponent of chivalric ideals and aims.

To name all the poets who had a share in developing the Arthurian legend would prove an impossible task, but Nennius, Gildas, Geoffrey of Monmouth, Wace, Layamon, Benoît de St Maur, Chrestien de Troyes, Marie de France, Hartmann von der Aue, and Wolfram von Eschenbach have, in English, French, and German, helped to develop the 'matter of Britain,' and have managed to connect it with 'the matter of France.'

During the age of metrical romances (1200 to 1500), all the already extant cycles were remodelled and extended. Not only were Greek and Latin epics translated so as to be within reach of all, but one country freely borrowed from another. Thus, the French romances of *Huon de Bordeaux* and *The Four Sons of Aymon* found many admirers in England, where the former later supplied Shakespeare with some of the characters for *A Midsummer Night's Dream*. It was to offset the very popular romance of Alexander, that some patriotic poet evolved the romance of Richard Coeur-de-Lion, explaining how this king earned his well-known nickname by wrenching the heart out of a lion!

Some of these romances, such as *Flores and Blancheflour*, have "the voluptuous qualities of the East," make great use of magic of all kinds, and show the idyllic side of love. The tragedy of love is depicted in the romance of *Tristram and Iseult*, where a love-potion plays a prominent part. But, although knightly love and valour are the stock topics, we occasionally come across a theme of Christian humility, like *Sir Isumbras*, or of democracy, as in *The Squire of Low Degree* and in the ballads of Robin Hood.

With the advent of Chaucer a new poet, a new language, and new themes appear. Many of his *Canterbury Tales* are miniature epics, borrowed in general from other writers, but retold with a charm all his own. The Knight's Tale, or story of the rivalry in love of Palamon and Arcite, the tale of Gamelyn, and that of Troilus and Cressida, all contain admirable epic passages.

Spenser, our next epic poet, left us the unfinished *Faerie Queene*, an allegorical epic which shows the influence of Ariosto and other Italian poets, and contains exquisitely beautiful passages descriptive of nature, etc. His allegorical plot affords every facility for the display of his graceful verse, and is outlined in another chapter.

There are two curious but little-known English

epics, William Warner's chronicle epic entitled *Albion's England* (1586), and Samuel Daniel's *Civil Wars.* The first, beginning with the Flood, carries the reader through Greek mythology to the Trojan War, and hence by means of Brut to the beginnings of English history, which is then continued to the execution of Mary Stuart. The second (1595) is an epic, in eight books, on the Wars of the Roses. Drayton also wrote, on the theme of the Civil Wars, an epic entitled *The Barons' Wars*, and undertook a descriptive and patriotic epic in *Polyolbion*, wherein he makes a tour of England, relating innumerable local legends.

Abraham Cowley composed an epic entitled *Davideis*, or the troubles of David. He begins this work in four books with a description of two councils held in Heaven and Hell in regard to the life of this worthy.

Dryden was not only a translator of the classic epics, but projected an epic of his own about Arthur. Almost at the same time Pope was planning to write one on Brut, but he too failed to carry out his intentions, and is best known as the translator of the *Iliad*, although some authorities claim the *Rape of the Lock* as a unique sample of the *épopée galante.*

The poet Keats, whose life was so short, left us a complete mythological epic in *Endymion*, a fragment of one in *Hyperion*, and a reproduction of one of the old romances in *Isabella, or the Pot of Basil.*

Shelley, Keats' contemporary, wrote poems abounding in epic passages—*Alastor, or the Spirit of Solitude*, *The Revolt of Islam*, *Adonais*, and *Prometheus Unbound*; while Byron's epical poems are *Manfred*, *The Corsair*, and *Don Juan* ; and Scott's, *The Lay of the Last*

Minstrel, *Marmion*, *The Lady of the Lake*, and *The Bridal of Triermain*.

The greatest of Coleridge's poems, *The Ancient Mariner*, is sometimes called a visionary epic, while his *Christabel* conforms more closely to the old *roman d'aventure*.

As the translator of the epical romances of *Amadis de Gaule* and *Palmerin*, Southey won considerable renown; he also wrote the Oriental epics *Thalaba* and *The Curse of Kehama*, as well as epical poems on *Madoc*, *Joan of Arc*, and *Roderick, the Last of the Goths*.

Moore, although pre-eminently a lyric poet, has left us the Eastern epic *Lalla Rookh*, and Lockhart some *Spanish Ballads* which paraphrase *The Cid*.

Among Macaulay's writings the *Lays of Ancient Rome* have epic qualities, which are also found in Leigh Hunt's *Story of Rimini*.

The plot of *Tristram* has been utilized both by Matthew Arnold and by Swinburne, while William Morris in *The Earthly Paradise*, *The Life and Death of Jason*, *The Defence of Guinevere*, and Sir Lewis Morris in the *Epic of Hades*, have also been inspired by the old classic stories.

It was the Victorian Poet Laureate Tennyson who gave the Arthurian legend its latest and most artistic touches in *Idylls of the King*. Some critics also claim his *Enoch Arden* as an example of the domestic epic.

Among recent writers, sundry novelists have been hailed as authors of prose epics. Thomas Westwood has composed in excellent verse *The Quest of the Sangreall*, Mrs. Trask *Under King Constantine*, a notable addition to the Arthurian Cycle, and Stephen Philips has sung of Ulysses and of King Alfred.

BEOWULF[1]

Introduction

The only Anglo-Saxon epic which has been preserved entire was probably composed in Sweden before the eighth century, and taken thence to England, where this pagan poem was worked over and Christianized by some Northumbrian bard. Although some authorities date it as far back as the fifth century, it is more generally assumed to have been composed in the seventh. The only manuscript of the poem, now preserved in the British Museum, dates back to the tenth century. It contains some 3182 lines, and is written in alliterative verse ; the lines are written in pairs, and each perfect pair contains the same sound twice in the first line and once in the second. Although the author of *Beowulf* is unknown, the poem affords priceless hints in regard to the armour, ships, and mode of life of our early Saxon forefathers. Many translations of the poem have been made, some in prose and others in verse, and the epic as it stands, consisting of an introduction and forty-two ' fits,' is the main text for the study of the Anglo-Saxon language.

The Epic

Hrothgar, King of Denmark, traces his origin to Skiold, son of Odin, who as an infant drifted to the shores of Denmark. This child lay on a sheaf of ripe wheat, surrounded by priceless weapons, jewels, and a wonderful suit of armour, which proved that he must be the scion of some princely race. The childless

[1] See also the author's *Myths and Legends of the Middle Ages*.

King and Queen of Denmark therefore gladly adopted him, and in due time he succeeded them and ruled over the whole country. When he died, his subjects, placing his body in the vessel in which he had come, set him adrift.

> Men are not able
> Soothly to tell us, they in halls who reside,
> Heroes under heaven, to what haven he hied.[1]

Hrothgar, his descendant, constructed a magnificent hall, called Heorot, wherein to feast his retainers and entertain them with the songs of the northern skalds.

> It burned in his spirit
> To urge his folk to found a great building,
> A mead-hall grander than men of the era
> Ever had heard of, and in it to share
> With young and old all of the blessings
> The Lord had allowed him, save life and retainers.

On the night of the inauguration of this building, the royal body-guard lay down in the hall to sleep; and, when the servants entered the place on the morrow, they were horrified to find floor and walls spattered with blood, but no other trace of the thirty knights who had rested there the night before. Their cry of horror aroused Hrothgar, who, on investigating, discovered gigantic footsteps leading straight from the hall to the sluggish waters of a mountain tarn, above which a phosphorescent light always hovered. These footsteps were those of Grendel, a descendant of Cain, who dwelt in the marsh, and who had evidently slain and devoured all the King's men.

Too old to wield a sword in person, Hrothgar

[1] The quotations from *Beowulf* are taken from Hall's translation.

offered a princely reward to whoever would rid his country of this terrible scourge. But, although many warriors gladly undertook the task, the monster proved too strong for all, and none save a minstrel—who hid in one corner of the hall—ever succeeded in escaping from his clutches. This minstrel, after seeing Grendel feed upon his companions, was so impressed by his horrible experience, that he composed a song about it, which he sang wherever he went, and once repeated for the entertainment of Higelac, King of the Geats, and his nephew Beowulf. In answer to their eager questions, the bard averred that the monster still existed and invariably visited the hall when a feast was held there. This was enough to arouse in Beowulf a burning desire to visit Denmark and rid the world of this scourge. Knowing that his nephew was very brave, and having had proof of his endurance (for the young man had once, in the course of a swimming match, stayed in the water five whole days and nights, killing many sea monsters who came to attack him), Higelac willingly allowed him to depart with fourteen chosen companions. Thus did Beowulf set out "over the Swan-Road" for Denmark, to offer his services to the King.

The foamy-necked floater fanned by the breeze,
Likest a bird, glided the waters,
Till twenty and four hours thereafter
The twist-stemmed vessel had travelled such distance
That the sailing-men saw the sloping embankments,
The sea-cliffs gleaming, precipitous mountains,
Nesses enormous: they were nearing the limits
At the end of the ocean.

On seeing a vessel with armed men approach their shores, the Danish coastguards challenged the newcomers, who explained that their intentions were purely friendly, and begged to be led to the King. After paying their respects to Hrothgar, Beowulf and his attendants offered their services to rid him of the terrible scourge which had preyed so long upon his people. The King thereupon ordered a feast to be prepared, and at its close allowed Beowulf to remain alone in the hall with his own men. Aware that no weapon could pierce the armed hide of the uncanny monster, Beowulf—who had the strength of thirty men—laid aside his armour and prepared to grapple with Grendel by main strength when he appeared.

> Then the brave-mooded hero bent to his slumber,
> The pillow received the cheek of the noble;
> And many a martial mere-thane attending
> Sank to his slumber.

Just as the chill of morning invades the hall, Beowulf hears stealthy steps approaching, and the great door bursts open, admitting a monster, all enveloped in clammy mist, who, pouncing upon one of the men, crunches his bones and greedily drinks his blood. Beowulf, intently watching the fiend, sees him stretch out a horny hand for another victim, and suddenly grasps it with such force and determination that the monster, notwithstanding frantic efforts, cannot free himself. A terrible struggle now takes place, in the course of which Beowulf and Grendel, wrestling madly, overturn tables and couches, shaking the hall to its very foundations. Nevertheless, Beowulf clings so fast to the hand and arm he had grasped, that the monster, in his endeavour to free himself, tears his arm out of its socket and disappears, uttering a blood-curdling cry, and leaving this trophy in the grasp of his foe. Mortally wounded, Grendel hastens back to his marsh, leaving a trail of blood behind him, while Beowulf, exhausted but triumphant, proudly exhibits the huge hand and limb which he has wrenched from the monster, declaring that it will henceforth serve to adorn Heorot.

When Hrothgar beholds it on the morrow and hears an account of the night's adventures, he warmly congratulates Beowulf, upon whom he bestows rich gifts, and in whose honour he holds a grand feast in the hall. While they are drinking and listening to the music of the skalds (who sing of Sigmund the dragon-slayer and of a fight at Finnsburgh), Wealtheow, Queen of Denmark, appears in their midst, and bestows upon Beowulf a wonderful necklace and a ring of the finest gold, bidding him wear them in memory of his triumph.

The feast over, Hrothgar escorts his guest to the palace, leaving his own men to guard Heorot overnight, for all feel confident Grendel has been too sorely wounded ever to appear again. But, while the warriors sleep peacefully, the giant's mother—an equally hideous monster—comes into the hall, secures her son's gory arm which hangs there as a trophy, and bears away Aeschere, one of the King's friends.

On learning of this loss on the morrow, Hrothgar is overcome with grief, and Beowulf volunteers to complete his work and avenge Aeschere by attacking Grendel's mother in her own retreat. But, knowing the perils he is facing, he makes his arrangements in case he should never return, before following the bloody traces left by the monsters. Then he hastens to the pool, where he finds Aeschere's head set aloft as a trophy! Gazing down into the waters, tinged with the monster's blood, he plunges boldly into their depths, where he swims about for a whole day seeking

Grendel's retreat. Guided at last by a phosphorescent gleam, our hero finally reaches a cave, after slaying on the way a number of monsters sent to check his advance. On nearing the giants' den, a strong eddy suddenly sweeps him within reach of Grendel's mother, who, clutching him fast, flings him on the floor, and is trying to find a joint in his armour, so as to kill him with her knife, when Beowulf, snatching a sword hanging from a rocky projection, deals her so fierce a blow that he severs her head from its trunk.

> Then he saw amid the war-gems a weapon of victory,
> An ancient giant-sword, of edges a-doughty,
> Glory of warriors : of weapons 'twas choicest,
> Only 'twas larger than any man else was
> Able to bear in the battle-encounter,
> The good and splendid work of the giants.
> He grasped then the sword-hilt, knight of Scyldings,
> Bold and battle-grim, brandished his ring-sword,
> Hopeless of living hotly he smote her,
> That the fiend-woman's neck firmly it grappled,
> Broke through her bone-joints, the bill fully pierced her
> Fate-cursèd body, she fell to the ground then :
> The hand sword was bloody, the hero exulted.
> The brand was brilliant, brightly it glimmered,
> Just as from heaven gem-like shineth
> The torch of the firmament.

The blood from this monster, pouring out of the cave, mingles with the waters without, which begin to seethe and bubble so ominously that Hrothgar and his men, convinced that Beowulf is dead, sadly depart. The hero's attendants, however, mindful of their orders, linger at the side of the mere, although they cherish small hope of ever beholding their master again.

Having disposed of Grendel's mother, Beowulf

rushes to the rear of the cave, where, finding Grendel dead, he cuts off his head, and with this trophy makes his way up through the tainted waters, which melt his sword, so that he has nothing but the hilt left on reaching the shore.

> The sword-blade began then,
> The blood having touched it, contracting and shrivelling
> With battle-icicles; 'twas a wonderful marvel
> That it melted entirely, likest to ice when
> The Father unbindeth the bond of the frost and
> Unwindeth the wave-bands, He who wieldeth dominion
> Of times and of tides: a truth-firm Creator.

Just as his followers are about to depart, Beowulf emerges from the waters; having beheld his trophy and heard his tale, they escort him back in triumph to Heorot, where the grateful Danes again load him with presents.

His task accomplished, Beowulf returns home, where he bestows the necklace he has won upon the Queen of the Geats, and continues faithfully to serve the royal couple, even placing their infant son upon the throne after their death, and defending his rights as long as he lives. Then the people elect Beowulf king, and during a reign of fifty years he rules them wisely and well. Old age has robbed Beowulf of part of his fabulous strength, when his subjects are suddenly dismayed by the ravages of a fire-breathing dragon, which has taken up its abode in some neighbouring mountains, where he gloats over a hoard of glittering gold. A fugitive slave having made his way into the monster's den during one of its absences and abstracted a small portion of its treasure, the incensed firedrake, in revenge, flies all over the land, vomiting fire and smoke in every direction, and filling all hearts with such terror that the people implore Beowulf to deliver them from this monster also.

Although Beowulf knows that he no longer enjoys his youthful vigour, he nevertheless sets out bravely with eleven men to attack the monster. On reaching the mountain gorge he bids his small troop stand still, and, advancing alone, challenges the beast to come forth. A moment later the mountain shakes as a fire-breathing dragon rushes out to attack Beowulf, who feels his fiery breath even through shield and armour. With deadly fury the dragon attacks the warrior, coiling his scaly folds round and round Beowulf, who vainly slashes at him with his sword, for the monster's scales make him invulnerable.

Seeing his master about to be crushed to death, Wiglaf—one of Beowulf's followers—now springs forward to aid him, thus causing sufficient diversion to enable Beowulf to creep beneath the dragon, and drive his sword deep into its undefended breast! Although the monster's coils now drop limply away from his body, poor Beowulf has been so sorely burned by its breath that he feels his end is near. Turning to his faithful follower, he thanks him for his aid, bidding him hasten into the cave and bring forth the treasure he has won for his people, that he may feast his eyes upon it before he dies.

> " Fare thou with haste now
> To behold the hoard 'neath the hoar-greyish stone,
> Well-lovèd Wiglaf, now the worm is a-lying,
> Sore-wounded sleepeth, disseized of his treasure.
> Go thou in haste that treasures of old I
> Gold-wealth may gaze on, together see lying
> The ether-bright jewels, be easier able,
> Having the heap of hoard-gems, to yield my
> Life and the land-folk whom long I have governed."

Sure that the monster can no longer molest them, the rest of the warriors press forward in their turn, and receive the farewells of their dying chief, who, after rehearsing the great deeds he has accomplished, declares himself ready to close honourably an eventful career. When he has breathed his last, his followers push the corpse of the dragon off a cliff into the sea, and erect on the headland a funeral barrow for Beowulf's ashes, placing within it part of the treasure he won, and erecting above it a memorial, or bauta stone, on which they carve the name and deeds of the great hero who conquered Grendel and saved them from the fiery dragon.

So lamented mourning the men of the Geats,
Fond-loving vassals the fall of their lord,
Said he was kindest of kings under heaven,
Gentlest of men, most winning of manner,
Friendliest to folk-troops and fondest of honour.

THE ARTHURIAN CYCLE

The Arthurian Cycle consists of a number of epics or romances dealing with King Arthur, the knights of his Round Table, or the ladies of his court. The Anglo-Norman *trouvères* arranged these tales in graduated circles round their nucleus, the legend of the Holy Grail. Next in importance to this sacred theme, and forming the first circle, were the stories of Galahad and Percival, who achieved the quest of the Holy Grail, of Launcelot and Elaine, and of Bors, who accompanied Galahad and Percival on their journey to Sarras. The second circle included the stories of Arthur and Guinevere, of Geraint and Enid, of Tristan and Isolde, of Pelleas and Ettarre, of Gareth and Lynette, of Gawain, and of Bedevere. The third and last circle dealt with the epics of Merlin and Vivien, Uther and Igerne, Gorlois, and Vortigern.

To give a complete outline of the adventures which befell all these knights and ladies in the course of seventeen epics and romances—of which many versions exist, and to which each new poet added some episode—would require far more space than any one volume would afford. A general outline will therefore be given of the two principal themes, the Quest of the Holy Grail and King Arthur and the Round Table, mentioning only the main features of the other epics as they impinge upon these two great centres.

Some of the greatest writers of the Arthurian Cycle have been Gildas, Nennius, Geoffrey of Monmouth, Wace, Robert de Borron, Marie de France, Layamon, Chrestien de Troyes, Benoît de St Maur, Gaucher, Manessier, Gerbert, Knot de Provence, Wolfram von Eschenbach, Gottfried von Strassburg, Hartmann von der Aue, Malory, Tennyson, Swinburne, Howard Pyle, Matthew Arnold, and Wagner. Still, almost every writer of note has had something to say on the subject, and thus the Arthuriana has become almost as voluminous as the Shakespeariana. The legend of Arthur, almost unknown before the twelfth century, so rapidly became popular all over Europe, that it was translated into every language and recited with endless variations at every fireside.

Robert de Borron is said to be mainly responsible for the tale of Merlin, the real poet of that name having been a bard at the court, first of Ambrosius Aurelianus and then of King Arthur. The Merlin of the romances was supposed to have owed his birth to the commerce of a fiend with an unconscious nun. A priest, convinced of the woman's purity of spirit, baptized her child as soon as it was born, thus defeating the plots of Satan, who had hoped that the son of a fiend would be able to outwit the plans of the Son of Man for human redemption. In early infancy, already, this Merlin showed his miraculous powers, for he testified in his mother's behalf when she was accused of incontinence.

In the meantime Constance, King of England, had left three sons, the eldest of whom, Constantine, had entered a monastery, while the two others were too young to reign. Drawn from his retirement to wear the crown, Constantine proved incapable of maintaining order, so his general, Vortigern, with the aid of the Saxon leaders Hengist and Horsa, usurped his throne. Some time after, wishing to construct an impregnable fortress on Salisbury Plain, Vortigern sent for a host of masons, who were dismayed to see the work they had done during the day destroyed every night.

On consulting an astrologer, Vortigern was directed to anoint the stones with the blood of a boy of five who had no human father. The only child corresponding to this description was Merlin, who saved himself from untimely death by telling the King that, if he dug into the earth, and drained the lake which he would find, he would discover broad stones beneath which two dragons slept by day, but fought so fiercely at night that they caused the tremendous earthquakes which shattered his walls. These directions were followed, the dragons were roused, and fought until the red one was slain and the two-headed white one disappeared. Asked to explain the meaning of these two dragons, Merlin declared that the white dragon with two heads represented the two younger sons of King Constance, who were destined to drive Vortigern away. Having thus spoken, Merlin disappeared, escaping the wrath of Vortigern, who wished to slay him.

Soon after, the young princes surprised and burned Vortigern in his palace, and recovered possession of their father's throne. Then, one of them dying, the other, assuming both their names, became Uther Pendragon, King of Britain. Such was his bravery that during his reign of seven years he became overlord of all the petty kings who had in the meantime taken possession of various parts of England. He was aided in this work by his prime minister, Merlin, whose skill as a clairvoyant, magician, inventor, and artificer of all kinds of things—such as armour which nothing could damage, a magic mirror, round table, and ring, and wonderful buildings—was of infinite service to his master.

There are various accounts of Arthur's birth; according to one, Uther fell in love with Gorlois' wife Igerne, who was already mother of three daughters. Thanks to Merlin's magic arts, Uther was able to visit Igerne in the guise of her husband, and thus begot a son, who was entrusted to Merlin's care as soon as born. Another legend declares that after Gorlois' death Uther Pendragon married Igerne, and that Arthur was their lawful child. Feeling he was about to die, and fearing lest his infant son should be made away with by the lords whom he had compelled to obedience, Uther Pendragon bade Merlin hide Arthur until he was old enough to reign over Britain. Merlin therefore secretly bore the babe to Sir Ector, who brought Arthur up in the belief that he was the younger brother of his only son, Sir Kay.

Arthur had just reached the age of eighteen when the Archbishop of Canterbury besought Merlin to select an overlord who would reduce the other kings to obedience, and thus restore peace, law, and order in Britain. Thereupon Merlin promised that a king would soon appear whose rights none would be able to dispute. Shortly after, on coming out of the cathedral one feast-day, the Archbishop saw a huge block of stone, in which was embedded an anvil, through which was thrust a beautiful sword. This weapon bore an inscription, stating that he who pulled it out and thrust it back should be the rightful heir to the throne.

Meantime a tournament had been proclaimed, and Sir Kay, having broken his sword while fighting, bade his brother Arthur get him another immediately. Unable to find any weapon in their tent, Arthur ran to the anvil, pulled out the sword, and gave it to Sir Kay. Seeing it in his son's hand, Sir Ector inquired how it had been obtained, and insisted upon Arthur's thrusting it back and taking it out more than once, before he would recognize him as his king. As none other could move the sword, and as Arthur repeatedly proved his claim to it on the great feast-days, he became overlord of all the petty kings. At Sir Ector's request he appointed Sir Kay as steward of his palace, and, thanks to the help of Merlin and of his brave knights, soon subdued the rebels, and became not only master of all England, but, if we are to believe the later romances, a sort of English Alexander, who, after crossing the Alps, became Emperor of the World!

During his reign Arthur fought twelve memorable

battles, and, not content with this activity, often rode out like other knights-errant in quest of adventure, challenging any who wished to fight, rescuing captives, and aiding damsels in distress. In these encounters Arthur wore the peerless armour made by Merlin, and sometimes carried a shield so brilliant that it blinded all who gazed upon it. It was, therefore, generally covered with a close-fitting case, which, like Arthur's helmet, bore as emblem a two-headed dragon. Having lost his divine sword in one encounter, Arthur was advised by Merlin to apply for another to Nimue, or Nymue, the Lady of the Lake. She immediately pointed out an arm, which, rising from the middle of the lake, brandished a magnificent sword. Springing into a skiff near by, Arthur was miraculously ferried to the centre of the lake; as soon as he grasped the sword, the mystic arm disappeared. Merlin now informed Arthur that, fighting with Excalibur, his wonderful sword, he could never be conquered, and that as long as its scabbard hung by his side he could not be wounded. Later on in the story, Arthur incurred the anger of one of his step-sisters, Morgana the Fay, who borrowed Excalibur under the pretext of admiring it, and had so exact a copy of it made that no one suspected that she had kept the magic sword until Arthur was wounded and defeated. He, however, recovered possession of Excalibur—though not of the scabbard—before he fought his last battle.

Bravery and romance were allied traits in Arthur's character; Guinevere having bent over him once when he lay half unconscious from a wound, he fell so deeply in love with her that he entered her father's service as garden boy. Guinevere discovered his identity, and, guessing what had brought him thither, teased him unmercifully. Shortly after, a neighbouring, very ill-favoured king declared that Guinevere's old father should be deprived of his kingdom unless she would consent to marry him, and defied in single combat any one who should dare to oppose him.

Arthur, having secretly provided himself with a white horse and armour, defeated this insolent suitor, and, after a few more thrilling adventures, arranged for his marriage to Guinevere in the fall of the year. By Merlin's advice he also begged his future father-in-law to give him, as wedding present, the Round Table which Merlin had made for Uther Pendragon. This was a magic board round which none but virtuous knights could sit. When led to a seat, any worthy candidate beheld his name suddenly appear on its back, in golden letters, which vanished only at his death, or when he became unworthy to occupy a seat at the Round Table. On one side of Arthur's throne was also the Siege Perilous, which none could occupy under penalty of destruction, save the knight destined to achieve the Holy Grail.

We are informed that Arthur sent his best friend and most accomplished knight, Launcelot, to escort Guinevere to Caerleon on Usk, where the wedding and first session of the Round Table were to take place on the self-same day. When this Launcelot was a babe, his parents were compelled to flee from a burning home. Overcome by sorrow and wounds, the poor father soon sank dying beside the road, and, while the mother was closing his eyes, the Lady of the Lake suddenly rose from her watery home, seized the babe, and plunged back with him into its depths. The widowed and bereft woman entered a

King Arthur
W. H. Margetson

convent, where she was known as the Lady of Sorrows, unaware that her son was being trained by Pellias—husband of the Lady of the Lake—to become the most famous knight of the Round Table. When he reached the age of eighteen the Lady of the Lake decided that it was time Launcelot should be knighted. So, on St John's eve—when mortals can see fairies—King Arthur and Sir Ector were led by a mysterious damsel and a dwarf to a place where Pellias and the Lady of the Lake begged them to knight their *protégé* and pupil, who was henceforth to be known as Launcelot of the Lake. Not only did Arthur gladly bestow the accolade upon the young man, but he took him with him to Camelot.

It was as a supreme honour and mark of confidence that Arthur sent Launcelot to meet and escort Guinevere. Some legends claim these two already loved each other dearly, others that they fell in love during the journey, others still that their guilty passion was due to a love potion, and a few that Guinevere, incensed by the behaviour of Arthur—whom some of the epics do not depict as Tennyson's "blameless king"—proved faithless in revenge later on. All the versions, however, agree that Launcelot cherished an incurable, guilty passion for Guinevere, and that she proved untrue to her marriage vows. Time and again we hear of stolen meetings, and of Launcelot's deep sorrow at deceiving the noble friend whom he continues to love and admire. This is the only blemish in his character, while Guinevere is coquettish, passionate, unfeeling, and exacting, and has little to recommend her save grace, beauty, and personal charm. At court she plays her part as queen and lady of the revels with consummate skill, and we have many descriptions of festivities of all kinds. During a maying party the Queen was once kidnapped by a bold admirer and kept for a time in durance vile. Launcelot, hastening after her, ruthlessly cut down all who attempted to check him, and, his horse falling at last beneath him, continued his pursuit in a wood-chopper's cart, although none but criminals were seen in such a vehicle in the Middle Ages. The Knight of the Cart was, however, only intent upon rescuing the Queen, who showed herself very ungrateful, for she often thereafter taunted him with this ride and laughed at the gibes the others lavished upon him. Twice Guinevere drove Launcelot mad with her taunts, and frequently she heartlessly sent him off on dangerous errands.

Launcelot, however, so surpassed other knights in courage and daring that he won all the prizes in the tournaments. A brilliant series of these contests was given by the King, who, having found twelve large diamonds in the crown of a dead king, offered one of them as prize in twelve successive years. Launcelot, having secured all but the last, decided to attend the last tournament in disguise, after carefully informing the King and Queen that he would not take part in the game.

Pausing at the Castle of Astolat, he borrowed a blank shield, and left his own in the care of Elaine, daughter of his host, who, although he had not shown her any attention, had fallen deeply in love with him. As a further disguise, Launcelot also wore the favour which Elaine timidly offered, and visited the tournament escorted by her brother. Once more Launcelot bore down all rivals, but he was so sorely wounded in the last encounter that he rode off without taking the prize. Elaine's brother, following him, conveyed him to a hermit's cell, where some poets claim that Elaine nursed him back to health. Be it noted that there are two Elaines in Launcelot's life : the daughter of Pelles, whom he is tricked into marrying, and who bears him Galahad, and the "lily maid of Astolat," whom later writers frequently confused with the former. According to some accounts Launcelot lived happily with the first Elaine in the castle he had conquered, Joyous Garde, until Queen Guinevere, consumed by jealousy, summoned them both to court. There she kept them apart, and so persecuted poor Elaine that she crept to a convent, where she died, after bringing Galahad into the world and predicting that he would achieve the Quest of the Holy Grail.

The other Elaine, as Tennyson so beautifully relates, dying of unrequited love, bade her father and brothers send her corpse down the river in charge of a dumb boatman. Everybody knows of the arrival of the funeral barge at court, of the reading of the letter in Elaine's dead hand, and of Launcelot's sorrow over the suffering he had unwittingly caused.

> And Lancelot answer'd nothing, but he went,
> And at the inrunning of a little brook
> Sat by the river in a cove, and watch'd
> The high reed wave, and lifted up his eyes
> And saw the barge that brought her moving down,
> Far off, a blot upon the stream, and said
> Low in himself, "Ah, simple heart and sweet,
> You loved me, damsel, surely with a love
> Far tenderer than my Queen's. Pray for thy soul ?
> Ay, that will I. Farewell too—now at last—
> Farewell, fair lily."

Lancelot and Elaine[1]

Launcelot and Guinevere are not the only examples in the Arthurian Cycle of the love of a queen for her

[1] The quotations are taken from Tennyson's *Idylls of the King*.

husband's friend, and of the latter's overwhelming passion for the wife of his master. Another famous couple, Tristram and Iseult, also claims our attention.

The legend of Tristram was already known in the sixth century, and from that time until now has been periodically rewritten and embellished. Like most mediæval legends, it begins with the hero's birth, gives in detail the whole story of his life, and ends only when he is safely dead and buried.

The main events in Tristram's very adventurous career begin with the elopement of his mother, a sister of King Mark of Cornwall. Then, while mourning for her beloved, this lady dies in giving birth to her son, whom she names Tristram, or the sad one.

Brought up by a faithful servant—Gouvernail or Kurvenal—Tristram learns to become a peerless hunter and musician. After describing sundry childish and youthful adventures in different lands, the various legends agree in bringing him to his uncle's court just as a giant champion named Morolt arrives from Ireland, claiming tribute in money and men unless some one can defeat him in battle. As neither Mark nor any of his subjects dare venture to face the challenger, Tristram volunteers to meet him. The battle takes place on an island, and, after many blows have been given and received and the end has seemed doubtful, Tristram (who has been wounded by his opponent's poisoned lance) kills him by a blow of his sword, a splinter of which remains embedded in the dead giant's skull. The latter's corpse is then brought back to Ireland to receive sepulchre at the hands of Queen Iseult, who, in preparing the body for the grave, finds the fragment of steel, which she treasures, thinking it may some day help her to find her champion's slayer and enable her to avenge his death.

Meanwhile Tristram's wound does not heal, and, having heard that Queen Iseult alone can cure him, he sails for Ireland, where he presents himself as the minstrel Tramtris, and rewards the care of the Queen and her daughter—who both bear the name of Iseult—by his sweet music.

On his return to Cornwall, Tristram, who has evidently been impressed by Princess Iseult's beauty, sings her praises so enthusiastically that King Mark decides to sue for her hand, and—advised by the jealous courtiers, who deem the expedition perilous in the extreme—selects Tristram as his ambassador.

On landing in Ireland, Tristram notices ill-concealed excitement, and discovers that a dragon is causing such damage in the neighbourhood that the King has promised his daughter's hand to the warrior who will slay the monster.

Nothing daunted, Tristram sets out alone, and beards the dragon in his den to such good purpose that he kills him and carries off his tongue as a trophy. But, wounded in his encounter, Tristram soon sinks unconscious by the roadside. The King's butler, who has been spying upon him and who deems him dead, now cuts off the dragon's head and lays it at the King's feet, claiming the promised reward.

Princess Iseult and her mother refuse, however, to believe that this man—a notorious coward—has performed any such feat, and hasten out to the battle-field. There they find not only the headless dragon, but the unconscious Tristram, and the tongue which proves him the real victor. To nurse him back to health is no great task for these ladies, who, like many of the heroines of the mediaeval epics and romances, are skilled leeches and surgeons.

One day, while guarding their patient's slumbers,

the ladies idly examine his weapons, and make the momentous discovery that the fragment of steel found in Morolt's head exactly fits a nick in Tristram's sword.

Although both had sworn vengeance, they decide that the service which Tristram has just rendered their country more than counterbalances his offence, and therefore let him go unscathed.

Fully restored to health, Tristram proves that the butler had no right to Iseult's hand, and, instead of enforcing his own claim, makes King Mark's proposals known. Either because such an alliance flatters their pride or because they dare not refuse, Iseult's parents accept in their daughter's name and prepare everything for her speedy departure. The Queen, wishing to save her daughter from the curse of a loveless marriage, next brews a love-potion which she bids Brengwain—her daughter's maid and companion—administer to King Mark and Iseult on their wedding night.

During the voyage across the Irish Channel, Tristram entertains Princess Iseult with songs and tales, until he becomes so thirsty that he begs for a drink. By mistake the love-potion is brought, and, as Iseult graciously dips her lips in the cup before handing it to her entertainer, it comes to pass that both partake of the magic draught, and thus become victims of a passion which naught can cure. But their love remains pure, and they continue the journey to Cornwall, where, in spite of all he suffers, Tristram delivers the reluctant bride into his uncle's hands.

Some legends claim that Iseult made her maid Brengwain take her place by the King's side on their wedding night, and that, although the Irish Princess dwelt in the palace at Cornwall, she never proved untrue to her lover Tristram. The romances now give us stolen interviews, temporary elopements, and hair-breadth escapes from all manner of dangers. Once, for instance, Iseult is summoned by her husband to appear before the judges and clear herself from all suspicion of infidelity by taking a public oath in their presence. By Iseult's directions, Tristram, disguised as a mendicant, carries her ashore from the boat, begging for a kiss as reward. This enables the Queen to swear truthfully that she has never been embraced by any man save King Mark and the mendicant who carried her ashore!

Tristram—like Launcelot—feels deeply the baseness of his conduct toward his uncle, and often tries to tear himself away, but the spell of the magic potion is too powerful to be broken. Once remorse and shame actually drive him mad, and he roams around the country performing all manner of frenzied deeds.

He too, when restored to his senses, visits Arthur's court, is admitted to the Round Table, and joins in the Quest for the Holy Grail, which, of course, he cannot achieve. But he does marvels in the matter of hunting and fighting, and having received another dangerous wound, wonders who besides Iseult of Cornwall can cure it? It is then that he hears for the first time of Iseult of Brittany (or of the White Hands), whose skill in leechcraft is proverbial, and, seeking her aid, he is soon made whole. But meantime the physician has fallen in love with her patient, and fancies her love is returned because every lay he sings is in praise of Iseult!

Her brother, discovering her innocent passion, reveals it to Tristram, who, through gratitude or to drive the remembrance of his guilty passion out of his mind, finally marries her. But even marriage cannot make him forget Iseult of Cornwall. The time comes when, wounded beyond the power of his wife's skill to cure, Tristram sends for Iseult of Cornwall, who, either owing to treachery or to accident, arrives too late, and dies of grief on her lover's corpse.

The legends vary greatly in the manner of Tristram's death ; in some he is slain by King Mark, who is justly angry to find him in his wife's company. Most of the versions, however, declare that the lovers were buried side by side, and that creepers growing out of their respective graves twined lovingly round each other.

Other beautiful episodes from old Welsh versions of the Arthurian legends are the stories of Geraint and Enid, of Pelleas and Ettarre, of Gareth and Lynette, which have received their latest and most beautiful setting at the hands of Tennyson, and the very tragic and pathetic tale of the twin brothers Balin and Balan, who, after many sinister happenings, failing to recognize each other, fight until one deals the " dolorous stroke " which kills his brother.

Were anyone patient enough to count the characters, duels, and hairbreadth escapes in Malory's *Morte d'Arthur*, the sum might well appal a modern reader. Magic, too, plays a prominent part in the Arthurian Cycle ; thus Merlin, under the influence of a magic ring given by the Lady of the Lake to her sister Vivien, becomes so infatuated with the latter lady, that she is able to coax from him all his secrets, and even to learn the spell whereby a mortal can be kept alive although hidden from all eyes. Having obtained the magic formula by bringing all her

The Passing of Arthur
Stella Langdale

coquettish wiles to bear upon besotted old Merlin, Vivien is said to have decoyed the wizard either to an enchanted castle, where she enclosed him in a stone sepulchre, or into the forest of Broceliande, in Brittany, where she left him spellbound in a flowering thorn-bush. Another legend, however, claims that, having grown old and forgetful, Merlin absent-mindedly took his seat in the Siege Perilous, only to be swallowed up by the yawning chasm which opened beneath his feet.

It was at the height of Arthur's prosperity and fame that the knights of the Round Table solemnly pledged themselves to undertake the Quest of the Holy Grail, as is described in a later chapter. Their absence, the faithlessness of the Queen, and the King's consciousness of past sins cast such a gloom over the once brilliant reunions of Camelot and Caerleon, as well as over the whole land, that Arthur's foes became bolder, and troubles thickened around him. Finally, most of the knights returned from the Quest sadder and wiser men, Launcelot was banished by the King to Joyous Garde, and was therefore not at hand when the last great fight occurred. Mordred, the Judas of the Arthurian Cycle—whom some poets represent as the illegitimate and incestuous son of Arthur, while others merely make him a nephew of the King—rebels against Arthur, who engages in his last battle near the Castle of Tintagel, where he was born.

> "King am I, whatsoever be their cry,
> And one last act of kinghood shalt thou see
> Yet, ere I pass." And uttering this the King
> Made at the man: then Modred smote his liege
> Hard on that helm which many a heathen sword
> Had beaten thin; while Arthur at one blow,
> Striking the last stroke with Excalibur,
> Slew him, and all but slain himself, he fell.

> So all day-long the noise of battle roll'd
> Among the mountains by the winter sea ;
> Until King Arthur's Table, man by man,
> Had fall'n in Lyonesse about their lord,
> King Arthur.
>
> *The Passing of Arthur*

Knowing that his wonderful blade Excalibur must return to its donor ere he departs, Arthur thrice orders Sir Bedevere to cast it into the mere. Twice the knight hides the sword instead of obeying, but the third time, having exactly carried out the royal orders, he reports having seen a hand rise out of the Lake, catch and brandish Excalibur, and vanish beneath the waters with it ! Arthur is next carried by Sir Bedevere down to the water's edge, where a mysterious barge receives the dying King. In this barge are three black-veiled queens—the King's step-sisters—and, when Arthur's head has been tenderly laid in the lap of Morgana the Fay, he announces that he is about to sail off to the Isle of Avalon.

> " I am going a long way
> With these thou seest—if indeed I go
> (For all my mind is clouded with a doubt)—
> To the island-valley of Avilion ;
> Where falls not hail, or rain, or any snow,
> Nor ever wind blows loudly ; but it lies
> Deep-meadow'd, happy, fair with orchard lawns
> And bowery hollows crown'd with summer sea,
> Where I will heal me of my grievous wound."
>
> So said he, and the barge with oar and sail
> Moved from the brink, like some full breasted swan.
>
> *The Passing of Arthur*

Although the Isle of Avalon was evidently a poetical mediaeval version of the " bourne whence no man returns," people long watched for Arthur's homecoming, for he was a very real personage to readers of epics and romances in the Middle Ages.

Guinevere—her sin having been discovered by her hitherto fabulously blind husband—took refuge in a nunnery at Almesbury, where she received a farewell visit from Arthur and an assurance of his forgiveness, before he rode into his last fight.

As for Launcelot, he, too, devoted his last days to penance and prayer in a monastery. There he remained until warned in a vision that Guinevere was dead. Leaving his cell, Launcelot hastened to Almesbury, where, finding Guinevere had ceased to breathe, he bore her corpse to Glastonbury—whither, according to some versions, Arthur had been conveyed by the barge and buried—and there laid her to rest at her husband's feet.

Then Launcelot again withdrew to his cell, where he died after six months' abstinence and prayer. It was his heir, Sir Ector de Maris, who feelingly pronounced the eulogy of the knight *par excellence* of the mediaeval legends in the following terms: "'Ah, Sir Lancelot,' he said, 'thou were head of all Christian knights; and now I dare say,' said Sir Ector, 'that, Sir Lancelot, there thou liest, thou were never matched of none earthly knight's hands; and thou were the courtliest knight that ever bare shield; and thou were the truest friend to thy lover that ever bestrode horse; and thou were the truest lover of a sinful man that ever loved woman; and thou were the kindest man that ever struck with sword; and thou were the goodliest person that ever came among press of knights; and thou were the meekest man, and the gentlest, that ever ate in hall among ladies; and thou were the sternest knight to thy mortal foe that ever put spear in rest.'"

ROBIN HOOD

Among the most popular of the prose epics is the story of Robin Hood, compiled from some two-score old English ballads, some of which date back at least to 1400. This material has recently been charmingly reworked by Howard Pyle, who has happily illustrated his own book. The bare outline of the tale is as follows:

In the days of Henry II there lived in Sherwood Forest the famous outlaw Robin Hood, with his band of sevenscore men. At eighteen years of age Robin had left Locksley to attend a shooting-match in a neighbouring town. While crossing the forest one of the royal gamekeepers tauntingly challenged him to prove his skill as a marksman by killing a deer just darting past them. But, when the unsuspecting youth brought down this quarry, the forester proposed to arrest him for violating the law. Robin, however, deftly escaped, and, when the keeper sent an arrow after him, retaliated by another, which, better aimed, killed one of the King's men!

Guilty of murder, although unintentional, Robin, knowing his life was forfeit, took to the forest, where he became an outlaw. In vain the Sheriff of Nottingham tried to secure him: Robin always evaded capture at his hands. Still he did not remain in hiding, but frequently appeared among his fellow-men, none of whom would betray him, although the sheriff promised a reward of £200 for his capture.

Once, while in quest of adventures, Robin met on a narrow bridge a stranger who refused to make way for him. Irritated by what he considered the man's insolence, Robin seized his quarter-staff, only to find that his antagonist more than matched him in the skilful use of this weapon. Then a false step suddenly toppled Robin over into the stream, where he might have perished had not some of his men leaped out of the thicket to his rescue. Vexed at being beaten at quarter-staff, Robin now proposed a shooting-match, and, his good humour entirely restored by winning a victory in this contest, he promptly enrolled the stranger in his band. His merry companions, on learning that the huge newcomer was John Little, ironically termed him Little John, by which name he became very famous.

Baffled in his attempts to secure Robin and unable to find anyone near at hand to serve a warrant upon him, the Sheriff hired a Lincoln tinker, who, entering an inn, loudly boasted how cleverly he was going to accomplish his task. Among his listeners was the outlaw, who enticed the tinker to drink, and had no difficulty in stealing his warrant.

The tinker, on awaking, was furious, and, coming face to face with Robin soon after, attacked him fiercely. Seeing his opponent was getting the better of him, Robin blew his horn, whereupon six of his men appeared to aid him. Awed by the sudden appearance of these men, who were all clad in Lincoln green, the tinker laid down his cudgel and humbly begged permission to join the band.

The baffled Sheriff now rode off to London to complain, but, when Henry heard that one of his officers could not capture an outlaw, he indignantly bade him leave the court and not appear there again until he had secured Robin. Dismayed at having incurred royal displeasure, the Sheriff resolved to accomplish by stratagem what he had failed to compass by force. He therefore proclaimed a shooting-match, and, feeling sure Robin would be among the competitors for the prize, posted a number of men to watch for him and arrest him. These sleuths recognized all the contestants present, except a dark man, with a patch over one eye, who did not in the least resemble the fair-haired, handsome Robin. Although one-eyed, the stranger easily bore away the prize, and when the Sheriff offered to take him into his service, curtly rejoined that no man should ever be his master. But that evening, in a secret glade in Sherwood Forest, Robin gleefully exhibited to his followers the golden arrow he had won, and, doffing his patch, remarked that the walnut stain, which had transformed a fair man into a dark one, would soon wear off.

Still, not satisfied with outwitting the Sheriff, Robin, anxious to apprise him of the fact, wrote a message on an arrow, which he boldly shot into the hall where his enemy was seated at a banquet. Enraged by this impudence, the Sheriff sent out 300 men to scour the forest, and Robin and his men were forced to hide.

Weary of inaction, Robin finally bade Will Stutely reconnoitre, report what the Sheriff was doing, and see whether it would be safe for him and his men to venture out. Garbed as a monk, Will Stutely sought the nearest inn, where he was quietly seated when some of the Sheriff's men came in. The outlaw was listening intently to their plans when a cat, rubbing against him, pushed aside his frock, and thus allowed the officer a glimpse of Lincoln green beneath its folds. To arrest the outlaw was but the matter of a moment, and Will Stutely was led off to prison and execution, while a friendly barmaid hastened off secretly to the forest to warn Robin of his friend's peril.

Robin Hood and the Sheriff of Nottingham 300

W. Otway Cannell

Determined to save Will from the gallows at any risk, Robin immediately set out with four of his best men and let them mingle among the people assembled near the gallows. Although disguised, the outlaws were immediately recognized by Will when he arrived with the Sheriff. Pressing forward as if to obtain a better view of the execution, the outlaws contrived to annoy their neighbours so sorely that a fight ensued, and, in the midst of the confusion, Little John, slipping close up to the prisoner, cut his bonds, knocked down the Sheriff, and escaped with all the band!

Life in the forest sometimes proved too monotonous to suit Robin, who once purchased from a butcher his horse, cart, and meat, and drove off boldly to Nottingham Fair. There he lustily cried his wares, announcing churchmen would have to pay double, aldermen cost price, housewives less, and pretty girls nothing save a kiss! The merry vendor's methods of trading soon attracted so many female customers that the other butchers became angry, but, deeming Robin a mere simpleton, invited him to a banquet, hoping to take advantage of him.

The Sheriff—who was present—blandly inquired of the butcher whether he had any cattle for sale, and arranged to meet him in the forest and pay 300 crowns in cash for 500 horned heads. But, when the gullible Sheriff reached the trysting-spot, he was borne captive to Robin's camp, where the chief, mockingly pointing out the King's deer, bade him take possession of 500 horned heads! Then he invited the Sheriff to witness games exhibiting the outlaws' strength and skill, and, after relieving him of his money, allowed him to depart unharmed.

More determined than ever to obtain revenge,

the Sheriff again proclaimed an archery contest, which Robin shunned. Little John, however, put in an appearance, won all the prizes, and even accepted the Sheriff's offer to serve him. But, living on the fat of the land in the Sheriff's household, Little John grew fat and lazy, quarrelled with the other servants, and finally departed with his master's cook and his silver!

Robin, although delighted to acquire a new follower, hotly reviled his companion for stealing the silver, whereupon Little John declared the Sheriff had given it to him, and volunteered to produce him to confirm his words. He therefore set out, and waylaid his late employer, who, thinking himself under the protection of one of his own men, innocently followed him to the outlaws' camp. When brought thus suddenly face to face with Robin, the Sheriff expected to be robbed or killed, but Robin, after ascertaining that the silver was not a free gift, gave it back to him and let him go.

Angry because Robin often twitted him with his stoutness, Little John once wandered off by himself in the forest, and meeting Arthur a Bland, challenged him to fight, little suspecting that Robin was watching them from a neighbouring thicket. From this hiding-place the chief of the outlaws witnessed Little John's defeat, and, issuing forth as soon as the fight was over, invited Arthur a Bland to join his band. The three men next continued their walk, until they met a "rose-leaf, whipped-cream youth," of whose modish attire and effeminate manners they made unmerciful fun. Boastfully informing his two companions that he was going to show them how a quarter-staff should be handled, Robin challenged the stranger, who, suddenly dropping his affected manners, snatched a stake from the hedge and proceeded to outfence Robin. In his turn Little John had a chance to laugh at his leader's discomfiture, and Robin, on learning that his antagonist was his nephew (who had taken refuge in the forest because he had accidentally killed a man), invited him to join his merry men.

Soon after Little John was dispatched for food, and the outlaws were enjoying a jolly meal " under the greenwood tree," when a miller came trudging along with a heavy bag of meal. Crowding around him, the outlaws demanded his money, and, when he exhibited an empty purse, Robin suggested that his money was probably hidden in the meal, and sternly ordered him to produce it without delay. Grumbling about his loss, the miller opened his sack, and began to fumble in it ; when all the outlaws were bending anxiously over it, he flung a double handful of meal into their eyes, thus blinding them temporarily. Had not other outlaws now rushed out of the thicket, the miller would doubtless have effected his escape, but the new arrivals held him fast until Robin, charmed with his ready wit, invited him to become an outlaw also.

Some time after this, Robin, Will Scarlet, and Little John discovered the minstrel Allan a Dale weeping in the forest because his sweetheart, fair Ellen, was compelled by her father to marry a rich old squire. Hearing this tale and sympathizing with the lovers, Robin engaged to unite them, provided he could secure a priest to tie the knot. When told that Friar Tuck would surely oblige him, Robin started out in quest of him, and, finding him under a tree, feasting alone and toasting himself, he joined in his merry meal. Then, under the pretext of saving his fine clothes from a wetting, Robin persuaded the friar to carry him pick-a-back across a stream. While doing so, the friar stole Robin's sword, and refused to give it back unless the outlaw carried him back. Following Friar Tuck's example, Robin slyly purloined something from him, and exacted a new ride across the river, during which Friar Tuck tumbled him over into the water. Robin, who had hitherto taken his companion's pleasantries good-naturedly, grew angry and began a fight, but soon, feeling he was about to be worsted, he loudly summoned his men. Friar Tuck in return whistled for his dogs, which proved quite formidable enough opponents to induce the outlaws to beg for a truce.

Robin now secured Friar Tuck to celebrate Allan's marriage, and laid clever plans to rescue Ellen from an unwelcome bridegroom. So all proceeded secretly or openly to the church where the marriage was to take place. Pretending to be versed in magic, Robin swore to the ecclesiastics present that, if they would only give him the jewels they wore, he would guarantee the bride should love the bridegroom. Just as the reluctant Ellen was about to be united to the rich old squire by these churchmen, Robin interfered, and (the angry bridegroom having flounced out of church) bribed the father to allow Friar Tuck to unite Ellen and Allan a Dale. As the bride undoubtedly loved her spouse, Robin claimed the jewels promised him, and bestowed them upon the happy couple, who adopted Sherwood Forest for their home.

Weary of the same company, Robin once dispatched his men into the forest with orders to arrest anyone they met and bring him to their nightly banquet. Robin himself sallied out too, and soon met a dejected knight, who declared that he felt too sad to contribute to the outlaw's amusement. When Robin questioned him in regard to his dejection, Sir Richard of the Lee explained that his son, having accidentally wounded his opponent in a tournament, had been obliged to pay a fine of £600 in gold and make a pilgrimage to Palestine. To raise the money for the fine, the father had mortgaged his estates, and was now about to be despoiled of them by the avaricious prior of Emmet, who demanded an immediate payment of £400 or the estate.

Robin, ever ready to help the poor and sorrowful, bade the knight cheer up and promised to discover some way to raise the £400. Meantime Little John and Friar Tuck—who had joined Robin's band—caught the Bishop of Hereford, travelling through the forest with a train of pack horses, one of which was laden with an iron-bound chest. After entertaining these forced guests at dinner, Robin made them witness his archers' skill and listen to Allan a Dale's music, ere he set forth the knight's predicament and appealed to the Bishop to lend him the necessary money. When the Bishop loudly protested he would do so gladly had he funds, Robin ordered his baggage to be examined and divided into three equal shares, one for the owner, one for his men, and one for the poor.

Such was the value of the third set aside for the poor that Robin could lend Sir Richard £500. Armed with this money—which he promised to repay within a year—Sir Richard presented himself before the prior of Emmet, who had hired the Sheriff and a lawyer to help him despoil the knight with some show of law and justice. It was therefore before an august board of three villains that Sir Richard knelt begging for time wherein to pay his debt. Virtuously protesting he would gladly remit £100 for prompt payment—so great was his need of money—the prior refused to wait, and his claim was duly upheld by lawyer and Sheriff. Relinquishing his humble position, Sir Richard then defiantly produced £300, which he forced the prior to accept in full payment! Soon after, the happy knight was able to repay Robin's loan, and gratefully bestowed fine bows and arrows on all the outlaws.

Little John, garbed as a friar, once set out for a neighbouring fair, and, meeting three pretty girls with baskets of eggs, gallantly offered to carry their loads. When merrily challenged to carry all three, Little John cleverly slung one basket round his neck by means of his rosary, and marched along carrying the other two and singing at the top of his lungs, while one of the girls beat time with his staff.

On approaching the town, Little John restored the baskets to their owners, and, assuming a sanctimonious bearing, joined two brothers of Fountains Abbey, whom he implored to give him a little money. As they turned a deaf ear to his request, Little John went with them, acting so strangely that he annoyed them sorely. He then declared that he would leave them if they would only give him two pennies, whereupon they rejoined they had no more than that for their own needs. Promising to perform a miracle, Little John plumped down upon his big knees in the middle of the road and loudly entreated St Dunstan to put money in their purses. Then jumping up, he seized their bags, vowing that anything above a penny was clearly his, since it was obtained through his prayers!

Robin, longing for a little variety, once met a beggar with whom he exchanged garments. Soon after, meeting four other mendicants, Robin joined them, and having gotten into a quarrel with them, had the satisfaction of routing all four. A little later he met a usurer, whom he induced to reveal the fact that he had never lost his money because he always carried his fortune in the thick soles of his shoes. Of course Robin immediately compelled the usurer to remove his foot-gear, and sent him home barefoot, while he rejoined his men and amused them with a detailed account of the day's adventures.

Queen Eleanor, having heard endless merry tales about Robin Hood, became very anxious to meet him, and finally sent one of her pages to Sherwood Forest to inform Robin that the King had wagered his archers would win all the prizes in the royal shooting-match. She, however, had wagered the contrary, and she promised Robin a safe-conduct for himself and his men if he would only come to court and display his skill.

Choosing Will Scarlet, Little John, and Allan a Dale as his companions, Robin attended the tournament and won all the prizes, to the great disgust of the King, the Sheriff, and the Bishop of Hereford, the latter of whom recognized the hated outlaw. On discovering that the King would not respect the safe-conduct she had given Robin, Eleanor sent him word : " The lion growls ; beware of thy head." This hint was sufficient to make Robin leave immediately, bidding his companions re-enter the forest by different roads and reserving the most difficult for himself.

Although Robin's men reached the forest safely, he himself was hotly pursued by the Sheriff's and

Bishop's troops. Once, when they were so close on his heels that it seemed impossible for him to escape, Robin exchanged garments with a cobbler, who was promptly arrested in his stead and borne off to prison. Such was Robin's exhaustion by this time that he entered an inn, and, creeping into bed, slept so soundly that only on awaking on the morrow did he discover that he had shared his bed with a monk. Slyly substituting the cobbler's garments for those of the sleeping monk, Robin peacefully departed, while the Sheriff's men, having discovered their mistake, proceeded to arrest the false cobbler! Meantime the Queen succeeded in softening the King's resentment, so Robin was allowed to rejoin his companions and his sweetheart, Maid Marian, who could shoot nearly as well as he.

Many years now elapsed, during which King Henry died and King Richard came to the throne. Robin, still pursued by the Sheriff, once discovered in the forest a man clad in horse-skin, who, having been an outlaw too, had been promised his pardon if he would slay Robin. Hearing him boast about what he would do, Robin challenged him first to a trial of marksmanship, and then to a bout of sword play, during which the strange outlaw was slain. Then, donning the fallen man's strange apparel, Robin went off to Nottingham in quest of more adventures.

Meanwhile, Little John had entered a poor hut, where he found a woman weeping because her sons had been seized as poachers and sentenced to be hanged. Touched by her grief, Little John promised to rescue them if she would only supply him with a disguise. Dressed in a suit which had belonged to the woman's husband, he entered Nottingham just as the Sheriff was escorting his captives to the gallows. No hangman being available, the Sheriff gladly hired the stranger to perform that office. While ostensibly fastening nooses around the three lads' necks, Little John cleverly whispered directions whereby they might escape. This part of his duty done, Little John strung his bow, arguing that it would be a humane act to shorten their agony by a well-directed shaft. But, as soon as his bow was properly strung, Little John gave the agreed signal, and the three youths scampered off, while he covered their retreat by threatening to kill anyone who pursued them.

The angry Sheriff, on perceiving Robin, who appeared at this moment, deeming him the man he had sent into the forest, demanded some token that he had done his duty. In reply Robin silently exhibited his own sword, bugle, and bow, and pointed to his blood-stained clothes. The officers having meantime captured Little John, the Sheriff allowed Robin—as a reward—to hang his companion. By means of the same stratagem as Little John had employed for the rescue of the youths, Robin saved his follower, and when the Sheriff started in pursuit, blew such a blast on his horn that the terrified official galloped off, one of Robin's arrows sticking in his back.

Two months later, there was great excitement in Nottingham, because King Richard was to ride through the town. The gay procession of knights, pages, and soldiers was viewed with delight by all the people, among whom Robin's outlaws were well represented. Riding beside the King, the Sheriff of Nottingham paled on recognizing in the crowd Robin himself, a change of colour which did not escape Richard's eagle eye. When the conversation turned upon the famous outlaw at the banquet that evening, and Sheriff and Bishop bitterly declared that Robin could not be captured, Richard exclaimed he would gladly give a hundred pounds for a glimpse of so extraordinary a man! One of the guests rejoined that he could easily obtain a glimpse of him by entering the forest in a monk's garb, a suggestion which so charmed the Lion-hearted monarch that he started out on the morrow with seven cowled men. They had not ridden far into the forest before they were arrested by a man in Lincoln green—Robin himself—who conducted them to the outlaws' abode.

As usual, the chance guests were entertained with a feast of venison and with athletic games, in the course of which Robin declared he would test the skill of his men, and that all who missed the bull's-eye should be punished by a buffet from Little John's mighty fist. Strange to relate, each man failed and was floored by Little John's blow, the rest roaring merrily over his discomfiture. All his men having tried and failed, Robin was asked to display his own skill for the stranger's benefit, and when he too shot at random all loudly clamoured that he must be punished too. Hoping to escape so severe a blow as Little John dealt, Robin declared it was not fitting that a chief should be struck by his men, and offered to take his punishment at his guest's hands. Richard, not sorry to take his revenge, now bared a muscular arm, and hit poor Robin so heartily that the outlaw measured his full length on the ground and lay there some time wondering what had occurred.

Just then the son of Sir Richard of the Lee rushed into the outlaws' camp, breathlessly crying that the King had left Nottingham and was scouring the forest to arrest them. Throwing back his cowl, Richard sternly demanded how one of his nobles dared reveal his plans to his foes, whereupon the young knight, kneeling before his monarch, explained how Robin had saved his father from ruin.

Richard, whose anger was a mere pretence, now informed Robin that he should no longer be persecuted, and proposed that he, Little John, Will Scarlet, and Allan a Dale should enter his service. The rest of the outlaws were appointed gamekeepers in the royal forests, a life which suited them admirably.

After spending the night in the camp of the outlaws, Richard rode away with his new followers, and we are told that Robin Hood served him to such good purpose that he soon earned the title of Earl of Huntington. Shortly after Richard's death, Robin, seized with a longing for the wild free life of his youth, revisited Sherwood Forest, where the first blast of his hunting-horn gathered a score of his old followers about him. Falling at his feet and kissing his hands, they so fervently besought him never to leave them again that Robin promised to remain in the forest, and did so, although King John sent for him several times, and finally ordered the Sheriff to arrest him.

By this time Robin was no longer a young man, and life in the open no longer proved as delightful as of yore. Seized with a fever which he could not shake off, Robin finally dragged himself to the priory of Kirk Lee, where he besought the prioress to bleed him. Either because she was afraid to defy the King or because she owed Robin a personal grudge, this lady opened an artery instead of a vein, and, locking the door of his room, left him there to bleed to death. The unsuspecting Robin patiently awaited her return, and, when he finally realized his plight and tried to summon aid, he was able to blow only the faintest call upon his horn. This proved enough, however, to summon Little John, who was lurking in the forest near by, for he dashed toward the priory, broke open the door, and forced his way into the turret-chamber, where he found poor Robin nearly dead.

At his cries, the prioress hastened to check the bleeding of Robin's wound, but too late! Faintly whispering that he would never hunt in the forest again, Robin begged Little John to string his bow, and raise him up so that he might shoot a last arrow out of the narrow window, adding that he wished to be buried where that arrow fell. Placing the bow in Robin's hand, Little John supported his dying master while he sent his last arrow to the foot of a mighty oak, and "something sped from that body as the winged arrow sped from the bow," for it was only a corpse that Little John laid down on the bed!

At dawn on the morrow six outlaws bore their dead leader to a grave which they had dug beneath the oak; above which was a stone which bore this inscription:

Here underneath this little stone
Lies Robin, Earl of Huntington,
None there was as he so good,
And people called him Robin Hood.
Such outlaws as he and his men
Will England never see again.
Died December 24th, 1247.

THE FAERIE QUEENE

Edmund Spenser, who was born in London in 1552, lived at Dublin as clerk to the Court of Chancery, and there wrote the *Faerie Queene*, of which the first part was published in 1589 and dedicated to Elizabeth. In this poem he purposed to depict the twelve moral virtues in twelve successive books, each containing twelve cantos, written in stanzas of eight pentameters followed by a hexameter. But he completed only six books of his poem in the course of six years.

Book I: The Legend of the Knight of the Red Cross, or of Holiness

The *Faerie Queene* is not only an epic but a double allegory, for many of the characters represent both abstract virtues and the noted people of Spenser's time. For instance, the poem opens with a description of the court of Gloriana, who personifies Elizabeth and is the champion of Protestantism. As queen of the fairy realm she holds annual festivals, in one of which the young peasant Georgos enters her hall. He kneels before her so humbly yet so courteously that, notwithstanding his rustic garb, she perceives he must be of noble birth. When he, therefore, craves as a boon the next adventure, Gloriana grants his request, on condition that he will serve her afterward for six years.

Shortly after, a beautiful lady, garbed in white but enveloped in a black mantle, rides up to court on a snow-white ass, leading a woolly lamb. She is followed by a dwarf, who conducts a war-steed, on which are piled all the arms of a knight. On approaching Gloriana, Una—the personification of Truth—explains that her royal parents are besieged in their capital by a dragon, which has slain all the warriors who have ventured to attack him.

On hearing Una beg for aid, Georgos eagerly steps forward to claim the task. Ill pleased to be given a peasant instead of the knight she was seeking, Una coldly bids Georgos—the personification of Holiness—

try on the armour she has brought, adding that, unless it fits him exactly, he need not expect to triumph. But no sooner has the youth donned the armour which the dwarf produces than all recognize with wonder that it must have been made for him, and Gloriana publicly dubs him " Knight of the Red Cross," because the armour which Una has brought bears that device.

Vaulting on his war-steed, Georgos now rides off with Una and the dwarf, and after crossing a wilderness enters a forest, where before long he descries the mouth of a cave, into which he feels impelled to enter. No sooner has he done so than he encounters a dragon—the personification of Heresy and Error—which attacks him with fury. A frightful battle ensues, in the course of which the Red Cross Knight is about to be worsted, when Una's encouragements so stimulate him that he slays the monster.

On seeing the exhaustion of her companion, Una realizes that he will require rest before undertaking further adventures, and therefore eagerly accepts an invitation tendered by a venerable old hermit who meets them. He leads them to his cell, where, after entertaining them all the evening with pious conversation, he dismisses them to seek rest. His guests have no sooner vanished than the hermit, Archimago—a personification of Hypocrisy—casts aside his disguise, and summons two demons, one of whom he dispatches to Hades to fetch a dream from the cave of Morpheus. This dream is to whisper to the sleeping Red Cross Knight that Una is not as innocent as she seems, while the other demon, transformed into her very semblance, is to delude the knight on awakening into believing his companion

The Faerie Queene

Gertrude Demain Hammond, R.I.

beneath contempt. This plot is duly carried out, and the Red Cross Knight, shocked by the behaviour of the sham Una, departs immediately, bidding the dwarf follow him. Riding along in a state of extreme disgust and irritation, the Red Cross Knight soon encounters Sansfoi—Faithless—accompanied by a lady clad in red, who is Duessa—a personification of Mary Queen of Scots, and also of falsehood and popery. The two knights immediately attack each other, and, when Georgos has slain his opponent, the lady beseeches him to spare her life, exclaiming that her name is Fidessa and that she is only too glad to be saved from the cruel Sansfoi. Deluded by her words and looks, the Red Cross Knight invites her to accompany him, promising to defend her from her foes.

They are riding along together, when the knight plucks a blossoming twig to weave a garland for his companion, and is dismayed to see blood trickle from the broken stem. Questioning the tree from which the branch was taken, Georgos learns that a knight and his wife have been transformed into plants by Duessa, who does not wish them to escape from her thraldrom. During this explanation, Georgos fails to notice how the lady in red trembles lest her victims recognize her, nor does he mark her relief at remaining undetected, thanks to the effectiveness of her disguise.

Riding on once more, the Red Cross Knight and his companion next draw near to a glittering castle, the stones of which seem covered with gold. Fidessa, who is familiar with this place, invites the knight to enter with her; and Georgos, unaware of the fact that this is the stronghold of Pride, not only consents, but pays respectful homage to the mistress of the castle, Queen Lucifera, whose attendants are Idleness, Gluttony, Lechery, Envy, Avarice, and Wrath. It is while sojourning in this castle that the Red Cross Knight one day sees Sansjoi—Joyless—snatch from his dwarf the shield won from Sansfoi. Angered by this deed of violence, Georgos draws his sword, and he would have decided the question of ownership then and there had not Lucifera decreed that he and his opponent should settle their quarrel in the lists on the morrow. During the ensuing night, Duessa secretly informs Sansjoi that the Red Cross Knight is he who slew his brother, and promises that, should he defeat his opponent, she will belong to him forever. On the morrow, in the midst of much feudal pomp, the duel takes place, and—although Duessa, fancying Sansjoi is about to win, loudly cheers him—the Red Cross Knight finally triumphs. Planting his foot upon his foe, Georgos would have ended Sansjoi's life had not Duessa enveloped her *protégé* in a cloud dense enough to hide him from his conqueror. After vainly seeking some trace of his vanished opponent, the Red Cross Knight is proclaimed victor, and goes back to the castle to nurse the wounds he has received.

Meanwhile Duessa steals into the deserted lists, removes the pall of cloud which envelops Sansjoi, and tenderly confides him to the Queen of Night, who bears him down to Hades, where Aesculapius heals his wounds. His victor, the Red Cross Knight, has not entirely recovered from this duel, when the dwarf rushes into his presence to report that while prowling round the castle he discovered a frightful dungeon, where men and women are imprisoned. When he declares that they are sojourning in a wicked place, the Red Cross Knight springs out of bed and, helped by his attendant, hastens away from a spot which now inspires him with unspeakable horror.

They have barely issued from the castle walls before Georgos realizes that he has been the victim of some baleful spell, for he now perceives that the building rests on a foundation of sand and is tottering to its fall, while the pomp which so dazzled him at first is merely outside show and delusion. Unaware, however, that Duessa has beguiled him, he regrets that she is not present to escape with him.

The latter, on returning to the castle to rejoin her victim, finds the Red Cross Knight gone, spurs after him, and on overtaking him gently reproaches him for abandoning her in such a place! Then she entices him to rest by a fountain, whose bewitched waters deprive the drinker of all strength, and offers Georgos a draught from this fountain. After he has drunk thereof, the giant Orgolio spurs out of the forest and, attacking him with a mighty club, lays him low and bears him off to his dungeon, to torture him for the rest of his life. Duessa humbly follows the giant, promising him her love, while the dwarf, who has watched the encounter from afar, sorrowfully collects his master's armour and, piling it hastily on his steed, rides off in quest of help.

Meanwhile the real Una, on awakening in the hermitage to learn that the Red Cross Knight and the dwarf have gone, rides after them as fast as her little white ass can trot. Of course her attempt to overtake her companions is vain, and after travelling a long distance she dismounts in a forest to rest. Suddenly she is almost paralyzed with fear, for a roaring lion bursts through the thicket to devour her. Still, in fairy-land wild beasts cannot harm kings' daughters, provided they are pure, so the lion—the personification of Courage—not only spares Una, but humbly licks her feet, and accompanies her as watch-dog when she resumes her journey. These two soon reach the house of Superstition, an old woman, whose daughter, Stupidity, loves a robber of churches. When this lover attempts to visit the house secretly by night, he is slain by the lion; whereupon the two women angrily banish Una. She is therefore again wandering aimlessly in the forest when Archimago meets her in the guise of the Red Cross Knight, for he wishes her to believe he is her missing champion. On perceiving the lion, however, the magician approaches Una cautiously, but the fair maiden, suspecting no fraud, joyfully runs to meet him.

> And weeping said: "Ah, my long-lacked Lord,
> Where have ye bene thus long out of my sight?"

They have not proceeded far before they encounter Sansloi—Lawless—brother of the two knights with whom Georgos recently fought. Anxious to avenge their death, this new-comer boldly charges at the wearer of the Red Cross. Although terrified at the mere thought of an encounter, Archimago is forced to lower his lance in self-defence, but, as he is no expert, he is overthrown at the first blow. Springing down from his steed, Sansloi sets his foot upon his fallen foe, and, in spite of Una's entreaties, proceeds to unlace his opponent's helmet in order to deal him a deadly blow. But no sooner does he behold the crafty lineaments of Archimago in place of those of the Red Cross Knight, than he contemptuously abandons his opponent to recover his senses at leisure, and starts off in pursuit of Una, whose beauty has charmed his lustful eye.

In a vain endeavour to protect his mistress, the lion next loses his life, and Sansloi, plucking the shrieking Una from her ass, flings her across his palfrey and rides off into the forest, followed by the little steed, which is too faithful to forsake its mistress. On arriving in the depths of the forest, Sansloi dismounts, but Una's cries attract a company of fauns and satyrs, whose uncanny faces inspire Sansloi with such terror that he flees, leaving his captive in their power. Notwithstanding their strange appearance, these wild men are essentially chivalrous, for they speedily assure Una no harm shall befall her in their company. In return she instructs them in regard to virtue and truth, until Sir Satyrane appears, who generously volunteers to go with her in search of the Red Cross Knight.

They presently encounter a pilgrim, who reports that the Red Cross Knight has just been slain in a combat by a knight who is now quenching his thirst at a neighbouring fountain. Following this pilgrim's directions, Sir Satyrane soon overtakes the reported slayer of Georgos, and while they struggle together, the terrified Una flees into the forest, closely pursued by the pilgrim, who is Archimago in a new disguise. Meantime the fight continues until Sansloi, severely wounded, beats a retreat, leaving Sir Satyrane too injured to follow Una. She, however, has meantime overtaken her dwarf, and learned from him that the Red Cross Knight is a prisoner of Orgolio. Thereupon she vows not to rest until she has rescued her companion. She and her dwarf are hastening in the direction in which the giant vanished with his victim, when they meet Prince Arthur—a personification of Leicester and of Chivalry—who, although he has never yet seen the Fairy Queen, is so deeply in love with her that he does battle in her name whenever he can. This prince is encased in magic armour, made by Merlin, and bears a shield fashioned from a single diamond, whose brightness is so dazzling that it must be kept covered, lest it blind all beholders.

After courteously greeting Una, the Prince, hearing her tale of woe, volunteers to accompany her and free the Red Cross Knight. When they reach the castle of Orgolio—Spiritual Pride—Arthur and his squire boldly summon the owner to come forth and fight. No answer is at first vouchsafed them, but after a blast from Arthur's magic bugle the gates burst open, and out of the stronghold rushes a seven-headed dragon, bearing on its back the witch Duessa. This monster is closely followed by the giant Orgolio, who engages in fight with Prince Arthur, while the squire, Timias, directs his efforts against the seven-headed beast. Although the Prince and his attendant finally overcome these terrible foes, their triumph is due to the fact that in the midst of the fray Prince Arthur's shield is accidentally uncovered, and its brightness quells both giant and beast. But no sooner are the fallen pierced with the victors' swords than they shrink to nothing, for they are mere "emptie bladers," or delusions of Archimago's devising.

On seeing the triumph won by her champions, Una congratulates them, and bids the squire pursue Duessa, who is now trying to escape. Thus enjoined, Timias seizes the witch, and, in obedience to Una's orders, strips her of her fine clothes and sends her forth in her original loathsome shape.

Meantime Una and the Prince boldly penetrate into the castle, and, passing hurriedly through rooms overflowing with treasures, reach a squalid dungeon, where they discover the Red Cross Knight almost starved to death. Full of compassion they bear him to comfortable quarters, where they proceed to nurse him back to health; and, when he is once more able to ride, he and Una resume their journey. As they proceed, however, Una becoming aware that her champion is not yet strong enough to do battle, conducts him to a house, where the wise old matron Religion, Doctor Patience, and three handmaidens, Faith, Hope, and Charity, nurse him to such good purpose that Georgos is soon stronger than ever. During his convalescence in this hospitable abode, the Red Cross Knight once wanders to the top of the hill of Contemplation, whence he is vouchsafed a vision of the New Jerusalem, and where he encounters an old man who prophesies that after fulfilling his present quest he will be known as "Saint George of mery England, the signe of victorcc." Modestly deeming himself unworthy of such distinction, the Red Cross Knight objects that a ploughman's son should not receive such honour, until the aged man informs him that he is in reality the son of the British king, stolen from his cradle by a wicked fairy, who, finding him too heavy to carry, dropped him in a field where a farmer discovered and adopted him. Notwithstanding this rustic breeding, it was Georgos' noble blood that urged him to seek adventures, and sent him to Gloriana's court, whence he sallied forth on his present quest.

After another brief sojourn in the house of Religion the Red Cross Knight and Una again set forth, and passing through another wilderness, reach a land ravaged and befouled by the dragon which holds Una's parents in durance vile. The lady is just pointing out her distant home to the Red Cross Knight, when she hears the dragon coming, and, bidding her champion fight him bravely, takes refuge in a cave near by. Spurring forward to encounter his opponent, the Red Cross Knight comes face to face with a hideous monster, sheathed in brazen scales and lashing a tail that sweeps over acres at a time. This monster is further provided with redoubtable iron teeth and brazen claws, and breathes forth sulphur and other deadly fumes.

Notwithstanding his opponent's advantages, Georgos boldly attacks him, only to find no weapon can pierce the metal scales. At the end of the first day's fight, the dragon withdraws, confident he will get the better of his foe on the morrow. At the close of the second day, the monster's tail whisks Georgos into a pool, whose waters fortunately prove so healing that this bath washes away every trace of weakness and restores him to health and strength. On the third day's encounter, the Red Cross Knight manages to run his sword into the dragon's mouth, and thus inflicts a deadly wound. Seeing her foe writhing at last in the agonies of death, Una joyfully emerges from her hiding-place, while the watchman on the castle tower loudly proclaims that they are free at last!

The poet vividly describes the relief of Una's parents on being able to emerge from their castle once more, and their joy on embracing the daughter who has effected their rescue. The castle inmates not only load Una with praise, but escort her and her champion back to their abode, where their marriage takes place amid general rejoicings. But, although the

Red Cross Knight would fain linger by Una, he remembers his promise to serve Gloriana for six years, and sets out immediately to redress other wrongs.

Book II: The Legend of Sir Guyon, or of Temperance

The next adventure in the *Faerie Queene* is that of Sir Guyon—personifying Temperance—who is escorted everywhere by a black-garbed palmer—Prudence or Abstinence—at whose dictation he performs all manner of heroic deeds. Journeying together they soon meet a squire, who reports that a lady has just been captured by a wicked knight, who is bearing her away. On hearing of this damsel's peril, Sir Guyon bids her squire lead them in the direction in which she vanished, declaring that he will save her if possible. He soon encounters a maiden with dishevelled locks and torn garments, who delays him by informing him that she has been ill-treated by a knight bearing the device of a red cross. Although loath to believe Georgos can be guilty of an unchivalric deed, Sir Guyon and the palmer promise to call him to account as soon as they overtake him. They no sooner do so, however, than he assures them that Archimago in his guise has been ranging through the forest, and that they must have met Duessa. Turning to punish the lying squire who led them astray, Sir Guyon now perceives he has vanished, and humbly begs pardon of the Red Cross Knight.

Shortly after, Sir Guyon is startled by loud shrieks, and, hastening in the direction whence they proceed, discovers a wounded lady and a dead knight. Close beside the lady is a young babe, whose innocent hands are dabbling in his parent's blood. On questioning the woman, Sir Guyon learns that her husband was bewitched by Acrasia—or Pleasure—who bore him off to the Bower of Bliss, a place where she detains her captives, feeding them on sweets until their manly courage is gone. On learning that her husband had fallen into the power of this enchantress, the lady had sought the Bower of Bliss and by dint of wifely devotion had rescued her spouse. But, even as they left, the witch bestowed upon them a magic cup, in which, little suspecting its evil powers, the wife offered water to her husband. No sooner had he drunk than blood gushed from his mouth and he died, whereupon, frantic at having unwittingly slain the man she loved, the lady had dealt herself a mortal wound with his sword.

Scarcely had the sufferer finished this account when she sank back lifeless. Sir Guyon and the palmer, after burying the parents, vainly tried to remove the blood-stains from the infant's hands. Then, unable to care properly for him themselves, they entrusted it to some ladies in a castle near by, bidding them call the babe Ruddy Main, or the Red Handed, and send him to court when he had grown up.

Having thus provided for the orphan, Sir Guyon, whose horse and spear meanwhile have been purloined by Braggadocchio, decides to recover possession of them, and to seek the Bower of Bliss to slay the witch Acrasia, who has caused such grievous harm. On this quest Sir Guyon and the palmer encounter the madman Furor, and then reach a stream which is too deep to ford. While they are seeking some conveyance to bear them across, they perceive a skiff rowed by a fair lady, Phaedria—or Mirth.

At their call she pushes her boat close to them, but no sooner has Sir Guyon sprung aboard than she pushes off, leaving the palmer behind in spite of all entreaties. Although impelled neither by oars nor sails, Phaedria's boat drifts rapidly over the Idle Sea, and Sir Guyon, on questioning its owner, learns they are bound for her magic realm.

They have scarcely touched the sedgy shores of a charming island, when a ruffian, Cymochles—or Deceit—bursts out of the thicket to claim the lady. Undaunted by the size of his challenger, Sir Guyon attacks him, and the duel might have proved fatal had not Phaedria cast herself between the champions, begging them not to quarrel in the land of love and delight. Thereupon Sir Guyon hotly informs her that he has no desire to slay Deceit or to claim her, and, seeing she cannot make any impression upon him, Phaedria angrily bids him re-enter the boat, which soon bears him to the place which he wished to reach.

Although still mourning the loss of his companion, the palmer, Sir Guyon decides to continue his quest for the Bower of Bliss. While passing through a dense thicket, his attention is attracted by a clank of metal, and peering through the branches he descries an old, dirt-encrusted man, surrounded by mounds of precious stones and coins, which keep dropping through his fingers. This creature is Mammon—God of Wealth—who is so busy counting his treasures that at first he pays no heed to Sir Guyon. When questioned, however, he boasts that he is more powerful than any potentate in the world, and tries to entice Sir Guyon to enter into his service by promising him much gold. For a moment Sir Guyon wavers, but finally decides not to accept the offer until he has ascertained whether Mammon's riches have been honestly gained. To show whence he draws them, the Money-god now conveys Sir Guyon to the bowels of the earth, and there lets him view his minions mining gold, silver, and precious stones, and thus constantly increasing his hoard. But, although sorely tempted, Sir Guyon perceives that Mammon's workmen are oppressed by Care and driven by Force and Fraud, who keep them constantly at work and never allow Sleep to approach them. This discovery makes him decide to have nothing to do with Mammon's treasures, although he is led into a hall where hosts of people are paying homage to the Money-king's daughter, who, he is told, will be his bride if he will only accept her father's offers. Coldly rejoining that his troth is already plighted, Sir Guyon refuses, only to emerge from this hall into a garden, through whose branches he catches fleeting glimpses of the underworld. In one of its rivers he even beholds Tantalus, undergoing torments from hunger and thirst, in punishment for sins committed while on earth.

After being subjected for three days to all the temptations of the underworld, Sir Guyon is led back to the light of day, where Mammon—who bitterly terms him a fool—abandons him.

The story now returns to the palmer, who, after watching Sir Guyon out of sight, wanders along the stream in quest of a vessel to follow his master. Several days later he manages to cross, only to hear a silvery voice calling for aid. Bursting through the thicket, he discovers Sir Guyon, lying on the ground, watched over by a spirit of such transcendent beauty that the palmer realizes it must be an angel even before he notes its diaphanous wings. This ministering spirit assures the palmer that Sir Guyon will soon recover, adding that although unseen he will continue to watch over him, and will help him to escape from all the dangers along his path. Then the heavenly spirit vanishes, and, while the palmer is bending over the fainting Sir Guyon, he sees two knights draw near, preceded by a page and followed by an old man. These knights are Cymochles and his brother, who have been brought hither by the old man Archimago, to slay Sir Guyon, whom they hate.

Drawing near, these ruffians thrust the palmer aside, but, while they are stripping the unconscious man of his armour, another knight suddenly draws near and attacks them. One of the brothers being without a sword, seizes that of Sir Guyon, although Archimago warns him that, as it once belonged to his antagonist, it will never harm him.

Prince Arthur, for it is he, now overcomes the ruffians, to whom he generously offers life, provided they will obey him hereafter. But, when they refuse these terms, he ruthlessly slays them, while Archimago and the page hurry away with all speed.

At this moment Sir Guyon recovers his senses, and is overjoyed to find the palmer beside him and to learn that Prince Arthur, who rescued him from the ruffians, is not far away.

After a brief rest, Prince Arthur and Sir Guyon depart together, the former explaining how anxious he is to do anything in his power for Queen Gloriana, whom he devotedly loves although he has never yet seen her. Conversing together, the two ride on to a castle, where no heed is paid to their request for a night's lodging. They are marvelling at such discourtesy, when a head is thrust over the battlement and a hoarse voice bids them flee, explaining that the castle has been besieged for seven years past by barbarians lurking in the forest, against whom no knight has been able to prevail.

While the watchman is thus accounting for his inhospitality, a rout of hungry barbarians bursts out of the forest and attacks Sir Guyon and Prince Arthur, both of whom fight to such good purpose that they utterly annihilate their assailants. Happy to be delivered from these foes, the inhabitants of the castle then open wide their gates. Our knights spend several days there resting from their labours, and perusing "old records from auncient times derivd," where they learn the history of all the British kings. Meantime the palmer, who has followed them thither, forges chains and a steel net, with which to capture and hold the witch Acrasia when the right time comes. When he has finished manufacturing these objects, he persuades Sir Guyon to start out once more. Reaching the water again, they board a vessel, which bears them safely past the Magnetic Rock, over the Sea of Gluttony, etc., to an island, whose beauty human imagination cannot conceive.

On landing, the travellers, to their surprise, encounter strange monsters, and are enveloped in dense mists, through which they hear the flapping of bat-like wings and catch glimpses of harpy-like creatures. Knowing that monsters and mists are mere delusions, Sir Guyon pays little heed to them, and the palmer soon disperses them by a touch from his magic staff. Still bearing the steel net and iron chains, this faithful henchman follows Sir Guyon into the enchanted bower of Acrasia, where he explains to his master that the animals he sees owe their present forms to the enchantress' power, for she always transforms her visitors into beasts.

Through an ivory gate—on which is carved the story of the Golden Fleece—the adventurers enter a hall, where a "comely personage" offers them wine. But Sir Guyon, knowing that a drop of it would have a baleful effect upon the drinker, boldly overturns the bowl. Then, threading his way through the Bower of Bliss, he reaches its innermost grove, although Phaedria tries to detain him. Pressing onward, Sir Guyon finally catches a glimpse of Acrasia herself, reposing upon a bed of flowers, and holding on her lap the head of an innocent youth, who is helpless owing to her spell. Silently signalling to the palmer, Sir Guyon spreads out the steel net, which they fling so deftly over witch and victim that neither can escape. Then Sir Guyon binds Acrasia fast, while the palmer removes the spell which she had laid upon her captives, and restores all the beasts on the island to their natural forms. Thereupon all profess gratitude, save one, whom the palmer grimly bids continue to be a pig.

Having thus happily achieved this quest, Sir Guyon and the palmer leave the island with Acrasia, who is sent under strong guard to the court of the Fairy Queen, where Gloriana is to dispose of her according to her good pleasure.

Book III: The Story of Britomart, or of Chastity

Britomart, only child of King Ryence, had from earliest childhood so longed to be a boy that, instead of devoting her time to womanly occupations, she practised manly sports until she became as expert a warrior as any squire in her father's realm.

One day, while wandering in the palace, she discovered in the treasure-room a magic mirror, fashioned by Merlin for her father, wherein one could behold the secrets of the future. Gazing into its crystal depths while wondering whom she should ultimately marry, Britomart suddenly saw a handsome knight, who bore a motto proclaiming that he was Sir Artegall, the Champion of Justice and proud possessor of Achilles' armour. No sooner had Britomart perceived this much than the vision faded. But the Princess left the room, feeling that henceforth she would know no rest until she had met her destined mate. When she confided this vision to her nurse Glauce, the worthy woman suggested that they go and consult Merlin, wearing the garb of men.

Early the next day, therefore, the two visited the magician, who, piercing their disguise, declared he knew who they were, and bade them ride forth as knight and squire to meet the person they sought. Thus encouraged, Britomart, wearing an Amazon's armour, and bearing a magic spear, set out on her quest, and met Prince Arthur and Sir Guyon, just after Acrasia had been dispatched to Gloriana's court and while they were in quest of new adventures.

Seeing a warrior approach, Sir Guyon immediately lowered his lance, but to his surprise was unhorsed by Britomart's invincible spear. She was about to dismount to dispatch her fallen foe with her sword, when the palmer loudly bade his master crave mercy, seeing it was useless to contend against magic weapons. Sir Guyon therefore surrendered, and he and Prince Arthur humbly offered to escort Britomart, whom they naturally took for a powerful knight.

They had not gone very far when they beheld at a distance a damsel dashing madly through the bushes, casting fearful glances behind her, for she was closely pursued by a grizzly forester. All their chivalric instincts aroused, Prince Arthur and his companions spurred hotly after the distressed damsel, while Britomart and her nurse calmly rode on, until they came to a castle, at whose gates one knight was desperately fighting against six. Britomart rode boldly to the rescue of the oppressed knight, and fought beside him to such good purpose that they defeated their assailants. Then entering the castle, Britomart and her nurse proceeded to tend their companion, the Red Cross Knight, who had received serious wounds.

Although he had noticed in the midst of the conflict that a golden curl had escaped from Britomart's helmet and fallen over her breast, and had thus discovered her sex, he courteously ignored it until they were about to ride away together, when he respectfully offered to serve as the lady's protector and escort. Thereupon Britomart explained who she was, adding that she was in quest of Sir Artegall, of whom she spoke rather slightingly, because she did not wish her companion to know how deeply she had fallen in love with a stranger. Judging from her tone that she did not approve of Sir Artegall, the Red Cross Knight hotly protested he was the noblest and most courteous knight that had ever lived, while

> The royall Maid woxe inly wondrous glad,
> To heare her Love so highly magnifyde.

Meantime, Prince Arthur and Sir Guyon, with their respective attendants, pursued the distressed damsel, riding through thick and thin until they came to cross-roads. Not knowing which path the fugitive had chosen, our heroes decided to part and ride along separate ways. Thus, it was Prince Arthur who first caught a glimpse of the maiden, who still kept glancing backward as if afraid; but, although he spurred on as fast as possible, he was not able to overtake her, and had to pause at nightfall to rest. On resuming his quest on the morrow, he soon encountered a dwarf, the servant of Lady Florimell, who had fled from court five days ago on hearing a rumour that her lover, Marinell, was slain. The poor damsel, while in quest of her lover, had been seen and pursued by an ill-favoured forester, and the dwarf feared some harm might have befallen her. To comfort this faithful henchman, Prince Arthur promised to go with him and rescue the unhappy damsel.

Meantime, undaunted by darkness, Florimell had ridden on until her weary steed paused before a hut deep in the woods. There she dismounted and humbly begged the old witch who lived there to give her some food. Moved by the distress of the stranger, the sorceress bade her dry her garments at her fire. While the lady was sitting there, the witch's son, a lazy, worthless fellow, suddenly entered; to see Florimell was to love her, so the uncouth rustic immediately began to court her with fruits and flowers which he sought in the forest. Fearing lest he should finally molest her, Florimell escaped from the hut on her palfrey, which she found in the witch's stable.

On awakening on the morrow to find their fair visitor gone, the witch and her son were in such despair that they let loose a wild beast, which they owned, bidding him track the missing girl. Before long, therefore, poor Florimell heard this monster crashing through the forest. Terrified at the thought of falling into its power, she urged her steed toward the seashore, in hopes of finding a boat and getting away. On reaching the water, she sprang off her steed, and, seeing a little skiff near by, stepped into it and pushed off, without securing the permission of the fisherman, who was sleeping at the bottom of the boat while his nets were drying on the sand.

Barely were they out of reach when the beast rushed down to the shore, pounced upon Florimell's horse and devoured it. The monster was still occupied thus when Sir Satyrane came riding along. He rashly concluded that the beast had devoured the rider too, a fear confirmed by the sight of Florimell's girdle on the sand. Attacking the monster, Sir Satyrane overcame and bound him fast with the girdle, but he had not proceeded far with his captive, when he spied a giantess bearing off an armed squire. In his haste to overtake her and rescue a fellow-man, Sir Satyrane spurred forward so hastily that the girdle slipped off the neck of the beast, which, finding itself free, plunged back into the forest. To attack the giantess, free her captive, and restore him to his senses proved short work for Sir Satyrane, who learned that the youth he had delivered was known as the Squire of Dames, because he constantly rode through the forest freeing damsels in distress.

Together with this companion, Sir Satyrane journeyed on until they encountered Sir Paridell, who told them that he was in quest of Florimell, who was wandering alone in the forest. Sir Satyrane informed Sir Paridell that the maiden must be dead, exhibiting as proof her girdle, and relating under what circumstances it had been found. Then all present took a solemn oath not to rest until they had avenged the lady's death. Riding together, these three knights, overtaken by a storm, asked for shelter in a neighbouring castle, only to be refused admittance. To escape from the downpour, they therefore took refuge with their steeds in a neighbouring shed, and were scarcely ensconced there when another stranger rode up seeking shelter also. As there was no room left, the first-comers forbade the stranger to enter, whereupon he challenged them to come forth and fight. Sir Paridell sallied out and began a duel, which was closely watched by his two companions. They, however, decided that the combatants were so exactly matched that it was useless to continue the fight, and suggested that they should join forces to make their way into the castle.

Before the determined attack of these knights and of their followers, Malbecco, owner of the castle, opened his gates, and the strangers proceeded to remove their armour and make themselves at home. The stranger knight was also "enforst to disaray"; the falling curls issuing from the helmet revealed a woman, none other than Britomart, and the marvelling knights "fed their hongry vew" on "the fairest woman-wight that ever eie did see."

The next day all left the castle save Sir Paridell, who had been so sorely wounded by Britomart that he was forced to remain for a while. Before long Britomart and her squire parted from Sir Satyrane and the Squire of Dames, and rode along until they beheld a shield hanging from a branch in the forest. They presently discovered its owner, Sir Scudamore, weeping beside a stream, because his bride, Amoret, had been stolen from him on his wedding day by the magician Busirane, who was trying to force her to marry him. Having heard this tale of woe, Britomart informed Sir Scudamore that instead of shedding vain tears they ought to devise means to rescue the captive lady. Encouraged by these words, Sir Scudamore donned his discarded armour and volunteered to guide Britomart to the magician's castle, explaining on the way that it was surrounded by a wall of fire through which none had been able to pass.

Undaunted by this information, Britomart pressed onward, and on reaching the castle declared her intention to charge through the flames. Although Sir Scudamore bravely tried to accompany her, he was driven back by the fierce heat, but Britomart passed through scatheless, and, entering the castle, found herself in a large room, whence led a door with the inscription 'Be bold.' After studying these words for a few moments, Britomart opened this door and passed through it into a second chamber, whose walls were lined with silver and gold, where she saw another door above which the same words were written twice. Opening this door also, Britomart entered a third apartment, sparkling with precious stones, in the centre of which she saw an altar surmounted by a statue of Love. Beyond was another door with the inscription 'Be not too bold.'

Pondering on the meaning of this warning, Britomart decided not to open it, but to take up her vigil fully armed beside the altar. As the clock struck midnight, the mysterious door flew open, and through its portals came in strange procession Fancy, Doubt, Desire, Danger, Fear, Hope, Dissemblance, Grief, Fury, and many others, leading the doleful Amoret, who had a dagger thrust into her heart and stumbled along in mortal pain. Although Britomart would fain have gone to Amoret's rescue, she was rooted to the soil by a spell too powerful to break, and, therefore, remained inactive while the procession circled around the altar, and again vanished behind the door, which closed with an ominous clang. Then only the spell lost its power, and Britomart, springing toward the door, vainly tried to open it. Unable to do so, she decided to continue mounting guard on this spot in hopes of catching another glimpse of the suffering lady. Twenty-four hours later the door reopened and the same procession appeared; it was about to vanish a second time when Britomart, by a violent effort, broke the spell and dashed into the next apartment before the door closed.

There, finding the magician Busirane on the point of binding Amoret fast to a post,

> So mightily she smote him, that to ground
> He fell halfe dead: next stroke him should have slaine,

had not Amoret reminded her that he alone could heal her wound and free the other inmates of the castle from magic thraldom. At the point of her sword, therefore, Britomart compelled the magician to undo his spells, and, when he had pronounced the necessary words, Amoret stood before her as whole and as well as on her wedding-morn when she was snatched away from her bridegroom. Britomart bade Amoret follow her out of the castle, assuring her that her husband was waiting without and would be overjoyed to see her once more. But the rescued lady was sorely dismayed on reaching the forest to find that Sir Scudamore and Britomart's nurse and squire had gone away. To comfort poor Amoret, Britomart suggested that they should ride after their companions, a proposal which Amoret gladly accepted.

Book IV: The Legend of Cambel and Triamond, or of Friendship

As Britomart conjectured, Sir Scudamore, deeming it impossible that she should survive the heat of the flames, had persuaded the nurse to ride on with him, in hope of encountering knights who would help him to rescue his bride.

They soon met a couple of warriors, who, on hearing their tale, laughingly assured them they need make no further efforts to rescue Amoret, as she had meantime been saved by a handsome young knight, with whom she was gaily riding through the forest. Incensed by this statement, Sir Scudamore offered to fight both informers, who, laughing at him for being jilted, rode contemptuously away. These two mockers had not gone very far, however, before they encountered a beautiful damsel, whom they mistook for the long-lost Florimell, but who was merely an image of her conjured up by the witch to comfort her son when he blubbered over the loss of his fair lady. As many knights were in quest of Florimell, some of them soon encountered the scoffers, who declared that they were leading the lady back to court. A little later the Squire of Dames found them contending for the possession of the false Florimell, and suggested that they should settle their difference at the court of Sir Satyrane, where a tournament had been proclaimed, and where Florimell's girdle was to be bestowed by the victor upon the fairest lady present. Both knights, anxious to win the girdle, thereupon set out for the tournament, where many others had assembled to take part in the knightly games.

On their way they overtake two knights, Cambel and Triamond, "that lincked rode in lovely wise," and hear the story of their friendship.

Here many feats of valour were performed before, on the third day, Sir Artegall entered the lists. To his surprise, however, he was unhorsed by a stranger knight, Britomart, who, unaware that her opponent was the lover she sought, bore off in triumph the girdle which her prowess had won. Then, summoning all the maidens present, she picked out the false Florimell as the greatest beauty and handed her the girdle. But, to the surprise of all present, the lady could not keep the girdle clasped about her waist, and, incensed at the mocking remarks of the bystanders, finally challenged the other ladies present to try it on. Thus it was ascertained that none could wear it save Amoret, evidently the only perfectly faithful lady present.

Having thus disposed of her prize, Britomart rode off with her companion, turning her back on the very man she was seeking. In the meantime Sir Scudamore, encountering Sir Artegall, and hearing that he had been defeated by the knight who had carried off Amoret, suggested that he should accompany him and seek revenge. They soon met Britomart, now riding alone through the forest, for, while she slept, Amoret had strayed from her side and got lost. Spurring forward to attack the stranger, Sir Scudamore was unhorsed at the first touch of her spear, and, when Sir Artegall came to his rescue, he also was disarmed. But in the midst of the fight, Britomart's helmet fell off, and both knights perceived that they had been defeated by a woman.

Humbly kneeling before her, they begged her pardon, Sir Scudamore realizing with joy that, as his wife had been travelling with a woman, his mad jealousy was without cause!

To justify her mistress, the nurse-squire now explained to both men how Britomart had seen Sir Artegall in the magic mirror, and was in quest of him because fate destined him to be her spouse. Happy at securing such a mate, Sir Artegall expressed deep joy, while Sir Scudamore clamoured to know what had become of his wife, and grieved to learn that she was lost. To comfort him, however, Britomart promised to assist in the recovery of his beloved, before she would consent to marry. Then all four proceeded to a neighbouring castle, where Sir Artegall was solemnly betrothed to Britomart, and where they agreed that their marriage would take place as soon as Amoret was found.

Meantime Timias, squire of Prince Arthur, seeking to trace the flying damsel, overtook the grim forester, with whom he had a terrible encounter. Sorely wounded in this fight, the poor squire lay in the forest until found by the nymph Belphebe, a twin sister of Amoret, who, in pity for his sufferings, bathed his wounds, laid healing herbs upon them, and did all she could to save his life. To her satisfaction, the wounded squire soon recovered consciousness, and she conveyed him to her bower, where she and her nymphs attended him until his wounds were entirely healed. During this illness Timias fell deeply in love with Belphebe; but, deeming himself of too lowly condition to declare his passion to a lady of high degree, he spent his days "in dolour and despaire." Belphebe renewed her efforts to cure him, until he was strong enough to accompany her into the forest. They were hunting there one day when Timias beheld a damsel fleeing from a misshapen monster, whom he attacked, but against whom he could not prevail, because the monster opposed the lady as a shield to every blow which Timias tried to deal him. It was only by a feint that Timias made the monster drop the lady, and he would surely have been slain by his opponent, had not his companion rescued him by a timely arrow. A little later Belphebe was horrified to find Timias bestowing fond kisses on the lady whom they had rescued. The angry nymph fled, unaware that Timias was kissing her own counterpart, for he had rescued her twin sister Amoret, who, after wandering away from the sleeping Britomart, had been seized by the monster from whose cave she had just managed to escape.

Bewildered to see Belphebe—whom he thought he was embracing—rush away, Timias now dropped Amoret to follow his charmer, but, unfamiliar with the forest pathways, he soon lost his way. In his grief he built himself a hut and dwelt in the forest, vowing not to go back in quest of Amoret, lest he thereby arouse the jealousy of his beloved. But to beguile his sorrow he carved Belphebe's name on every tree, and was kissing these marks when he was discovered by Prince Arthur, who fancied he had gone mad!

The squire had also found a dove which had lost its mate, and, realizing that they were fellow sufferers, bound round the bird's neck a ruby heart which Belphebe had given him. The dove, flying back to its mistress, enticed her, by fluttering a few paces ahead of her, to the place where Timias was kissing her name carved upon a tree. Convinced of his fidelity by such a proof of devotion, Belphebe reinstated Timias in her favour, and once more ranged the forest with him, hunting all kinds of game, until poor Timias was wounded by the Blatant Beast—Slander—a monster from whose jaws he was fortunately rescued by Prince Arthur.

After a partial recovery, Timias rode off with his master, to whom he confided how he had abandoned Amoret in the forest, and from whom he inquired whether any further news had been heard about her. To Timias' satisfaction Arthur assured him that she had safely rejoined her husband, who, finding her wounded in the forest, had carried her off to a castle and tenderly nursed her back to health. It was only after witnessing the joyful celebration of the long-postponed wedding festivities of this reunited couple, that Sir Arthur had started off on his recent quest for his squire.

In the meantime the real Florimell, cast into the sea by the angry fisherman whose vessel she had entered without permission, had been conveyed by sea-nymphs to Proteus' hall, where, after witnessing the nuptials of the Thames and Medway, she learned that her lover Marinell was recovering from his wound under the care of his goddess mother. He had, however, been pining for her, and recovered perfect health and happiness only when they were joined in wedlock.

Book V: The Legend of Sir Artegall, or of Justice

Sir Artegall, the noble champion of justice (the Lord Deputy of Ireland), sets forth at Gloriana's behest to defend Irena, or Ireland. He is attended by Talus, an iron man, whose flail threshes out falsehood. They have not proceeded very far before they come across a knight bending over a headless lady. They learn that a passing ruffian has not only carried off the knight's mate, but left in her stead a dame whom he beheaded because she pursued him.

Provided with a description of the armour and accoutrements of the ruffian, the iron page sets out in pursuit of him, and stuns him. Then, having bound him fast, he leads him and his captive back to his master and to the mourning knight. Then the ruffian, Sir Sanglier, coldly asserts he has nothing to do with the headless lady, but that the living one belongs to him. Finding it impossible to decide which tells the truth, Sir Artegall decrees that the second lady shall be beheaded also, but, while Sanglier readily agrees to this Solomon-like judgment, the true lover vehemently pleads for the lady's life, declaring he would rather know her safe than be proved right. Fully satisfied now that Sir Sanglier is at fault, Sir Artegall metes out justice and continues his quest.

Before very long he encounters a dwarf who announces that Florimell's wedding will take place three days hence, and suggests that, before appearing there, Sir Artegall defeat a Saracen who mounts guard over a neighbouring bridge, despoiling all those who pass for the benefit of his daughter. Such an undertaking suits Sir Artegall, who not only slays both the giant and his daughter, but razes their castle to the ground. Shortly after, on approaching the sea-shore, Sir Artegall perceives a charlatan provided with scales in which he pretends to weigh all things anew. Thereupon Sir Artegall, by weighing such intangible things as truth and falsehood, right and wrong, demonstrates that the charlatan's scales are false, and, after convicting him of trickery, drowns him in the sea.

The poet now ably describes the wedding of Florimell and Marinell and the tournament celebrated in their honour, which Sir Artegall attends, wearing Braggadocchio's armour as a disguise. He helps Marinell to win the prize which is to be bestowed upon Florimell, but, when the moment comes to award it, Braggadocchio boldly produces the false Florimell, so exactly like the true one that they cannot be told apart. Sir Artegall, however, ruthlessly exposes the trick, whereupon the false Florimell vanishes, leaving nothing behind her save the wrongfully appropriated girdle, which reverts at last to its legitimate owner. Braggadocchio is about to steal away, when Sir Guyon suddenly steps forward, demanding the return of his stolen steed. When Braggadocchio boldly asserts that the steed he rides is his own, Sir Artegall inquires of each what secret tokens the animal bears, and thus enables Sir Guyon to prove ownership.

Sir Artegall, after leaving the marriage hall, journeys to the sea-shore, where he discovers twin brothers quarrelling for the possession of two damsels, one of whom claims ownership to a huge coffer. Artegall checks this fight, and on inquiring into its cause, learns that the twin brothers were awarded neighbouring islands, and that the storms and the sea have carried off half the land of the one and added it to the possessions of the other. Thus, one twin has become richer than the other, and the heiress, who had promised to marry the poorer brother, has transferred her affections and possessions to the richer twin. On her way to join him, however, she suffered shipwreck and arrived at his island penniless. But the chest containing her treasures was in due time washed back to the smaller island, where, in the meantime, the discarded *fiancée* of the richer brother has taken refuge. As the wealthy twin declared, with reference to the land, that what the sea brought he had a right to keep, Sir Artegall decides he shall now abide by his own words, and that, since the sea conveyed the treasure-chest to his brother, he has no further claim upon it. Having thus settled this dispute, Artegall rides on until he meets a troop of Amazons about to hang an unfortunate man. At his bidding, Talus delivers this victim, Sir Turpine, a knight who came hither intending to fight the Amazons. As the Queen of these warrior-women has slain many men, Artegall challenges her to issue from her stronghold and fight with him.

We now have a brilliant description of Radigonde's appearance and of the duel, in which, blinding him by her beauty, she prevails over Artegall. She then triumphantly bears him off to her castle, after ordering the execution of Sir Turpine and Talus, who contrive to escape. But Sir Artegall, now a prisoner, is reduced to slavery, forced to assume a woman's garb and to spin beside his fellow-captives, for the Amazon Queen wishes to starve and humble her captives into submission to her will.

Having made good his escape, Talus informs Britomart that her lover is a prisoner, whereupon she sets out to rescue him, meeting with extraordinary adventures by the way, in which she triumphs, thanks to her magic spear.

While spending a peaceful night in the Temple of Isis, Britomart is favoured with a vision, inspired by which she challenges Radigonde, who in the midst of the encounter turns to flee. But Britomart pursues her into her stronghold, whence she manages to rescue Artegall. Setting him free, she bids him continue his adventurous quest.

Sir Artegall and his faithful squire next espy a maiden fleeing before two knights, but before they can overtake her, they notice that a new-comer slays one pursuer, while the other turns back. Urged by the maiden, Artegall kills the second persecutor, and only then discovers that the knight who first came to her rescue is Arthur. They learn that the maid is a servant of Mercilla (another personification of Elizabeth), and that her mistress is sorely beset by the Soldan, to whose evil wife Adicia she recently sent the maiden to carry a message. Dismissed like a dog by the "proude Dame" Adicia, the poor maid was then pursued by two Saracen knights, who were determined to secure her as a prize. Artegall now proposes to assume the armour of one of the dead knights, and thus disguised to convey the maiden back to the Soldan's court. Arthur is to follow under pretence of ransoming the captive, knowing that his offer will be refused so insolently that he will have an excuse to challenge the Soldan. All this comes to pass, and thanks to his magic shield Arthur triumphs. Adicia, on learning that her husband has succumbed, endeavours to take her revenge by slaying the captive maid, but Artegall defends her and drives the Soldan's wife into the forest, where she is transformed into a tiger.

Arthur and Sir Artegall now gallantly offer to escort the maid home, although she warns them that Guyle lies in wait by the roadside, armed with hooks and a net to catch all travellers who pass his cave. But, thanks to the bravery, strength, and agility of Arthur, Artegall, and Talus, Guyle's might is broken, and the maid triumphantly leads the three victorious champions to Mercilla's castle. After passing through its magnificent halls, they are ushered by Awe and Order into the presence of the Queen, whose transcendent beauty and surroundings are described at length. While the Queen is seated on her throne, with the English lion at her feet, Duessa (Mary Queen of Scots) is brought before her and is proved guilty of countless crimes; but, although she deserves death, Mercilla, too merciful to condemn her, sets her free.

During their sojourn at Mercilla's elegant court, Artegall and Arthur see two youths appear to inform the Queen that their mother Belge, or Belgium, a widow with seventeen sons, has been deprived of twelve of her offspring by a three-headed monster, Gereones (the personification of Philip the Second of Spain, the ruler of three realms). This monster invariably delivers his captives into the hands of the Inquisition, by which they are sorely persecuted. Arthur steps forward, offering to defend the widow and her children. Mercilla grants his request without demur, and Arthur hurries away, only to find that Belge has been driven out of her last stronghold by a faithless steward (Alba). But, thanks to Arthur's efforts, this steward is summoned forth, defeated in battle, and the lady reinstated in her domain.

Gereones now dauntlessly attacks Arthur, whom Belge secretly instructs to overthrow an idol in the neighbouring church, after which he will triumph without difficulty. While Arthur is thus rescuing Belge, Artegall and Talus have again departed to free Irena from her oppressor Grantorto. On their way to Ireland, they meet a knight, who informs them that Irena is doomed to perish unless a champion defeats Grantorto in duel. Thereupon Artegall swears to champion Irena's cause, but, on the way to keep his promise, pauses to rescue a distressed knight (Henry IV. of France), to whom he restores his lady Flourdelis, whom Grantorto is also trying to secure.

Artegall, the champion, reaching the sea-shore, at last finds a ship ready to sail for Ireland, where he lands, although Grantorto has stationed troops along the shore to prevent his doing so. These soldiers are soon scattered by Talus' flail, and Artegall, landing, forces Grantorto to bite the dust. Having thus freed Irena, he replaces her on her throne and restores order in her dominions, before Gloriana summons him back to court.

On the way thither Sir Artegall is beset by the hags Envy and Detraction, who are so angry with him for freeing Irena that they not only attack him themselves, but turn loose upon him the Blatant Beast (Slander). Although Talus would fain annihilate this infamous trio with his dreaded flail, Artegall decrees they shall live, and, heedless of their threats, hurries on to report success to his beloved mistress.

Book VI: The Legend of Sir Calidore, or of Courtesy

Sir Calidore, who, in the poem, impersonates Courtesy (or Sir Philip Sidney), now meets Artegall, and informs him that the Queen has despatched him to track and slay the Blatant Beast—an offspring of Cerberus and Chimera—whose bite inflicts a deadly wound. When Artegall reports having recently met that thousand-tongued monster, Calidore spurs off, and soon falls in with a squire bound to a tree. Pausing to free this captive, he learns that the unfortunate youth has been illtreated by a neighbouring villain, who exacts the hair of every woman and the beard of every man passing his castle, because his lady-love wishes a cloak woven of female hair and adorned with a fringe of beards. It was because the captive had vainly tried to rescue a poor lady from this tribute that he had been bound to this tree. Sir Calidore decides to end such doings for ever, and riding up to the castle pounds on its gates until a servant opens them wide. Forcing his way into the castle, Sir Calidore slays all who oppose him, and thus reaches the villain, with whom he fights until he compels him to surrender and to promise never to exact such tribute again.

Having settled this affair to his satisfaction, Sir Calidore rides on until he meets a youth on foot, bravely fighting a knight on horseback, while a lady anxiously watches the outcome of the fray. Just as Calidore rides up, the youth strikes down his opponent, a deed of violence justified by the maiden, who explains how the man on horseback was illtreating her when the youth came to her rescue. Charmed by this display of courage on the part of an unarmed man, Sir Calidore proposes to take the youth as his squire, and learns that he is Tristram of Lyonnesse, son of a king, and in quest of adventures.

Accompanied by this squire, who now wears the armour of the slain knight, Sir Calidore journeys on, until he comes across a sorely wounded knight, a victim of the very man whom his new squire slew. They convey this wounded man to a neighbouring castle, thereby earning the gratitude of his companion, a lady who mourns over his unconscious form.

The owner of the castle, father of the wounded man, is so grateful to his rescuers that he receives them with kindness. But he cannot account for the presence of the lady, until she explains that his son loved her and often met her in the forest. After nursing her lover until he is out of danger, Priscilla expresses a desire to return home, but is at a loss how to account to her parents for her prolonged absence. Sir Calidore, who volunteers to escort her, suggests that he shall bear to her father the head of the knight whom Tristram slew, stating that this villain was carrying her off when he rescued her. This tale so completely blinds Priscilla's father that he joyfully welcomes his daughter home, expressing great gratitude to her deliverers ere they pass on.

Calidore and his squire have not journeyed far before they perceive a knight and his lady sporting in the shade. So joyful and innocent do they seem that the travellers gladly join them, and, while the men converse together, Lady Serena strays into a neighbouring field to gather flowers. Suddenly the Blatant Beast pounces upon her, and is about to bear her away when her cries startle her companions. They immediately dart to her rescue. Calidore, arriving first, forces the animal to drop poor Serena, then, knowing that her husband will attend to her, continues to pursue the fleeing monster.

On reaching his beloved Serena, Sir Calespine finds her sorely wounded and in need of immediate care. Tenderly placing her on his horse, he supports her fainting form through the forest. During one of their brief halts, he beholds a bear carrying an infant, and rushes after the animal to rescue the child. Only after a prolonged pursuit does he achieve his purpose, and, not knowing how else to dispose of the babe, carries it to a neighbouring castle, where the lady gladly adopts it, because she and her husband have vainly awaited an heir. But Sir Calespine is unable to retrace his steps to his wounded companion, who soon after is found by a gentle savage. This man is trying to take her to some place of safety when he is overtaken by Arthur and Timias, who, seeing Serena in his company, fancy she is his captive. She, however, hastens to assure them that the wild man is more than kind, and relates what has occurred. As Serena and Timias have both been poisoned by the bites of the Blatant Beast, Arthur takes them to a hermit, who undertakes to cure them, but finds the task hopeless.

The learned hermit's healing arts having all proved vain, he finally resorts to prayer, and thus cures his guests, who, when healed, decide to set out together in quest of Sir Calespine and Arthur. The latter has meantime departed with the wild man, hoping to overtake Sir Turpine, who, as we have seen, had escaped from Radigonde. They track the villain to his castle and forcing an entrance, fight with him, sparing his life only because the lady of the castle pleads in his behalf.

Sir Turpine now succeeds in persuading two knights to pursue and attack Sir Arthur, but this hero proves too strong to be overcome, and, after disarming his assailants, demands why they have attacked him. When they reveal Turpine's treachery, Arthur regrets having spared his opponent, and decides that having overcome him once by force he will now resort to strategy. He, therefore, lies down, pretending to be asleep, while one of the knights rides back to report his death to Turpine. This plan is duly carried out, and Sir Turpine, coming to gloat upon his fallen foe, is seized by Arthur, who hangs him to a neighbouring tree.

In the meantime Serena and Timias proceed on

their way until they meet a lady and a fool (Disdain and Scorn), who are compelled by Cupid to wander through the world, rescuing as many people as they have made victims. When the fool attempts to seize Timias, Serena, terrified, flees into the forest.

Before long Sir Arthur manages to overtake his squire, driven by Scorn and Disdain, and immediately frees him. Then, hearing what penalty Cupid has imposed upon the couple, he decides they are sufficiently punished for the wrong they have done and lets them go.

Meanwhile Serena has wandered, until, utterly exhausted, she lies down to rest. While sleeping she is surrounded by savages, who propose to sacrifice her to their god. They are on the point of slaying her when Sir Calepine comes to her rescue, unaware at the moment that the lady whose life he has saved is his beloved wife.

Still pursuing the elusive Blatant Beast, Sir Calidore comes to a place where shepherds are holding a feast in honour of Pastorella, the adopted daughter of the farmer Melibee, and the beloved of young Coridon, a neighbouring shepherd. Coridon fears Sir Calidore will prove a rival for the affections of Pastorella, but Calidore disarms his jealousy by his perfect courtesy, which in time wins Pastorella's love.

One day the lonely Sir Calidore, seeking Pastorella, catches a glimpse of the Graces dancing in the forest to the piping of Colin Clout (a personification of Spenser). Shortly after, Calidore has the good fortune to rescue Pastorella from a tiger, just after Coridon has deserted her through fear.

To reward the bravery of Calidore, who has saved her from death, Pastorella lavishes her smiles upon him, until a brigand raid brings ruin and sorrow into the shepherd village, for the marauders not only carry off the flocks, but drag Pastorella, Coridon, and Melibee off to their underground retreat.

In that hopeless and dark abode the captain of the brigands is beginning to cast lustful glances upon Pastorella, when merchants arrive to purchase their captives as slaves. The captain refuses to part with Pastorella, although he is anxious to sell Coridon and Melibee, but the merchants insist upon having the maid, and seeing that they cannot obtain her by fair means resolve to employ force. The result is a battle, in the midst of which Coridon escapes, Melibee and the brigand captain are slain, and Pastorella faints and is deemed dead.

Sir Calidore, who has been absent for a while, comes back to find the shepherd village destroyed and Coridon wandering disconsolate among its ruins. From him he learns all that has happened, and, going in quest of Pastorella's remains, discovers that she is alive. He then manages by stratagem not only to rescue her, but to slay both merchants and robbers, and to recover the stolen flocks and also much booty. All the wealth thus obtained is bestowed upon Coridon to indemnify him for the loss of Pastorella, who accompanies her true love Calidore during the rest of his journeys.

Being still in quest of the ever fleeing Blatant Beast, Calidore conducts Pastorella to the castle of Belgard, whose master and mistress are passing sad because they lost their only child in its infancy. Wondering how such a loss could have befallen them, Calidore learns that the knight and lady, being secretly married, had entrusted their child to a handmaiden, ordering her to provide for its safety until they could acknowledge its existence. The faithless maid, however, had basely abandoned the child in the forest, where she was found and adopted by Melibee.

During Pastorella's sojourn in this castle the lady discovers on her breast a birth-mark, which proves that she is her long-lost daughter. While Pastorella is thus happy in the company of her parents, Calidore overtakes the Blatant Beast, and leads it safely muzzled through admiring throngs to Gloriana's feet. But, strange to relate, this able queen does not keep the monster securely chained, for it soon breaks its bonds, and the poet closes with the statement that it is again ranging through the country, and tearing even poems to pieces :

> Ne spareth he most learned wits to rate,
> Ne spareth he the gentle Poet's rime ;
> But rends without regard of person or of time.

PARADISE LOST

Book I

After intimating that he intends "no middle flight," but proposes to "justify the ways of God to man," Milton states that the Fall was due to the serpent, who, in revenge for being cast out of Heaven with his hosts, induced the mother of mankind to sin. He tells how, hurled from the ethereal sky to the bottomless pit, Satan lands in a burning lake of asphalt. There, oppressed by the sense of lost happiness and lasting pain, he casts his eyes about him, and, flames making the darkness visible, beholds those enveloped in his doom suffering the same dire pangs. Full of immortal hate, unconquerable will, and a determination never to submit or yield, Satan, confident that his companions will not fail him, determines to continue his struggle with the Almighty for the mastery of Heaven.

Beside Satan, on the burning marl, lies Beelzebub, his bold compeer, who dreads the pursuit of the Almighty and further punishment. But Satan, rejoining that "to be weak is miserable, doing or suffering," urges that they try to pervert God's designs. Then, gazing upward, he perceives that God has recalled His avenging hosts, that the rain of sulphur has ceased, and that lightning no longer furrows the sky. He therefore seizes the opportunity to rise from the burning lake and take measures to redeem their losses.

"Seest thou yon dreary plain, forlorn and wild,
The seat of desolation, void of light,
Save what the glimmering of these livid flames
Casts pale and dreadful? Thither let us tend
From off the tossing of these fiery waves:
There rest, if any rest can harbour there,
And, reassembling our afflicted pow'rs,
Consult how we may henceforth most offend
Our Enemy, our own loss how repair,
How overcome this dire calamity,
What reinforcement we may gain from hope,
If not, what resolution from despair."

Striding through parting flames to a neighbouring hill, Satan gazes around him, contrasting the mournful gloom of this abode with the refulgent light to which he has been accustomed, and, notwithstanding the bitter contrast, concluding, "better to reign in Hell than serve in Heaven," ere he bids Beelzebub call the fallen angels.

Beelzebub summons the legions lying on the asphalt lake, "thick as autumnal leaves that strew the brooks of Vallombrosa." Like sentinels caught sleeping, they hastily arise, and, numerous as the locusts which ravaged Egypt, flutter around the cope of Hell before alighting at their master's feet. Among them Milton describes various deities, later to be worshipped as gods in Palestine, Egypt, and Greece. Then, contrasting the downcast appearance of this host with its brilliancy in heaven, he goes on to tell how they saluted Satan's banner with "a shout that tore Hell's concave, and beyond frighted the reign of Chaos and old Night." Next, their standards fluttering in the breeze, they perform their wonted evolutions, and Satan, seeing so mighty a host still at his disposal, feels his heart distend with pride.

Although he realizes that these spirits have forfeited Heaven to follow him, he experiences merely a passing remorse ; he declares that the strife they waged was not inglorious, and that although defeated they may yet regain possession of their native seat. He suggests that, as they now know the strength of their opponent and realize that they cannot overcome Him by force, they damage the new world which the Almighty has recently created, for submission were unthinkable weakness.

To make their new quarters habitable, the fallen angels, under Mammon's direction, mine gold from the neighbouring hills and mould it into bricks, wherewith they erect Pandemonium, "the high capital of Satan and his peers." This hall, constructed with speed and ease, is brightly illuminated, and, after Satan and his staff have entered, the other fallen angels crowd beneath its roof in the shape of pygmies, and "the great consult" begins.

Book II

On a throne of dazzling splendour sits Satan, surrounded by his peers. Addressing his followers, he declares that, having forfeited the highest position, he has lost more than they, and that, since he suffers the greatest pain, none will envy him his pre-eminence. When he bids them suggest what they shall do, Moloch votes in favour of war, stirring up his companions with a bellicose speech. Belial, who is versed in making "the worse appear the better reason," urges guile instead of warfare, for they have tested the power of the Almighty and know that He can easily outwit their plans. In his turn, Mammon favours neither force nor guile, but suggests that, since riches abound in this region, they content themselves with piling up treasures.

All having been heard, the fallen angels decide, since it is impossible again to face Michael's dreaded sword, that they will adopt Beelzebub's suggestion and try to find out whether they cannot settle more comfortably in the recently created world. Satan next inquires who will undertake to reconnoitre, and, as no one volunteers, he declares that the mission of greatest difficulty and danger rightly belongs to him, bidding the fallen angels meanwhile keep watch lest further ill befall them.

The "consult" ended, the angels resume their wonted size and scatter through Hell, some exploring its recesses, where they discover huge rivers, regions of fire and ice, and hideous monsters, while others beguile their time by arguing on "foreknowledge, will, fate," and other questions of philosophy, or join in antiphonal songs.

Meanwhile Satan has set out on his dreadful journey, wending his way straight to the gates of Hell, before which stand two formidable shapes, one woman down to the waist and thence scaly dragon, while the other, a grim, skeleton-like shape, wears a royal crown and brandishes a spear. Seeing Satan approach, this monster threatens him, whereupon a dire fight would ensue, did not the female step between them, declaring that she is Sin, Satan's daughter, and that in an incestuous union they two engendered Death, whom even they cannot subdue. She adds that she dare not unlock the gates, but, when Satan urges that if she will only let him pass, she and Death will be supplied with congenial occupation in the new world, she produces a key, and flings wide the massive doors which no infernal power can ever close again. Through these gaping portals may be descried Chaos, where hot and cold, moist and dry contend for mastery, and where Satan will have to make his way through the elements in confusion to reach the place whither he is bound.

The poet now graphically describes how, on the wing or on foot, Satan scales high battlements and plunges down deep abysses, thus gradually working his way to the place where Chaos and Night sit enthroned, contemplating the world which hangs from Heaven by a golden chain. Addressing these deities, Satan commiserates them for having lost both Tartarus, now the abode of the fallen angels, and the region of light occupied by the new world. When he proposes to restore to them that part of their realm by frustrating God's plans, they gladly speed him toward earth, whither " full fraught with mischievous revenge, accursed, and in a cursèd hour he hies."

Book III

After a pathetic invocation to light, the offspring of Heaven, whose rays will never shine through *his* darkness, Milton expresses a hope that, like other blind poets and seers, he may describe all the more clearly what is ever before his intellectual sight. Then he relates how the Eternal Father, gazing downward, contemplates Hell, the newly-created world, and the wide cleft between, where He descries Satan hovering "in the dun air sublime." Summoning His hosts, the Almighty addresses His Only Begotten Son—whose arrival in Heaven has caused Satan's rebellion—and, pointing out the Adversary, declares that he is bent on revenge which will redound on his own head. Then God adds that, whilst the angels fell by their own suggestion, and are hence excluded from all hope of redemption, man, on the other hand, will fall deceived by Satan, so that, although he will thus incur death, he will not forever be unforgiven if some one will pay the penalty of his sin. Because none of the angels feel holy enough to make so great a sacrifice, "silence was in Heaven," until the Son of God, "in whom the fullness dwells of love divine," seeing that man will be lost unless He intervenes, declares His willingness to surrender to death all of Himself that can die. He entreats, however, that the Father will not leave Him in the loathsome grave, but will permit His soul to rise victorious, leading to Heaven those ransomed from sin, death, and Hell through His devotion. The angels, on hearing this proposal, are filled with admiration, and the Father, bending a loving glance upon the Son, accepts His sacrifice, proclaiming that He shall in due time appear on earth in the flesh to take the place of our first father, and that, as in Adam all were lost, so in Him all shall be saved. Then, further to recompense His Son for His devotion, God promises that He shall reign His equal for ever and judge mankind, ere He bids the heavenly host worship their new Master. Removing their crowns of amaranth and gold, the angels kneel before Christ in adoration, and, tuning their harps, sing the praises of Father and Son, proclaiming the latter " Saviour of men."

While the angels are thus occupied, Satan, speed ing through Chaos, passes through a place peopled by the idolatries, superstitions, and vanities of the world, all of which are doomed to be punished here later on. Then, past the stairway leading up to Heaven, he hurries to a passage leading down to earth, toward which he whirls through space, landing at last upon the sun. There, in the guise of a stripling cherub, Satan tells the archangel Uriel that, having been absent at the time of the creation, he longs to behold the earth and to glorify God. Uriel proudly rejoins that he witnessed the performance, and describes how at God's voice darkness fled and solids converged into spheres, which began to roll in their appointed orbits. Then he points out to Satan the newly-created earth, whither the Evil Spirit eagerly speeds.

> Thus said, he turned, and Satan, bowing low,
> As to superior Spirits is wont in Heav'n,
> Where honour due and reverence none neglects,
> Took leave, and toward the coast of Earth beneath,
> Down from th' Ecliptic, sped with hoped success,
> Throws his steep flight in many an aery wheel,
> Nor stayed till on Niphates' top he lights.

Book IV

Wishing his voice were loud enough to warn our first parents of coming woe and thus forestall the misfortunes ready to befall them, the poet describes how Satan, with hell raging in his heart, gazes from the hill, upon which he has alighted, into Paradise. The fact that he is outcast both from Heaven and earth fills Satan with alternate sorrow and fierce wrath, and under the impulse of these emotions his features become fearfully distorted. These changes and his fierce gestures are seen by Uriel, who curiously follows his flight, and who now for the first time suspects that he may have escaped from Hell.

After describing the wonders of Eden and giving free rein to his poetic fancy, Milton relates how Satan, springing over the dividing wall, alights within its precincts, and in the guise of a cormorant perches upon a tree, whence he beholds two God-like shapes "clad in naked majesty." One of these is Adam, formed for contemplation and valour, the other Eve, formed for softness and grace. They sit beneath a tree, the beasts of the earth playing peacefully around them, and Satan, watching them, wonders whether they are destined to occupy his former place in Heaven, and vows he will ruin their present happiness and deliver them up to woe! After arguing that he must do so to secure a better abode for himself and his followers, the fiend transforms himself first into one beast and then into another, and, having approached the pair unnoticed, listens to their conversation. He learns Eve's wonder on first opening her eyes and gazing around her on the flowers and trees, her amazement at her own reflection in the water, her obedience to a voice which promised to lead her to her counterpart, who would make her mother of the human race. But, the figure which she thus found proving less attractive than the one she had just seen in the waters,

The Garden of Eden
John Martin

she was about to retreat, when Adam claimed her as the other half of his being. Since then, the twain have dwelt in bliss in this garden, where all things are at their disposal save the fruit of one tree. Thus Satan discovers the prohibition laid upon our first parents. He immediately decides to bring about their ruin by inciting them to scorn the divine command, assuring them that the knowledge of good and evil will make them equal to God, and having devised this means of compassing his purpose, he steals away to elaborate his plans.

Meantime, near the eastern gate of Paradise, Gabriel, chief of the angelic host, watches the joyful evolutions of the guards who at nightfall issue forth to patrol the boundaries of Paradise. While he is thus engaged, Uriel comes gliding down through the evening air on a sunbeam, to warn him that one of the banished host has escaped, and was seen at noon near these gates. Gabriel assures Uriel that no creature of any kind has passed through them, and that if an evil spirit has overleapt the earthly bounds he will be discovered before morning, no matter what shape he has assumed. While Uriel returns to his post in the sun, grey twilight steals over the earth, and Gabriel, having appointed bands of angels to circle Paradise in opposite directions, dispatches two of his lieutenants to search for the hidden foe.

Our first parents, after uniting in prayer, are about to retire, when Eve, who derives all her information from Adam, asks why the stars shine at night, when they are asleep and cannot enjoy them? In reply Adam states that the stars gem the sky to prevent darkness from resuming its sway, and assures his wife that while they sleep angels mount guard, for he has often heard their voices at midnight. Then the pair enter the bower selected for their abode by the sovereign planter, a spot where the loveliest flowers bloom in profusion, and where no bird, beast, insect, or worm dare venture.

In the course of their search, the angels Ithuriel and Zephon reach this place in time to behold a toad crouching by the ear of Eve, trying by devilish arts to reach the organs of her fancy. Touched by Ithuriel's spear—which has the power of compelling all substances to assume their real form—this vile creature instantly assumes a demon shape. On recognizing a fiend, Ithuriel demands how he escaped and why he is here. Whereupon Satan haughtily rejoins that the time was when none would have dared treat him so unceremoniously, nor would have needed to ask his name. Zephon recognizes their former superior, Lucifer, and gazes sadly on his tarnished glory. Both angels now escort their captive to Gabriel, who, recognizing the prisoner from afar, also comments on his faded splendour. Then, addressing Satan, Gabriel demands why he has broken his prescribed bonds? Satan defiantly retorts that prisoners invariably try to escape, that no one courts torture, and that, if God meant to keep the fiends for ever in durance vile, He should have barred the gates more securely. But, even by escaping from Tartarus, Satan cannot evade his punishment, and Gabriel warns him that he has probably increased his penalty sevenfold by his disobedience. Then he tauntingly inquires whether pain is less intolerable to the archfiend's subordinates than to himself, and whether he has already deserted his followers. Wrathfully Satan boasts that, fiercest in battle, he alone had courage enough to undertake this journey to ascertain whether it were possible to secure a pleasanter place of abode. As in the course of his reply he contradicts himself, the angel terms him a liar and hypocrite, and bids him depart, vowing that should he ever be found lurking near Paradise again, he will be dragged back to the infernal pit and bound in chains lest he escape again! This threat arouses Satan's scorn and makes him so insolent, that the angels, turning fiery red, close around him, threatening him with their spears! Glancing upward and perceiving by the position of the heavenly scales that the issue of a combat would not be in his favour, Satan wrathfully flees with the vanishing shades of night.

Book V

Morning having dawned, Adam awakens refreshed, only to notice the flushed cheeks and discomposed tresses of his companion, from whom, when he awakens her, he learns of a dream wherein a voice urged her to go forth and walk in the garden. Eve goes on to describe how, gliding beneath the trees, she came to the one bearing the forbidden fruit, and descried among its branches a winged shape, which bade her taste of the apples and not despise the boon of knowledge. Although chilled with horror at the mere suggestion, Eve admits that she yielded, because the voice assured her that one taste would enable her to wing her way through the air like the angels and perchance visit God! Her desire to enjoy such a privilege became so intense that when the fruit was pressed to her lips she tasted it, and had no sooner done so than she soared upward, only to sink down and awaken at Adam's touch!

Comforting his distressed consort, Adam leads her into the garden to prune over-luxuriant branches and to train vines from tree to tree. While they are thus occupied, the Almighty summons Raphael, and, after informing him that Satan has escaped from Hell and has found his way to Paradise to disturb the felicity of man, bids the archangel hasten down to earth; there, conversing "as friend with friend" with Adam, he shall warn him that he has the power to retain or forfeit his happy state, and shall caution him against the wiles of the fiend, lest, after wilfully transgressing, man should protest that he had not been forewarned.

Past choirs of angels, through the golden gate, and down the mighty stairs, Raphael flits, reaching earth in the shape of a six-winged cherub, whose iridescent plumes seem to have been dipped in heaven's own dyes. On beholding this visitor, Adam bids Eve collect her choicest fruit, and, while she hastens away "on hospitable thoughts intent," he advances to meet Raphael, knowing that the latter brings some divine message. After hailing Eve with the salutation later addressed to Mary, the angel proceeds to Adam's lodge and shares his meal, admitting that in Heaven the angels partake of spiritual food only, although they are endowed with senses like man.

On discovering that he may question Raphael—save in regard to matters which are to be withheld for a while longer—Adam asks for information regarding things which have troubled him. Inferring from the angel's words that their bliss is not secure, he learns that as long as he proves obedient his happiness will continue, but that, having been created as free as the angels, he must choose his lot.

Adam next asks to be told about Heaven, and Raphael considers how he shall relate, in terms intelligible to a finite mind, things which even angels fail to conceive in their entirety, and which it may not be lawful to reveal. Still, knowing that he can vouchsafe a brief outline of all that has hitherto occurred, Raphael describes how the Almighty, after creating the Son, bade the angels bow down and worship Him. He states that, during the night following this event, Lucifer, angry because he was no longer second in Heaven, withdrew to that quarter of the sky entrusted to his keeping, and there suggested to Beelzebub rebellion against God, who required them to pay servile tribute to His Son! Arguing that they would be gradually reduced to slavery, Satan induced one-third of the heavenly hosts to rebel, for only one of his followers, Abdiel, refused to believe his specious words. In his indignation, Abdiel burst forth into flame, denounced Lucifer, and departed to report to the Almighty what he had heard. He alone proved faithful among the faithless, and as he passed out from among them, the rebel angels, resenting his attitude, overwhelmed him with their scorn.

> From amidst them forth he passed,
> Long way through hostile scorn, which he sustained
> Superior, nor of violence feared aught;
> And with retorted scorn his back he turned
> On those proud towers to swift destruction doomed.

The Almighty, however, did not require Abdiel's warning, for the all-seeing eye had already descried what had occurred, and had pointed out to the Son how Lucifer, devoured by pride, was about to rise up against them.

Book VI

In spite of the speed with which he travels, Abdiel requires all night to cross the distance which separates the apostate angels from the heavenly throne. The news he bears being already known in Heaven, the angels joyfully welcome him and conduct him to the throne, whence, from a golden cloud, issues a voice proclaiming "Well done." Next God bids Michael lead forth a host equal in number to those who are arraying themselves in battle, and who would dispute with the Almighty the sovereignty of Heaven. Michael is ordered to oppose Lucifer and to hurl him into the gulf of Tartarus, whose fiery mouth will open wide to receive him. A moment later trumpets sound in Heaven, and the angelic legions sally forth to battle for God and for His Messiah. The evil angels, whose glory has not yet been dimmed, meet this host in squadrons, at the head of which rides Lucifer (or Satan as he is generally called after he becomes an apostate), in his sun-bright chariot. On beholding him, Abdiel marvels because he still retains a God-like semblance, and warns him that he will soon pay the penalty of his folly. In return Satan terms Abdiel a common deserter, and overwhelms him with scorn, to which this angel pays little heed, realizing that by serving a divine Master he enjoys more freedom than independent Satan.

After exchanging Homeric taunts, they begin the fight, and Abdiel's first dart causes the arch-enemy to recoil and almost sink to the ground. But, when the divine host clamour that Satan is overcome, he promptly recovers his footing, and, retreating into the ranks of his army, directs their resistance to the foe. The battle now rages with such fury that the heavens resound. Many deeds of eternal fame are wrought, for Satan proves almost equal to Michael, who with his two-handed sword strikes down whole squadrons at one blow. But wounds inflicted on angels are no sooner made than healed, and those who sink down disabled are soon back in the thick of the fight. The moment comes, however, when Michael's sword inflicts so deep a wound in Satan's side that, for the first time, he experiences pain. Seeing him fall, his adherents bear him away from the field of battle. He is soon healed, " for spirits, that live throughout vital in every part, . . . cannot but by annihilation die," but Michael, thus temporarily deprived of his greatest opponent, attacks Moloch, while Uriel, Raphael, and Abdiel vanquish other potent angels who have dared to rebel against God.

After describing the battle-field, strewn with shattered armour and broken chariots, Raphael pictures the dismay in the ranks of the rebel angels, and describes how Satan drew away his troops so that they might rest and be ready to renew the fray on the morrow. In the silence of that night, he also consults with his adherents how to fight to better advantage on the morrow, strong in the knowledge that they can never be permanently wounded. The demons feel confident that, granted better arms, they could secure the advantage, so, when one of their number suggests the manufacture of cannon, all gladly welcome the idea. Under Satan's direction some of the evil angels draw from the ground metal, which, molten and poured into moulds, furnishes the engines of destruction they are seeking. Meanwhile others collect ingredients for ammunition, and, when morning dawns, they have a number of weapons ready for use, which they cunningly conceal in the centre of their fourfold phalanx as they advance.

In the midst of the second encounter, Satan's squadrons suddenly draw aside to let these cannons belch forth the destruction with which they are charged, an unexpected broadside which fells the good angels in thousands; but, although hosts of them are thus laid low, others spring forward to take their place. On seeing the havoc wrought by their guns, Satan and his host openly rejoice; but the good angels, perceiving that weapons are useless against this artillery, throw them away, and, picking up the hills, hurl them at their opponents, whom they bury beneath the weight of mountains. In fact, had not the Almighty checked this outburst of righteous anger, the fiends would doubtless have been buried so deep they never would have reappeared!

On the third day the Almighty proclaims that, as both forces are equal in strength, the fighting will never end unless He interferes. He therefore summons His Only Begotten Son to wield the thunderbolts, the weapons of God alone. Ever ready to do His Father's will, the Son accepts, mounts a chariot borne by four cherubs, and sets forth, attended by 20,000 saints, who wish to witness His triumph. On seeing Him approach, the good angels exult, while the wicked are seized with terror, although they disdain to flee. Bidding the angelic host watch Him triumph single-handed over the foe, the Son of God changes His benignant expression into one of wrath, and hurls His thunderbolts to such purpose that the rebels long for the mountains to cover them as on the previous day. With these divine weapons Christ ruthlessly drives Satan and his hosts out of the confines of Heaven, over the edge of the abyss, and hurls them down into the bottomless pit, sending after them peal after peal of thunder, together with dazzling flashes of lightning, but mercifully withholding His deadly bolts, as He purposes not to annihilate the rebels, but merely to drive them out of Heaven. Thus, with an "unsufferable noise" which the poet graphically describes, Satan and his host fall through space and land nine days later in the fiery lake! After pursuing the foe far enough to make sure that they will not return, the Messiah re-enters Heaven in triumph, greeted by saints and angels with hymns of praise.

This account of the war in Heaven concluded, Raphael informs Adam that Satan, leader of these fallen angels, envying his happy state, is now plotting to seduce him from his allegiance to God, and thus compel him to share his eternal misery.

> "But listen not to his temptations; warn
> Thy weaker; let it profit thee to have heard,
> By terrible example, the reward
> Of disobedience. Firm they might have stood,
> Yet fell. Remember, and fear to transgress."

Book VII

At Adam's request Raphael next tells how the earth was created; he explains that, as Satan had seduced one-third of the inhabitants of Heaven. God decided to create a new race, whence angels could be recruited to repeople His realm. In terms simple enough to make himself understood, Raphael relates how the Son of God, passing through the heavenly gates and viewing the immeasurable abyss, decided to evolve from it a thing of beauty. He adds that the Creator made use of the divine compasses, "prepared in God's eternal store," to circumscribe the universe, thus setting its bounds at equal distance from its centre. Then His spirit, brooding over the abyss, permeated Chaos with vital warmth, until its various components sought their appointed places, and earth " self-balanced on her centre hung." Next the light evolved from the deep began to travel from east to west, and " God saw the Light was good."

On the second day God created the firmament, on the third separated water from dry land, and on the fourth covered the earth with plants and trees, each bearing seed to propagate its kind. Then came the creation of the sun, moon, and stars to rule day and night and divide light from darkness, and on the fifth day the creation of the birds and fishes, whom God bade multiply until they filled the earth. Only on the sixth and last day did God call into life cattle and creeping things, which issued out of the earth full-grown and perfect-limbed. Then, as there was still wanting a creature endowed with reason to rule the rest, God created man in His own image, fashioning him from clay and breathing life into his nostrils. After thus creating Adam and his consort Eve, God blessed them both, bidding them be fruitful, multiply and fill the earth, and hold dominion over every living thing upon it. Having placed creatures so richly endowed in Paradise, God left them free to enjoy all that it contained, save the fruit of the tree of knowledge of good and evil, in regard to which He warned them " in the day thou eatest thou diest." Then, His work finished, the Creator returned to Heaven, where He and the angels spent the seventh day resting from their work.

Book VIII

Not daring to intrude upon the conversation of Adam and Raphael, Eve waits at a distance, knowing that her husband will tell her all she need learn.

Meanwhile, further to satisfy his curiosity, Adam inquires how the sun and stars move so quietly in their orbit. Raphael rejoins that, although the heavens are the book of God, wherein man can read His wondrous works, it is difficult to make anyone understand the distances separating the various orbs. To give Adam some idea of them, Raphael declares that he—whose motions are not slow—set out from Heaven at early morn and arrived at Eden only at midday. Then he describes the three rotations to which our earth is subject, names the six planets, and assures Adam that God holds them all in His hand and prescribes their paths and speed.

In his turn, Adam entertains Raphael with an account of his amazement when he awoke on a flowery hillside, and gazed upon the sky, the woods, and the streams ; his gradual acquaintance with his own person and powers, the naming of the animals, and his awe when the divine Master led him into Paradise and warned him not to touch the central tree. After describing his loneliness on discovering that all living creatures went about in pairs, Adam tells how, after he had complained to the Creator, a deep sleep fell upon him, during which a rib was removed from his side from which to fashion Eve. Joined by the Creator Himself to this bone of his bone and flesh of his flesh, Adam dwells fondly on his nuptial bliss, and artlessly inquires whether angels marry and are given in marriage. Raphael rejoins that in Heaven love so refines the thoughts and enlarges the heart, that none save spiritual communion is necessary to secure perfect bliss. Then, seeing the sun about to set, the angel takes leave of Adam and wends his way back to Heaven, while the father of mankind rejoins his waiting wife.

Book IX

The poet warns us that there will be no more conversation between man and angels; his song must now change to a tragic note, because vile distrust has entered Paradise. He describes how Satan, driven away from Eden by Gabriel, circles around the earth seven days and nights without rest, and at the end of that time re-enters Paradise by an underground river and in the guise of a mist. Then, perched as a bird upon the tree of knowledge of good and evil, Satan decides to approach our first parents in the guise of a loathsome serpent and to seek his revenge, although fully aware that the consequences will recoil upon himself. Finding a serpent asleep, Satan enters its body and creeps along the paths of Paradise, hoping to find Adam and Eve apart, for he deems it will be easier to work on one at a time.

Morning having come, Adam and Eve awake, and after their usual song of praise set out to attend the garden. But Eve insists that when they are together they allow themselves to be distracted from their labours, and proposes that they should work independently until the noon hour brings them together to share their simple repast. Although reluctant to be parted from his beloved, Adam at length yields to her pleading. Thus, the serpent, ranging through the garden, perceives Eve alone among the roses, and rejoices that he can make his first attempt upon the one whom he rightly deems the weaker vessel. Although not without compunction, he wends his way toward her and startles her by addressing her in a human voice. When she inquires how it happens that a beast can communicate with her, the serpent rejoins that, although at first speechless like other beasts, he no sooner tasted a certain fruit than he was gifted with greater knowledge than he had yet enjoyed, and endowed with the power of speech. Thinking that this fruit might have equally beneficial effects upon her and make her more nearly equal to her consort, Eve longs to partake of it also, and readily follows her guide to the centre of the garden. But, when the serpent points out the forbidden tree, Eve shrinks back, until the tempter assures her that God's prohibition was not intended to be obeyed. He argues that, although he has tasted the fruit, he continues to live—nay, more, has obtained new faculties —and thus induces Eve to pluck and eat the fruit. As it touches her lips, nature gives " signs of woe," and the guilty serpent slinks back into the thicket, leaving Eve to feast upon the fruit, the taste of which affords her keener delight than she had ever experienced. She promises to care for the tree, and then wonders whether Adam will perceive any difference in her, and whether it will be wise to tell him the happiness that she has tasted. Although at first doubtful, Eve, fearing lest death should part her from Adam, determines to induce him to share this food too, for she loves Adam too dearly to live or die without him.

> " Confirmed then I resolve
> Adam shall share with me in bliss or woe.
> So dear I love him, that with him all deaths
> I could endure, without him live no life."

Eve therefore hastens to Adam, and volubly explains that the tree is not what God depicted, for the serpent, having tasted of its fruit, has been endowed with eloquence so persuasive that he has induced her to taste it also. Horror-stricken, for he realizes that his wife is lost, Adam asks himself how he will exist without her, and is amazed that she should have yielded to the very first onslaught of their foe. But after a first outburst of grief, he vows that he will share her doom and die with her. He then accepts the fruit which she tenders, and nature again shudders, for Adam, although not deceived, yields to temptation because of his love for Eve. No sooner have both fed upon the tree than its effects become patent, for it kindles within them the never-before-experienced sense of lust. The couple therefore emerge on the morrow from their bower, their innocence lost, and overwhelmed, for the first time in their lives, by a crushing sense of shame. In his new knowledge of good and evil, Adam reproaches his wife, wailing that never more shall they behold the face of God, and he suggests that they weave leaf-garments to hide their nakedness. So the first couple steal into the thicket to fashion fig-leaf girdles, which they bind about them, reviling each other for having forfeited their former happy estate.

Book X

Meanwhile, Eve's fall has been reported in Heaven by the angelic guards, whom the Almighty reassures, for He knew that the Evil Spirit would succeed and that man would fall. He then decrees that, as man has transgressed, his sentence shall be pronounced, and that the one best fitted for such a task is the Son, man's Mediator. Ready to do His Father's will in Heaven as upon earth, the Son departs, promising to temper justice with mercy, so that God's goodness will be made manifest, and adding that the doom of the absent Satan shall also be pronounced.

Escorted to the gates of Heaven by the angelic host, the Redeemer descends alone to earth, where

He arrives in the garden in the cool of the evening. At His summons Adam and Eve emerge from their hiding-place, and Adam shamefacedly explains that they hid because they were naked. His very words convict him of guilt, and his Master inquires whether they have eaten of the forbidden fruit. Unable to deny his transgression, Adam confesses " in evil strait this day I stand before my Judge," for he must either accuse himself wrongfully or lay the guilt upon the wife whom it is his duty to protect. When he adds that the woman gave him the fruit whereof he did eat, the Judge sternly demands whether Adam was bound to obey his consort, reminding him that woman was made subject to man, and declaring that by yielding to Eve's persuasions he incurred equal guilt. Then turning to the woman, the Judge demands what she had done, and Eve, abashed, confesses that the serpent beguiled her until she ate. Having thus heard both culprits, the Judge pronounces sentence upon the serpent in veiled terms, for, as yet, man is not to understand what is divinely planned. Then, having disposed of the arch-enemy, he predicts that Eve will bring forth her children in suffering and will be subject to her husband's will, ere He informs Adam that henceforth he will have to earn his bread by the sweat of his brow, for the earth will no longer bear fruit for him without labour. Having thus pronounced His judgment, the Judge postpones the penalty of death indefinitely, and taking pity upon our first parents, clothes them in the skins of beasts, to enable them to bear the harsher air to which they are soon to be exposed.

Meanwhile Sin and Death peer forth through Hell's open gateway, hoping to catch some glimpse of returning Satan. Weary of waiting, Sin finally suggests to Death the folly of remaining idle, since Satan cannot but succeed, and proposes that they follow him over the abyss, building as they go a road to facilitate intercourse hereafter between Hell and earth. This proposal is approved by Death, whose keen nostrils already descry the smell of mortal change, and who longs to reach earth and prey upon all living creatures. These two terrible shapes, therefore, venture out through the waste, and fashion of stone and asphalt a broad highway from the gates of Hell to the confines of the newly-created world. "With pins of adamant and chains they made all fast—too fast they made, and durable."

They have barely finished this causeway when Satan—still in the likeness of an angel—comes flying toward them, for after seducing Eve he has lurked in the garden until from a safe hiding-place he heard the threefold sentence pronounced by the Judge. He too does not grasp his doom, but, realizing that humanity is in his power, is hastening back to Hades to make the joyful fact known. On encountering Sin and Death, Satan congratulates them upon their engineering skill and sends them on to work their will in the world, while he speeds along the path they have made to tell the fallen angels all that has occurred. In obedience to his orders a number of these are mounting guard, but Satan, in the guise of a ministering spirit, passes through their midst unheeded, and only after entering Pandemonium allows his native majesty to shine forth. On becoming aware that he is once more present, the demons welcome him with a mighty shout. By an impressive gesture Satan imposes silence, and describes his journey, his success, and the ease with which they can pass to and fro now that Sin and Death have paved their way. To satisfy their curiosity he relates by what means he tempted woman, and, although he admits that he was cursed as well as the fallen, does not appear dismayed. Raising their voices to applaud him, his adherents are now surprised to hear themselves hiss, and to discover they have all been transformed into serpents. Then Satan himself, in the form of a dragon, guides them to a grove near by, where they climb the trees to feed on apples of Sodom, "fruitage fair to sight," whose bitter ashes offend their taste, a performance to be renewed yearly on the anniversary of the temptation.

Meanwhile, Sin and Death having entered Paradise —where they are not yet allowed to touch human beings—lay low herbs, fruit, flowers, and beasts, all of which are now their legitimate prey. Pointing out their ravages, the Almighty explains that, had man not disobeyed, these despoilers would never have preyed upon the newly-created world, where they are now to have full sway until the Son hurls them back into Hades. The angels praise the ways of the Almighty, which are ever just, and laud His Son as the destined restorer of mankind. The Almighty now directs that the sun shall move so as to subject the earth to alternate cold and heat, thus making winter follow summer. The planets, too, are to shed malignant influences upon the earth, whose axle is slightly turned, while violent winds cause devastation, and enmity is kindled between creatures which have hitherto lived in peace. Adam, on perceiving these changes, becomes conscious that they are the effect of his transgression, and is plunged in such grief that God's order to increase and multiply seems horrible. He murmurs aloud, but, after a while, realizing that he was left free to choose between good and evil, he acknowledges the justice of his punishment. The fact that God does not immediately visit upon him the penalty he has incurred does not, however, comfort him, because he longs for death to end his sorrows. On seeing her husband's grief, Eve now offers to go in quest of their Judge, imploring Him to visit upon her alone the penalty of sin. Her readiness to sacrifice herself touches Adam, who replies that, since they are one, they must share what awaits them. When Eve shrinks from bearing children foredoomed to woe and death, Adam reminds her that it is only through repentance and obedience that they can appease their Judge.

Book XI

In this state of humility and repentance, our first parents are viewed compassionately by the Redeemer, who, gathering up their prayers, presents them to the Father as the first-fruits which have sprung from His mercy.

> " See, Father, what first-fruits on Earth are sprung
> From Thy implanted grace in Man—these sighs
> And prayers, which in this golden censer, mixed
> With incense, I, Thy priest, before Thee bring,
> Fruits of more pleasing savour, from Thy seed
> Sown with contrition in his heart, than those
> Which, his own hand manuring, all the trees
> Of Paradise could have produced, ere fallen
> From innocence."

In reply to the touching intercession of this advocate, the heavenly Father promises that the culprits shall be forgiven, provided their repentance is sincere, but insists that in the meantime they be ejected from Paradise. Michael and the cherubs chosen for this office are instructed to mount guard day and night, lest the fiend return to Paradise, or the human pair re-enter and partake of the tree of life and thus escape the penalty of death. But, before driving out our first parents, Michael is to reveal to Adam all that awaits his race in the future, emphasizing the promise that salvation shall come through his seed. These orders received, the archangel wends his way down to earth, where, dawn having appeared, Adam and Eve once more issue from their bower.

Night has brought some comfort, and Adam exclaims that, since the penalty of death is to be postponed, they must show their penitence by labouring hard, working henceforth side by side as contentedly as their fallen state will allow. On the way to the scene of their wonted labours, they notice an eagle pursuing another bird, and see wild beasts hunting one another. While Adam seeks to interpret these ominous signs, he descries a bright light travelling rapidly toward them, and informs Eve that some message is on its way. He is not mistaken, for Michael soon emerges from this cloud of light; bidding Eve retire, Adam steps forward to receive him.

Clad in celestial panoply, the angel announces that he has been sent to inform Adam that, although the penalty of death is indefinitely postponed, he shall no longer inhabit Paradise, but must go forth into the world and till the ground from which he sprang. Horror-stricken at these tidings, Adam remains mute, and Eve, "who unseen yet all had heard," wails aloud at the thought of leaving Paradise. The angel bids her dry her tears and follow her husband, making her home wherever he abides. Then Adam wonders whether by incessant prayer and penitence he can induce the Almighty to alter His decree and let them remain in Paradise, for he had hoped to point out to his descendants the places where he met and conversed with his Maker. Michael rejoins that he will find God everywhere, and invites Adam to follow him to the top of a neighbouring hill. He has meanwhile enveloped Eve in slumbers, which will hold her entranced while he reveals to Adam the earth's kingdoms and their glory.

> "Know I am sent
> To show thee what shall come in future days
> To thee and to thy offspring. Good with bad
> Expect to hear, supernal Grace contending
> With sinfulness of men—thereby to learn
> True patience, and to temper joy with fear
> And pious sorrow, equally inured
> By moderation either state to bear,
> Prosperous or adverse: so shalt thou lead
> Safest thy life, and best prepared endure
> Thy mortal passage when it comes. Ascend
> This hill; let Eve (for I have drenched her eyes)
> Here sleep below while thou to foresight wakest,
> As once thou slept'st, while she to life was formed."

From a hill in Paradise, after instilling into Adam's eyes three drops of water from the well of life, Michael vouchsafes him a glimpse of all that is to take place upon our earth. Thus, Cain and Abel first pass before their father's eyes, but death is so unintelligible to Adam that the angel has to explain what it means. Overwhelmed at the thought that so awful a thing has come into the world through his transgression, Adam is further horrified when the angel reveals all the suffering which will visit mankind, explaining that, since much of it will be due to evil living, it behoves Adam to observe temperance in food and drink. But he warns him that, in spite of all precautions, old age will come upon him as a precursor of death. In a panorama Adam sees all that is to occur until the Deluge, and, watching Noah construct the ark, wails because his progeny is to be destroyed by the Flood. The angel, however, demonstrates that the righteous will be saved, and that from them will descend a race more willing to obey God's commands. The dove and the rainbow, therefore, instil comfort into Adam's heart, as does God's promise that day and night, seed-time and harvest, shall hold their course until new heavens and earth appear wherein the just shall dwell.

Book XII

Having depicted a world destroyed and foreshadowed a world restored, the angel shows Adam how man will migrate to a plain, where by means of bricks and bitumen an attempt will be made to erect a tower to reach Heaven. When Adam expresses displeasure that one of his race should defy God, Michael assures him that he rightly abhors disobedience, and comforts him by revealing how one righteous man, in whose seed all nations shall be blessed, is to be brought out of that country into the Promised Land.

The angel names Abraham, and depicts his life, the captivity in Egypt, the exodus, and the forty years in the desert. He also vouchsafes to Adam a glimpse of Moses on Mount Sinai receiving the tables of the law, and appointing the worship which the Chosen People are to offer to their Creator. When Adam wonders at the number of laws, Michael rejoins that sin has many faces, and that, until blood more precious than that of the prescribed sacrifices has been shed, no suitable atonement can be made.

After describing how under the Judges and then under the Kings the people of Israel will continue their career, the angel designates David as the ancestor of the Messiah, whose coming will be heralded by a star which will serve as guide to Eastern sages. He adds that this Messiah will descend from the Most High by a virgin mother, that His reign will extend over all the earth, and that, by bruising the serpent's head, He will conquer Sin and Death. This promise fills Adam's heart with joy, because it partly explains the mysterious prophecy, but, when he inquires how the serpent can wound such a victor's heel, Michael rejoins that, in order to overcome Satan, the Messiah will incur the penalty of death, revealing how, after living hated and blasphemed, He will prove by His death and resurrection that Sin and Death have no lasting power over those who believe in His name. Full of joy at the promise that the Messiah will lead all ransomed souls to a happier Paradise than the one which he has forfeited, Adam declares that since such good is to proceed from the evil he has done, his repentance will be the less bitter.

Between the death of Christ and His second coming, the angel adds that the Comforter will dwell upon earth with those who love their Redeemer, helping them to resist the onslaughts of Satan, and that in spite of temptation many righteous will ultimately reach heaven, to take the place of the outcast angels.

"Till the day
Appear of respiration to the just
And vengeance to the wicked, at return
Of Him so lately promised to thy aid,
The Woman's Seed, obscurely then foretold,

> Now amplier known thy Saviour and thy Lord;
> Last in the clouds from Heaven to be revealed
> In glory of the Father, to dissolve
> Satan with his perverted World, then raise
> From the conflagrant mass, purged and refined,
> New Heavens, new Earth, Ages of endless date
> Founded in righteousness and peace and love,
> To bring forth fruits, joy, and eternal bliss."

The angel bids Adam not to seek to know any more, enjoining upon him to add deeds to knowledge, to cultivate patience, temperance, and love, and promising, if he obeys, that Paradise will reign in his heart. Then, pointing out that the guards placed around Eden are waving their flashing swords and that it is time to awaken Eve, he bids Adam gradually impart to her all that he has learned. When they rejoin Eve, she tells how God sent her a dream which has soothed her heart and filled it with hope, making her realize that, although she has sinned and is unworthy, through her "the Promised Seed shall all restore."

Then the angel takes Adam and Eve by the hand and leads them out by the eastern gate into the world. Gazing backward, our first parents catch their last glimpse of Paradise and behold at the gate the angel with a flaming sword. Thus, hand in hand, dropping "some natural tears," they pass out into the world to select their place of rest, having Providence only for their guide.

PARADISE REGAINED

Having sung of Paradise Lost, Milton proposes as theme for a new epic *Paradise Regained.* In it he purposes to sing of "deeds above heroic, though in secret done," and to describe how Christ was led into the wilderness to be tempted by Satan.

Book I

While baptizing in the Jordan, John suddenly beheld Christ approaching, and, although he at first demurred, yielded at last to His request to baptize Him too, whereupon a heavenly voice proclaimed Christ the Son of God. This voice was heard not only by John and his disciples, but also by the Adversary, who, ever since the Fall, had been roaming around the world, and who for years past has been closely watching the promised Redeemer in hope of defeating His ends.

Suddenly realizing that the conflict between them is about to begin, Satan hastens back to hell to take counsel with his crew. When all are assembled, he reminds them how long they have ruled the earth, adding that the time has come when their power may be wrested from them, and the curse spoken in Eden fulfilled. He fears Jesus is the promised Messiah, and points to His miraculous birth, to the testimony of the precursor, John, and to the heavenly proclamation when He was baptized. Besides, Satan has recognized in Christ's lineaments the imprint of the Father's glory, and he avers that, unless they can defeat the Son, they will forfeit all they have gained. Realizing, however, that this task is far greater than the one which he undertook centuries before—when he winged his way through chaos to discover the new world and tempt our first parents—he volunteers to undertake it in person, and all the evil spirits applaud him. This settled, Satan departs to carry out the second temptation.

Meantime another assembly has been held in

Heaven, where, addressing the archangel Gabriel, the Almighty informs him that he will soon see the fulfilment of the message which he bore some thirty years previously to Mary. He adds that His Son, whom He has publicly recognized, is about to be tempted by Satan, who, although he failed in the case of Job, is undertaking this new task confident of success. The Almighty also predicts that Satan will again be defeated, but declares that Christ is as free to yield or resist as Adam when first created, and that before sending Him out to encounter Sin and Death He means to strengthen Him by a sojourn in the desert. On hearing that Satan's evil plans will be frustrated, the angels burst into a hymn of triumph with which Heaven resounds.

> So spake the eternal Father, and all heaven
> Admiring stood a space; then into hymns
> Burst forth, and in celestial measures mov'd,
> Circling the throne and singing, while the hand
> Sung with the voice, and this the argument:
> "Victory and triumph to the Son of God,
> Now ent'ring His great duel, not of arms,
> But to vanquish by wisdom hellish wiles!
> The Father knows the Son; therefore secure
> Ventures His filial virtue, though untried,
> Against whate'er may tempt, whate'er seduce,
> Allure, or terrify, or undermine.
> Be frustrate, all ye stratagems of hell,
> And, devilish machinations, come to nought."

During this time the Son of God, after lingering three days by the Jordan, is driven by the Holy Spirit into the wilderness, where He spends His time meditating upon the great office He has undertaken as Saviour of mankind. In a grand soliloquy we hear how since early youth He has been urged onward by divine and philosophical influences, and how, realizing that He was born to further truth, He has diligently studied the law of God. Thus, ere yet His age " had measured twice six years," our Lord could measure His learning with that of the rabbis in the temple. Ever since that time He has longed to end brutality, to further all that is good, and to win all hearts to God. He recalls the stories His mother told Him in regard to the Annunciation, to His virgin birth, and to the Star of Bethlehem, and comments upon the fact that the Baptist immediately knew Him and that a voice from Heaven hailed him as the Son of God!

Although Christ realizes that He has been sent into the wilderness by divine power, and that His future way lies " through many a hard assay " and may lead even to death, He does not repine. Instead He spends the forty days in the wilderness fasting, preparing Himself for the great work which He is called upon to accomplish, and paying no heed to the wild beasts which prowl around Him without doing Him any harm.

It is only when, after forty days' fast, Christ is weak with hunger, that Satan approaches Him in the guise of an old peasant, pathetically describing the difficulty of maintaining life in the wilderness. Then he adds that he saw Jesus baptized in the Jordan, and begs Him, if He is the Son of God, to turn the stones around Him into food, thereby relieving Himself and His wretched fellow-sufferer from the pangs of hunger.

Jesus, however, merely reproaches the tempter, rejoining, " Man lives not by bread only, but by each word proceeding from the mouth of God," and explaining that He knows Satan for what he is. Unable to conceal his identity any longer, the evil spirit admits that he has come straight from Hell, but adds that God gave him power to test Job and to punish Ahab. He argues that the Almighty, who fed the Israelites with manna and supplied Elijah with miraculous food, does not intend to starve His only Son. Then Satan explains that he is not the foe of men, since through them he gained what he has gained, and has often helped them by oracles and omens. In spite of these arguments, Jesus refuses to listen to him, and announces that He is sent to execute His Father's will.

> "God hath now sent His living Oracle
> Into the world to teach His final will,
> And sends His Spirit of Truth henceforth to dwell
> In pious hearts, an inward oracle
> To all truth requisite for men to know."

Thus baffled, Satan vanishes "into thin air diffused," and night steals over the desert, where fowls seek their nests, while the wild beasts "come forth the woods to roam."

Book II

John the Baptist and his disciples, made anxious by Jesus' long absence, now begin to seek Him as the prophets sought Elijah, fearing lest He too may have been wafted up to Heaven. Hearing Simon and Andrew wonder whither He has gone and what He is doing, Mary relates the extraordinary circumstances which accompanied her Son's birth, mentioning the flight into Egypt, the return to Nazareth, and other occurrences during the youth of our Lord. She declares that, ever since Gabriel's message fell upon her ear, she has tried to prepare herself for the fulfilment of a promise then made to her, and has often wondered what Simeon meant when he cried that a sword would pierce her very soul! Yet she recalls how, when her Son was twelve years of age, she grieved over His loss, until she found Him in the temple, when He excused Himself by stating that He must be about His Father's business. Ever since then Mary has patiently awaited what is to come to pass, realizing that the child she bore is destined to great things.

> Thus Mary, pond'ring oft, and oft to mind
> Recalling what remarkably had passed
> Since first her salutation heard, with thoughts
> Meekly composed awaited the fulfilling.

Satan, having hastened back to the infernal regions, reports the ill success of his first venture, and the effect which his first temptation had upon our Lord. Feeling at a loss how to proceed, he invites the demons to assist him with their counsel, warning them this task will prove far more difficult than that of leading Adam astray. Belial, the most dissolute spirit in Hell, then proposes that Satan tempt Jesus with women, averring that the female sex possesses so many wiles that even Solomon, wisest of kings, succumbed. But Satan scornfully rejects this proposal, declaring that He whom they propose thus to tempt is far wiser than Solomon and has a much more exalted mind. Although certain that Christ will prove impervious to the bait of the senses, Satan surmises that, owing to a prolonged fast, He may be susceptible to the temptation of hunger, so, taking a select band of spirits, He returns to the desert to renew his attempts in a different form.

Transferring us again to the solitude, the poet describes how our Saviour passed the night dreaming of Elijah fed by the ravens and of Daniel staying his hunger with pulse. Awakened at last by the song of the larks, our Lord rises from His couch on the hard ground, and, entering a fertile valley, encounters Satan, who, superbly dressed, expresses surprise that He should receive no aid in the wilderness when Hagar, the Israelites, and Elijah were all fed by divine intervention. Then Satan exhibits the wonderful banquet he has prepared, inviting Christ to partake of it; but the Son of God quietly replies that He can obtain food whenever He wishes, and hence need not accept what He knows is offered with evil intent. Seeing that our Lord cannot be assailed on the ground of hunger, Satan causes the banquet to vanish, but remains to tempt Christ with an offer of riches, artfully setting forth the power that can be acquired by their means. He adds that, since Christ's mind is set on high designs, he will require greater wealth than stands at the disposal of the Son of Joseph the carpenter. But, although Satan offers to bestow vast treasures upon him, Christ rejects this proffer also, describing what noble deeds have been achieved by poor men such as Gideon, Jephtha, and David, as well as by certain Romans. He adds that riches often mislead their possessor, and so eloquently describes the drawbacks of wealth that Satan realizes the uselessness of pursuing this attempt.

Book III

Again complimenting Christ on His wisdom, Satan rehearses the great deeds performed by Philip of Macedon and by Julius Caesar, who began their glorious careers earlier in life than He. Then, hoping to kindle in Jesus' heart a passion for worldly glory, Satan artfully relates that Caesar wept because he had lived so long without distinguishing himself; but our Lord quietly demonstrates the futility of earthly fame, compared to real glory, which is won only through religious patience and virtuous striving, such as was practised by Job and Socrates. When Christ repeats that He is not seeking His own glory, but that of the Father who sent Him, Satan reminds Him that God is surrounded with splendour, and that it behoves His Son to strive to be like Him. But Jesus rejoins that, while glory is the essential attribute of the Creator, no one else has a right to aspire to it.

Undeterred by these checks, Satan changes his theme, and reminds Christ that, as a descendant of David, He is not only entitled to the throne, but is expected to free Judea from Roman oppression. He states that the holy temple has been defiled, that injustice has been committed, and urges that even the Maccabees resorted to arms to free their country. Christ rejoins that no such mission has been appointed for Him, and adds:

> "Who best
> Can suffer best can do; best reign, who first
> Well hath obeyed; just trial, ere I merit
> My exaltation without change or end."

Then, turning upon His interlocutor, Christ inquires why he is so anxious to promote the one whose rise will entail his fall? To which Satan replies that, having no hope, it little behoves him to obstruct the plans of Christ, from whose benevolence alone he expects some mitigation of his punishment. Then, feigning to believe that Christ has refused his offers simply because He has only seen Jerusalem and the towns of Galilee, Satan conveys Him in the twinkling of an eye to the summit of a mountain, whence, pointing eastward, he shows Him all the great kingdoms of Asia. He reveals the glories of Assyria, Babylonia, and Persia—of whose histories he gives a brief *résumé*—before pointing out a large Parthian army setting out to war against the Scythians, for he hopes by this martial display to convince Christ that, in order to obtain a kingdom, He must resort to military force. Then he adds that he can easily enlist the services of this army, with which Christ can drive the Romans out of Judea, and triumphantly reign over the land of His ancestors, whence His glory will extend far and wide, until it far surpasses all that Rome and Caesar achieved. Jesus, however, demonstrates the vanity of all military efforts, declaring that His time has not yet come, but assuring him that He will not be found wanting when the moment comes for Him to ascend the throne, for He hopes to prove an able ruler.

Then He reminds Satan how he tempted David to take a census against God's wish, and led Israel astray, until the Ten Tribes were taken into captivity in punishment for their idolatry. He also comments upon Satan's extraordinary anxiety to restore the very people whose foe he has always been, as he has proved time and again by leading them into idolatry, adding that God may yet restore them to their liberty and to their native land. These arguments silence even Satan, for such is ever the result when " with truth falsehood contends."

Book IV

With all the persistency of his kind, Satan refuses to acknowledge himself beaten, and, leading Christ to the western side of the mountain, reveals to Him all the splendour of Rome, exhibiting its Capitol, Tarpeian Rock, triumphal arches, and the great roads along which hosts are journeying to the Eternal City. After thus dazzling him, Satan suggests that Christ oust Tiberius (who has no son) from the imperial throne, and make Himself master not only of the realm of David, but of the whole Roman Empire, establishing law and order where vice now reigns.

Although Satan eagerly proffers his aid to accomplish all this, our Lord rejoins that such a position has no attraction for Him, adding that, as long as the Romans were frugal, mild, and temperate, they were happy, but that, when they became avaricious and brutal, they forfeited their happiness. He adds that He has not been sent to free the Romans, but that, when His season comes to sit on David's throne, His rule will spread over the whole world and will dwell there without end.

> " Know, therefore, when My season comes to sit
> On David's throne, it shall be like a tree
> Spreading and overshadowing all the earth,
> Or as a stone, that shall to pieces dash
> All monarchies besides throughout the world;
> And of My kingdom there shall be no end:
> Means there shall be to this, but what the means,
> Is not for thee to know, nor Me to tell."

Pretending that Christ's reluctance is due to the fact that He shrinks from the exertions necessary to obtain this boon, Satan offers to bestow it freely upon Him, provided He will fall down and worship him. Christ rebukes the tempter, saying, " Thou shalt worship the Lord thy God, and only Him shalt serve," and reviling him for his ingratitude. Satan then proposes to make Him famous through wisdom, and exhibits Athens—that celebrated centre of ancient learning—offering to make Him master of all its schools of philosophy, oratory, and poetry, and thus afford Him ample intellectual gratification. But Jesus rejects this offer also, after proving the vanity and insufficiency of heathen philosophy and learning, and after demonstrating that many books are a weariness to the flesh, and that none compare with those which are the proudest boast of God's Chosen People.

> "However, many books,
> Wise men have said, are wearisome: who reads
> Incessantly, and to his reading brings not
> A spirit and judgment equal or superior
> (And what he brings, what needs he elsewhere seek?),
> Uncertain and unsettled still remains,
> Deep versed in books and shallow in himself,
> Crude or intoxicate, collecting toys
> And trifles for choice matters, worth a sponge,
> As children gathering pebbles on the shore."

Irritated by the failure of all his attempts, Satan next taunts his opponent by describing the sufferings and humiliations which He will have to undergo, until, seeing this too has no effect, he suddenly bears Him back to the wilderness, where he leaves Him for the night, during which he sends a terrific storm to appal Him. Even in sleep Jesus is haunted by dreams and spectres sent by the tempter, but at dawn all these visions disappear, the storm dies down, and a lovely morning greets Him when He awakes.

Once more Satan appears to warn our Lord that the dreams of the night and the horrors of the tempest were foreshadowings of what He will have to undergo. In spite of this, Christ assures him he is toiling in vain; whereupon, swollen with rage, Satan confesses that ever since he heard Gabriel's announcement to the shepherds in regard to Christ's birth, he has watched Him, hoping to get some hold upon Him during His infancy, youth, or early manhood. He now inquires whether Christ is really his destined foe, and reluctantly admits that he has failed in all his endeavours to tempt Him. But one last test still remains, for Satan suddenly conveys Christ to the topmost pinnacle of the Temple of Jerusalem, bidding Him demonstrate His divinity by fearlessly casting Himself down, "For it is written, 'He will give command concerning Thee to His angels.'"

Not only does our Lord reprove the tempter, but so calmly manifests His divine power by standing erect on this dangerous point, that Satan—like all other defeated monsters, such as the Sphinx—falls howling down into the infernal regions. At the same time angels convey our Lord to a lovely valley, where they minister unto Him with celestial food and celebrate His victory with a triumphal hymn, for the Son of God has successfully resisted the tempter, before whom Adam succumbed, and has thereby saved man from the penalty of his sin.

Henceforth Satan will never again dare set foot in Paradise, where Adam and his chosen descendants shall dwell secure, while the Son of Man completes the work He has been sent to do.

> Thus they the Son of God, our Saviour meek,
> Sung victor, and, from heavenly feast refreshed,
> Brought on His way with joy. He, unobserved,
> Home to His mother's house private returned.

GERMAN EPICS

GERMAN literature begins after the great migrations (*circa* 600), and its earliest examples are traditional songs of an epic character, like the *Hildebrandslied.* Owing to diversities of race and speech, there are in southern and northern Germany various epic cycles which cluster around such heroes as Ermanrich the Goth, Dietrich von Bern, Theodoric the East Goth, Attila the Hun, Gunther the Burgundian, Otfried the Langobardian, and Siegfried—perchance a Frisian, or, as some authorities claim, the famous Arminius who triumphed over the Romans.

The *Hildebrandslied* relates how Hildebrand, after spending thirty years in Hungary, returns to North Italy, leaving behind him a wife and an infant son Hadubrand. A false rumour of Hildebrand's death reaches Hungary, where Hadubrand has achieved great renown as a warrior; so, when in quest of adventure the young man meets his father, he deems him an impostor and fights with him. . . . At this point the poem breaks off, leaving us uncertain whether the father or son was victorious. But later poets, such as Kasper von der Rhön, give the story a happy ending, thus avoiding the tragic note struck in the case of Sorab and Rustem (p. 515).

There existed so many of these ancient epic songs that Charlemagne undertook to collect them, but Louis I, his all too pious son, destroyed this collection on his accession to the throne, because these epics glorified the pagan gods which his ancestors had worshipped!

Still not all the Teutonic epics are of pagan origin,

for in the second period we find such works as Visions of Judgment (*Muspilli*), lives of saints, and biblical narratives like *Heiland* (the Saviour), *Judith*, the *Exodus*, *Der Krist* by Otfried, and monkish-political works like the *Ludwigslied*, or history of the invasion of the Normans. There is also the *Waltharslied*, or *Lay of Walter of Aquitaine*, which, although written in Latin, shows many traces of its German origin. The *Waltharslied* is an epic of the Burgundian-Hunnish cycle, written by Ekkehard of St. Gall before 973. It relates the escape of Walter of Aquitaine and his betrothed Hildegund from the court of Attila, where the young man was detained as a hostage. After describing their preparations for flight, and their method of travel and camping, the poet relates how they are overtaken in the Vosges Mountains by a force led by Gunther and Hagen, who wish to secure the treasures they are carrying. Warned in time by Hildegund—who keeps watch while he sleeps—Walter dons his armour, and single-handed disposes of many foes. When Gunther, Hagen, and Walter alone survive, although sorely disabled, peace is concluded, and the lovers resume their journey and safely reach Aquitaine, where they reign happily for thirty years.

In the third period "the crusades revived the epic memories of Charlemagne and Roland and of the triumphs of Alexander," thus giving birth to a *Rolandslied* and an *Alexanderlied*, as well as to endless chivalric epics, or romances in verse and prose.

The *Rolandslied* relates the marriage and banishment of Charlemagne's sister Bertha, the birth of Roland, the manner in which he exacted tribute from his playmates to procure clothes, his first appearance in his uncle's palace, his bold seizure of meat and drink from the royal table to satisfy his mother's needs, Charlemagne's forgiveness of his sister for the sake of her spirited boy, the episode regarding the giant warrior in the Ardennes, the fight with Oliver, the ambush at Roncevaux, and ends with Roland's death and the punishment of the traitor Ganelon. But later legends claim that Roland, recovering from the wounds received at Roncevaux, returned to Germany and to his *fiancée* Aude, who, deeming him dead, had meantime taken the veil. We next have Roland's sorrow, the construction of his hermitage at Rolandseck, whence he continually overlooks the island of Nonnenwörth and the convent where his beloved is wearing her life away in prayers for his soul. This cycle concludes with Roland's death and burial on this very spot, his face still turned toward the grave where his beloved rests.

In the Langobardian cycle[1] stands out the tale of *Rother*, supposed to be Charlemagne's grandfather. We are told of the abduction by Rother of the Emperor's daughter, of her recovery by her father, and of Rother's pursuit and final reconquest of his wife. The next epic in the cycle, *Ortnit*, related the marriage of this king to a heathen princess, her father's gift of dragon's eggs, and the hatching of these monsters, which ultimately cause the death of Ortnit and infest Teutonic lands with their progeny. Then come the legends of Hug-Dietrich and Wolf-Dietrich, which continue the Langobardian cycle and pursue the adventures of Ortnit to his death.

The legend of *Herzog Ernst* is still popular, and relates how a Duke of Bavaria once made a pilgrim-

[1] See the author's *Myths and Legends of the Middle Ages.*

age to Jerusalem and lived through endless thrilling adventures on the way.

The greatest of all the German epics is undoubtedly the *Nibelungenlied*, which is often termed the *Iliad* of Germany, while *Gudrun* is considered its *Odyssey*. This latter folk epic relates how Hagan, son of a king, was carried off at seven years of age by a griffin. But, before the monster or its young could devour him, the sturdy child effected his escape into the wilderness, where he grew up with chance-found companions. Rescued finally by a passing ship, these young people are threatened with slavery, but spared so sad a fate thanks to Hagan's courage. Hagan now returns home, becomes king, and begets a child, whose daughter, Gudrun, is carried away from her father and her lover by a Prince of Zealand. On his way home, the kidnapper is overtaken by his pursuers, and wages a terrible battle on the Wülpensand, wherein he proves victorious. But the kidnapper cannot induce Gudrun to accept his attentions, although he tries hard to win her love. His mother, exasperated by this resistance, finally undertakes to subdue Gudrun by dint of hardships, and even sends her out barefoot in the snow to wash the household linen. While thus engaged, Gudrun and her faithful companion are discovered by the brother and the lover of the Princess; these young men arrange the dramatic rescue of the damsels, whom they marry.[1]

Next in order come the philosophic epics of Wolfram von Eschenbach, including the immortal *Parzifal*—which has inspired both Tennyson and Wagner—and the poetic tales of Gottfried of Strassburg, whose *Tristan und Isolde*, though unfinished, is a fine

[1] Detailed accounts of *Gudrun* and others of these subordinate epics can be found in the author's *Myths and Legends of the Middle Ages*.

piece of work. Hartmann von der Aue is author of *Erek*[1] *und Enide*, of *Der arme Heinrich*—which served as a foundation for Longfellow's *Golden Legend*—and of *Iwein* or *The Knight with the Lion.*

Among the Minnesingers of greatest note are Walther von der Vogelweide, and Wolfram von Eschenbach. Their favourite themes were court epics, dealing especially with the legends of Arthur, of the Holy Grail, and of Karl der Grosse. Many of these epics are embodied in the *Heldenbuch*, or Book of Heroes, compiled in the fifteenth century by Kaspar von der Rhön, while the *Abenteuerbuch* contains many of these legends as well as *Der Rosengarten* and *König Laurin.*

In the second part of the thirteenth century artificiality and vulgarity began to preponderate, provoking as counterweights didactic works such as *Der Krieg auf der Wartburg.*

The fourteenth century saw the rise of the free cities, literary guilds, and five universities. It also marks the cultivation of political satire in such works as *Reinecke Fuchs*, and of narrative prose chronicles like the *Lüneburger*, *Alsatian*, *and Thuringian Chronicles*, which are sometimes termed prose epics. The *Volksbücher* also date from this time, and have preserved for us many tales which would otherwise have been lost, such as the legends of the *Wandering Jew* and *Dr Faustus.*

The age of Reformation proved too serious for poets to indulge in any epics save new versions of *Reinecke Fuchs* and *Der Froschmeuseler*, and after the Thirty Years' War the first poem of this class really worthy of mention is Klopstock's *Messias*, an epic in twenty books on the life and mission of

[1] 'Erek' is the German, 'Erec' the French, name for Geraint.

Christ and the fulfilment of the task for which He was foreordained.

Contemporary with Klopstock are many noted writers, who distinguished themselves in what is known as the classic period of German literature. This begins with Goethe's return from Italy, when he, with Schiller's aid, formed a classical school of literature in Germany.

While Schiller has given us the immortal epic drama *William Tell*, Goethe produced the idyllic epic *Hermann und Dorothea*, the dramatic epic *Faust*, and an inimitable version of the animal epic *Reinecke Fuchs*.

Wieland also was a prolific writer in many fields; inspired by the *Arabian Nights*, Shakespeare's *Midsummer Night's Dream*, and *Huon de Bordeaux*,[1] he composed an allegorical epic entitled *Oberon*, wherein "picture after picture is unfolded to his readers," and which has since served as a theme for musicians and painters.

Since Goethe's day Wagner has made the greatest and most picturesque use of the old German epic material, for the themes of nearly all his operas are drawn from this source.

THE NIBELUNGENLIED[2]

The *Nibelungenlied*, or 'Song of the Nibelungs,' was written about the beginning of the thirteenth century, although it relates events dating back to the sixth or seventh. Some authorities assert that it consists of twenty songs of various dates and origin, others that it is the work of a single author. The latter ascribe the poem to Conrad von Kürenberg, Wolfram von Eschenbach, Heinrich von Ofter-

[1] See *Myths and Legends of the Middle Ages*. [2] *Ibid.*

dingen, or Walther von der Vogelweide. The poem is divided into thirty-nine 'adventures,' and contains 2459 stanzas of four lines each. The action covers a period of about thirty years, and is based on materials taken from the Frankish, Burgundian, Austro-Gothic, and Hunnish saga cycles.

Dietrich von Bern, one of the characters, is supposed to be Theodoric of Italy, while Etzel has been identified with Attila the Hun, and Gunther with a King of the Burgundians who was destroyed with all his followers by the Huns in 436.

First Adventure

Three Burgundian princes dwell at Worms on the Rhine, where, at the time when the poem opens, their sister Kriemhild is favoured by a vision wherein two eagles pursue a falcon and tear it to pieces when it seeks refuge on her breast.

A dream was dreamt by Kriemhild the virtuous and the gay,
How a wild young falcon she train'd for many a day,
Till two fierce eagles tore it; to her there could not be
In all the world such sorrow as this perforce to see.[1]

Knowing her mother skilled at interpreting dreams, Kriemhild inquires what this means, and learns that her future spouse will be attacked by grim foes. This note of tragedy, heard already in the very beginning of the poem, is repeated at intervals until it seems like the reiterated tolling of a funeral bell.

Second Adventure

The poem now transfers us to Xanten on the Rhine, where King Siegmund and his wife hold a tournament for the coming of age of their only son Siegfried, who

[1] All the quotations are from Lettsom's translation.

distinguishes himself greatly and on whose behalf his mother lavishes rich gifts upon all present.

> The gorgeous feast it lasted till the seventh day was o'er;
> Siegelind the wealthy did as they did of yore;
> She won for valiant Siegfried the hearts of young and old
> When for his sake among them she shower'd the ruddy gold.

Third Adventure

Hearing of the beauty of Kriemhild, Siegfried decides to go and woo her, taking with him only a troop of eleven men. His arrival at Worms causes a sensation, and Hagen of Tronje—a cousin of King Gunther—informs his master that this visitor once distinguished himself by slaying a dragon, and that he is the owner of the vast Nibelungen hoard. This treasure once belonged to two brothers, who implored Siegfried to divide it between them, a task which he undertook in exchange for the sword—Balmung—which lay on top of the heap of gold. But no sooner had he made the division than the brothers mortally wounded each other and died on their heaps of gold, leaving their treasure to Siegfried, who thus became the richest man in the world.

On hearing the new-comer announce that he has come to challenge Gunther to a duel, the Burgundians are dismayed, but they soon succeed in disarming their guest, and finally persuade him to remain with them a year, entertaining him with games and tournaments, in which Siegfried distinguished himself greatly, to the satisfaction of Kriemhild, who witnesses his prowess through a latticed window.

Fourth Adventure

Toward the end of Siegfried's visit, it is reported that the Kings of Saxony and Denmark are

Siegfried captures the King of Denmark 402

Willy Pogany

advancing with 4000 men. The dismay of the Burgundians is such that Siegfried proposes to go forth and overpower the enemy with a force of merely 1000 men. Only too glad to accept this offer, Gunther allows Siegfried to depart, and is overjoyed when the young hero comes back with two prisoner monarchs in his train. The messenger who announces Siegfried's triumph is richly rewarded by Kriemhild, who flushes with pleasure on hearing the praise bestowed upon her hero.

Fifth Adventure

After describing the tournament held at Worms in honour of this victory, the poet tells us how Siegfried and Kriemhild met there face to face, and how they fell in love with each other at first sight.

> Now went she forth, the loveliest, as forth the morning goes
> From misty clouds out-beaming; then all his weary woes
> Left him, in heart who bore her, and so, long time, had done.
> He saw there stately standing the fair, the peerless one.

Siegfried now came forward as a suitor for Kriemhild's hand, a proposal which Gunther was glad to accept in his sister's name.

Sixth Adventure

He bargained, however, that before Siegfried claimed his bride he should go with him to Isenland, and help him win Brunhild, the loveliest woman in the world. Gunther needs Siegfried's help in his wooing, because Brunhild has vowed to marry only the man who can throw a spear and a stone farther than she, and surpass her in jumping. Siegfried vainly tries to dissuade Gunther, and, when he decides to accompany him in his quest, suggests that Hagen and another knight form their train. Kriemhild provides the travellers with suitable garments, made by her own hands, and the four embark on a small vessel, in which they sail down the Rhine and out to sea, reaching Isenland twelve days later. As they near this land, Siegfried strictly charges his companions to tell every one he is Gunther's vassal, and acts as if such were indeed his real station.

Seventh Adventure

Gazing out of her window, Brunhild perceives the approaching ship, and, recognizing within it Siegfried—who visited her realm once before—her heart beats with joy at the thought that he has come to woo her. She is, however, amazed to see him hold Gunther's stirrup when they land, and to learn that it is the King of Burgundy who sues for her hand. In her disappointment Brunhild grimly warns the new-comer that, unless he prove successful, he and his men must die.

> "He must cast the stone beyond me, and after it must leap,
> Then with me shoot the javelin; too quick a pace you keep;
> Stop and awhile consider, and reckon well the cost,"
> The warrioress made answer, "ere life and fame be lost."

Undeterred by this threat, Gunther volunteers to undergo the test, but he quails when he sees the heavy spear which Brunhild brandishes, and when he perceives that twelve men stagger beneath the weight she proposes to throw. He is, however, somewhat reassured when Siegfried whispers he need but go through the motions, while his friend, concealed by the Tarncappe—the cloak of invisibility which endows the wearer with the strength of twelve men—will perform the required feats in his behalf.

Said he, "Off with the buckler and give it me to bear,
Now, what I shall advise thee, mark with thy closest care.
Be it thine to make the gestures, and mine the work to do."
Glad man was then King Gunther, when he his helpmate knew.

In the first test Brunhild casts a spear with such force that both Gunther and his invisible companion stagger and nearly fall, but, just as she is about to cry victory, Siegfried sends back the spear butt-end foremost and brings her to her knees. Veiling her dismay at this first defeat, Brunhild hurls the stone to a great distance and lands beside it with a flying leap. In Gunther's place the invisible Siegfried hurls the same stone much farther than Brunhild, and seizing Gunther by his belt jumps with him to the spot where it alighted. Having thus been outdone, Brunhild no longer refuses her hand to Gunther, who appears triumphant, although his prospective bride looks strangely solemn and angry.

Eighth Adventure

As Brunhild summons to her castle a large number of warriors, under pretext of celebrating her nuptials, Siegfried sails off unseen to the land of the Nibelungs, where he batters at his castle gate demanding admittance. The wary dwarf guardian of the Nibelung hoard refuses to admit him, but Siegfried fights him, and after conquering him compels him to recognize his authority. Then he bids a thousand Nibelung warriors accompany him back to Isenland, and Brunhild, seeing this force approaching and learning from Gunther that it is part of his suite, no longer dares to resist.

Ninth Adventure

The fair bride, escorted by all these men, now sails across the sea and up the Rhine. As they near

Burgundy, Gunther decides to send word of their arrival, and persuades Siegfried to act as his messenger, assuring him that he will earn Kriemhild's gratitude.

> Said he, "Nay, gentle Siegfried, do but this journey take,
> Not for my sake only, but for my sister's sake.
> You'll oblige fair Kriemhild in this as well as me."
> When so implor'd was Siegfried, ready at once was he.

Tenth Adventure

Siegfried receives the fair lady's hearty thanks, and acts as her escort when she hastens down to the bank to welcome her brother and his bride. The poem then describes the kissing, speeches, and grand tournament held to welcome Brunhild, as well as the banquet during which Siegfried publicly reminds Gunther that he promised him Kriemhild's hand as soon as Brunhild was won. Gunther then sends for his sister, although his new wife openly wonders that he should bestow her hand upon a mere vassal. Silencing his bride's objections, Gunther confers Kriemhild's hand upon Siegfried, and thus two bridal couples sit side by side at the evening meal.

The hour having come for retiring, Gunther, attempting to embrace his bride, is dismayed to find himself seized, bound fast, and hung up on a peg, where he dangles all night in spite of piteous entreaties to be set free. It is only a moment before the servants enter on the morrow that Brunhild consents to release her spouse, and when the bridegrooms appear in public, everybody notices that while Siegfried is radiant, Gunther's brow is clouded by a heavy frown. In the course of the day, the King of Burgundy confides to his new brother-in-law the cause of his displeasure, whereupon Siegfried promises to don his cloud cloak that evening and compel Gunther's bride to treat her husband henceforth with due respect. True to this promise, Siegfried, unseen, follows Gunther and Brunhild into their apartment, and, the lights having been extinguished, wrestles with the bride until she acknowledges herself beaten. She believes she is yielding to Gunther, but it is Siegfried who snatches her girdle and ring before leaving Gunther to reap the benefit of his victory, for Brunhild, having submitted to a man, loses her miraculous strength. Meanwhile Siegfried returns to Kriemhild, imprudently relates how he has been occupied, and bestows upon her the girdle and ring.

Eleventh Adventure

The wedding festivities finished, Siegfried returns to Xanten with his bride, who is escorted thither by her faithful henchman Ekkewart, who has vowed to follow her wherever she goes. Siegfried's parents not only receive the bride cordially, but relinquish their throne to the young couple, who live together most happily and are overjoyed at the advent of a son.

Twelfth Adventure

Ten whole years elapse ere Brunhild asks Gunther why his vassal Siegfried has never yet come to Worms to do homage? Although Gunther now assures his wife that Siegfried is a king in his own right, she nevertheless insists that her brother-in-law and his wife should be invited to Worms, a suggestion which Gunther is only too glad to carry out.

Thirteenth Adventure

Overjoyed at the prospect of revisiting the scene of their courtship, Siegfried and Kriemhild return to Worms, leaving their infant son at home, but taking with them Siegfried's father, Siegmund, who has recently lost his wife. To honour her sister-in-law, Brunhild welcomes Kriemhild with the same state that heralded her own entrance at Worms. Banquets and tournaments also take place, whereat the two queens try to outshine each other. One day, while sitting together extolling their husbands' virtues, a quarrel arises, during which Brunhild curtly informs Kriemhild that her husband can scarcely be as great as she pretends, seeing that he is merely Gunther's vassal!

Fourteenth Adventure

Of course Kriemhild hotly denies this, and, when Brunhild insists, declares she will prove her husband's superiority by claiming precedence at the church door. In wrathful mood, both ladies deck themselves magnificently and arrive simultaneously to attend mass, escorted by imposing trains. Seeing Kriemhild make a motion as if to enter first, Brunhild bids her pause, and the two ladies begin an exchange of uncomplimentary remarks. In the heat of the quarrel Kriemhild insinuates that Brunhild granted Siegfried bridal favours, and in proof thereof exhibits Brunhild's girdle and ring! Brunhild immediately sends for Gunther, who, helpless between two angry women, summons Siegfried. Bluntly declaring that wives should be kept in order, Siegfried undertakes to discipline Kriemhild, provided Gunther will reduce Brunhild to subjection, and publicly swears that he never approached the Burgundian queen in any unseemly way. In spite of this public apology, Brunhild refuses to be comforted, and, as her husband utterly refuses to take active measures to avenge her, she finally prevails upon his kinsman Hagen to take up her quarrel. Under the mistaken impression that she has been grievously wronged by Siegfried, Hagen urges Gunther to attack his brother-in-law, until the weak king yields to the pressure thus brought to bear by his angry wife and kinsman.

> None urged the matter further, except that Hagen still
> Kept ever prompting Gunther the guiltless blood to spill;
> Saying, that, if Siegfried perish'd, his death to him would bring
> The sway o'er many a kingdom. Sore mourn'd the wavering king.

Fifteenth Adventure

A cunning plan is now devised by Hagen, whereby Siegfried is informed that the monarchs he once conquered have again risen up in rebellion. Of course Siegfried volunteers to subdue them once more, and Kriemhild, hearing that he is about to start for war, expresses great anxiety for his safety. Under pretext of sympathy, Hagen inquires why Kriemhild feels any dread, seeing that the dragon's blood had rendered him invulnerable, and learns that Siegfried can be injured in a spot between his shoulders, because a lime-leaf, sticking fast there, prevented the blood from touching that spot.

> " So now I'll tell the secret, dear friend, alone to thee
> (For thou, I doubt not, cousin, will keep thy faith with me),
> Where sword may pierce my darling, and death sit on the thrust,
> See, in thy truth and honour how full, how firm my trust ! "

Under pretext of protecting this vulnerable point, Hagen persuades Kriemhild to embroider a cross on her husband's garment over the fatal spot. Then, sure now of triumphing over this dreaded foe, he feigns that the kings have sent word they will submit, and proposes that instead of fighting they all go hunting in the Odenwald.

Sixteenth Adventure

Troubled by strange forebodings, Kriemhild tries to prevent Siegfried from joining the chase, but, laughing at her fears, he departs joyfully, although he is never to see her again. After describing the game slain in the course of this day's hunt, the poet declares that Siegfried captured a live bear and playfully let it loose in camp, to the horror of his fellow-hunters. Then, feeling thirsty, Siegfried loudly begins to call for drink, and, discovering that owing to a mistake the wine has been conveyed to another part of the forest, proposes that he, Gunther, and Hagen should race to a neighbouring spring, undertaking to perform the feat in full armour while his companions run in light undress. Although handicapped, Siegfried arrives first, but courteously steps aside to allow Gunther to take a drink, as he wishes to remove his armour before quenching his thirst. But when he, in his turn, stoops over the fountain, Hagen, after slyly removing his weapons out of his reach, steals up behind him and runs a spear through the spot where the cross is embroidered on his doublet. Mortally wounded, Siegfried turns, and, grasping his shield, hurls it at the traitor with such force that he dashes it to pieces.

E'en to the death though wounded, he hurl'd it with such power
That the whirling buckler scatter'd wide a shower
Of the most precious jewels, then straight in shivers broke.
Full gladly had the warrior ta'en vengeance with that stroke.

Sinking to the ground after this effort, Siegfried

The Death of Siegfr ed

H. Hendrich

expends his last breath in beseeching Gunther to watch over his wife. Gazing down at the corpse, Gunther, afraid to acknowledge so dastardly a deed, suggests that they spread the report that Siegfried was slain by brigands while hunting alone in the forest. Hagen, however, proud of his feat, does not intend to subscribe to this project, and plots further villainy while following the body back to Worms.

Seventeenth Adventure

The funeral train arriving there at midnight, Hagen directs the bearers to lay Siegfried's body at Kriemhild's door, so that she may stumble over it when she comes out at dawn on her way to mass. On perceiving that the dead body over which she has fallen is that of her beloved husband, Kriemhild faints, while her women raise a mournful cry.

Roused from his slumbers by the terrible news, old Siegmund joins the mourners, and he and the Nibelung knights carry the body to the minster, where Kriemhild insists that all those who took part in the hunt shall file past it, for she hopes thereby to detect her husband's murderer. (Mediaeval tradition averred that a dead man's wounds bled whenever his murderer drew near.) Siegfried's wounds drop blood at Hagen's touch, and Kriemhild publicly denounces him as the murderer of her husband.

> It is a mighty marvel, which oft e'en now we spy,
> That, when the blood-stain'd murderer comes to the murder'd
> nigh,
> The wounds break out a bleeding, then too the same befell,
> And thus could each beholder the guilt of Hagen tell.

But, instead of showing remorse, Hagen boldly proclaims that he merely did his duty when he slew the man who cast a slur upon the honour of his queen.

Eighteenth Adventure

Having laid his beloved son to rest, old Siegmund returns home, after vainly urging Kriemhild to leave the place where Siegfried is buried and return to her son, for, although Kriemhild's mother and brothers show her every mark of sympathy, Brunhild reveals no pity.

> Meanwhile sat misproud Brunhild in haughtiness uncheck'd;
> Of Kriemhild's tears and sorrows her it nothing reck'd.
> She pitied not the mourner; she stoop'd not to the low.
> Soon Kriemhild took full vengeance, and woe repaid with woe.

Nineteenth Adventure

Three years elapse before Hagen suggests to Gunther that his sister send for the Nibelung hoard which was given her on her marriage. Intending to employ it to buy masses and avengers for Siegfried, Kriemhild gladly consents, and we are told that twelve wagons travelled four nights and days to convey the store of gold from the Nibelung castle to the sea, whence it was carried to Kriemhild at Worms. With such a treasure at her disposal the widowed queen proceeds to win so many adherents that Hagen, fearing this gold may prove dangerous, advises her brothers to take possession of it. No sooner have they done so than Hagen buries it in the Rhine, telling none but his masters in what place it is hidden.

Twentieth Adventure

Having lost his first wife, Etzel, King of Hungary, now deems it advisable to marry again and secure an heir to his realm. As no other woman seems so fitted for this exalted station as Kriemhild, Etzel sends his chief nobleman, Rudiger, to Worms with his proposal. After tarrying a few days on the way with his wife and daughter, this ambassador proceeds to Worms, where he is welcomed by Hagen, who had formerly spent several years as a hostage at Etzel's court. Rudiger having made his errand known, Gunther asks for three days' time to ascertain his sister's wishes. Flattered by the prospect of such an alliance, Gunther hopes that Kriemhild will accept Etzel's proposal, but Hagen rejoins that should she secure such powerful allies, she might in time punish them for Siegfried's death. At first the widowed Kriemhild refuses to listen to Etzel's offers, but, when Rudiger swears to avenge her past or future ills, she suddenly announces her consent.

Then swore to her Sir Rudiger and all his knightly train
To serve her ever truly, and all her rights maintain,
Nor e'er of her due honours scant her in Etzel's land.
Thereto gave the good margrave th' assurance of his hand.

Then thought the faithful mourner, "With such a host of friends
Now the poor lonely widow may work her secret ends,
Nor care for what reflections the world on her may cast.
What if my lost beloved I may revenge at last?"

Then, still escorted by the faithful Ekkewart and carrying off with her the small portion of the Nibelungen treasure which she still retains, Kriemhild starts out for Hungary.

Twenty-first Adventure

The three Burgundian princes escort their sister to the Danube and, taking leave of her there, allow her to proceed with Rudiger to Passau, where her uncle, Bishop Pilgrin, gives her a warm welcome. Thence the travellers proceed to Rudiger's castle, where his wife and daughter entertain their future queen, who bestows upon them costly treasures. Resuming her journey, Kriemhild is now met on all sides by the ovations of her future subjects.

Twenty-second Adventure

When Etzel and his chief noblemen finally meet her, Kriemhild courteously kisses her future spouse, as well as the men whom he points out as worthy of such distinction. Among these is Dietrich of Bern, one of the heroes of the poem, and it is under his escort that the King and Queen of Hungary proceed to Vienna, where their marriage festivities last seventeen days.

Twenty-third Adventure

Seven years elapse, and, although Kriemhild has a son by Etzel, she still grieves for Siegfried and continually broods over her wrongs. One day she suddenly suggests that King Etzel invite her kinsmen to Hungary, and, when he consents, gives special instructions to the bards who bear the message to make sure that Hagen accompanies her brothers.

Twenty-fourth Adventure

After fourteen days' journey the minstrels reach Worms and deliver their message. All are in favour of accepting this invitation save Hagen, who remarks that such friendliness seems suspicious. When his master retorts that a guilty conscience harbours fear, Hagen stoutly avers that he is ready to serve as guide, suggesting, however, that they journey fully armed, with an escort of 1000 men, so as to cope with treachery should such occur.

Twenty-fifth Adventure

Dismissed with the old queen's blessing, the Burgundians leave Brunhild and her son in charge of a steward, and set out. As they are now sole possessors of the great Nibelung hoard, the poet terms them Nibelungs in the remainder of his work. Under the guidance of Hagen, who alone knows the way, the party reaches the banks of the Danube, where, finding no vessels to ferry them across, Hagen bids them wait until he provide means of transportation. Walking down the river, he surprises three swan-maidens bathing, and by capturing their garments, induces them to predict the future. Although one promises him all manner of pleasant things to recover her plumes, her companions, having secured theirs, warn Hagen that none but the priest will return safely to Burgundy.

> "Turn, while there's time for safety, turn, warriors most and least;
> For this, and for this only, you're bidden to the feast,
> That you perforce may perish in Etzel's bloody land.
> Whoever rideth thither, Death has he close at hand."

They inform him that he can secure a boat by assuring the ferry-man on the opposite bank that his name is Amalung. Thanks to this hint, Hagen induces the ferry-man to cross the river and springs into his boat, before the man, discovering the trick, attacks him with his oar. Forced to defend himself, Hagen slays the ferry-man, takes possession of his boat, and then proceeds to convey relays of the Burgundian army across the river. During his last journey, perceiving the chaplain on board and wishing to give the lie to the swan-maidens' prophecy, Hagen flings the priest into the water; but the long ecclesiastical garments buoy up their wearer and enable him to regain the bank which he has just left, whence he makes his way back to Burgundy. On witnessing the priest's escape, Hagen realizes that none of the rest will return, so he grimly destroys the boat as soon as all have passed. Then he directs his friends to ride onward, leaving him to guard their rear, for he knows that the boatman's friends will pursue and attack them.

Twenty-sixth Adventure

Although Hagen's apprehensions are soon justified, the Burgundians fight so bravely that their assailants are defeated. A little farther on they find a man sleeping by the roadside, and discover it is Ekkewart, lying in wait to warn them that Kriemhild harbours evil intentions. But, undeterred by this warning also, the Burgundians continue their journey, and visit Bishop Pilgrin and Rudiger on their way.

Twenty-seventh Adventure

While they are enjoying the hospitality of Rudiger, who lavishes gifts upon his guests, Hagen suggests that a marriage be arranged between Giseler, the youngest Burgundian prince, and Rudiger's daughter. In compliance with this suggestion, a formal betrothal takes place.

> Then had the bride and bridegroom within a ring to stand,
> For such was then the custom; a merry stripling band
> Encircled the fair couple, and gaz'd on them their fill,
> And thought the while as idly as think young people still.

This ceremony over, Rudiger prepares to guide the Burgundians to Etzel's court, where Kriemhild is rejoicing to think they will soon appear.

Twenty-eighth Adventure

So patent are Kriemhild's evil intentions, that Dietrich of Bern and his faithful henchman Hildebrand also caution the Burgundians to be on their guard. This second warning impresses the visitors, who at Hagen's suggestion announce that they will retain their weapons for three days. When they arrive at the palace, Kriemhild cordially embraces her youngest brother, but refuses the same welcome to the two others, and grimly asks Hagen whether he has brought her gold. When he bluntly rejoins that her treasures will remain in the Rhine until Doomsday, she abruptly turns her back upon him, and invites the rest to enter the palace, leaving their arms at the door. Hagen announces that his masters have vowed to spend the next three days in arms, a measure which Dietrich openly approves, informing Kriemhild frankly that he is sure she means no good.

Twenty-ninth Adventure

Although the three royal brothers accompany Kriemhild into the palace, Hagen lingers at the door, and, inviting the minstrel Volker to sit on the bench beside him, confides to him his fears, entreating him to stand by him, and promising to do the same in his behalf should the need occur.

> "Tell me now, friend Volker, will you stand me by,
> If these men of Kriemhild's would my mettle try?
> Show me, if you love me, faithful friend and true!
> And when you need my service I'll do as much for you."

On seeing her foe so close at hand, Kriemhild summons four hundred warriors, and bids them attack Hagen, for at present *he* is the only one against whom she has sinister designs. To prove to the men that Hagen is guilty, she offers to meet and question her foe in their presence. On seeing her coming, Volker suggests that they rise in token of respect, but Hagen grimly rejoins that Kriemhild would merely take such politeness as a proof of weakness. Instead of rising, he therefore ostentatiously lays Siegfried's sword across his lap. After taunting Hagen with slaying her husband—a charge he does not deny—Kriemhild orders her men to slay him, but a single glance of his fiery eyes sends them back cringing, and the Queen cannot prevail upon them to renew the attack. Volker and Hagen boldly join their friends in the banquet-hall, where Etzel—who is depicted as an inoffensive, unsuspicious old man—bids them welcome.

Thirtieth Adventure

On their way to their sleeping quarters that night, the Burgundians are jostled by some Huns, who, instigated by Kriemhild, are evidently seeking to provoke a quarrel. The Burgundians, however, reach their sleeping apartment in safety, where Hagen and Volker watch all night at the door to guard against surprise. It is well for them that they do so, for at midnight Kriemhild dispatches a force to attack them, but again the Huns shrink away appalled on meeting Hagen's menacing glance.

Thirty-first Adventure

At dawn the Burgundians, still fully armed, march off to church, and after service proceed with the

King and Queen to view a tournament held in their honour. In these games Rudiger and Dietrich both refuse to take part, lest an accident should occur. Their previsions are justified, for, when Volker inadvertently slays a Hun, Kriemhild loudly clamours for vengeance, although her husband implores that peace be maintained. Fomented by Kriemhild's secret efforts, such bad feelings have arisen among the Huns against their guests, that Etzel's own brother finally undertakes to compass their death. Meanwhile the old king, having invited the Burgundians to a banquet, is surprised to see the princes arrive fully armed, but tries to show his friendship by promising that they shall bring up his son.

Thirty-second Adventure

While the Burgundians are banqueting with the King of Hungary, their men are resting in the hall where they slept, under the charge of Dankwart, Hagen's brother. There they are suddenly attacked by some Huns, and, although they manage to slay most of their first assailants, the deaths they deal kindle lasting animosity in the breast of the rest of the Huns. New forces therefore press into the hall, until all the Burgundians are slain, save Dankwart, who, cutting his way through the enemy's serried ranks, rushes into the hall where his brother is feasting.

> "Be stirring, brother Hagen, you're sitting all too long.
> To you and God in heaven our deadly strait I plain;
> Yeomen and knights together lie in their quarters slain."

Thirty-third Adventure

No sooner has this cry reached his ear, than Hagen, whipping out his sword, cuts off the head of Etzel's child, which bounces into its mother's lap. Then, calling to his brother to prevent any escape, Hagen shears off the hand of the minstrel who invited them to Hungary, before he begins slashing right and left. Paralyzed by the sight of their headless son, Etzel and Kriemhild sit immovable on their thrones, while Hagen dispatches Volker to help Dankwart guard the door, and bids his masters make use of their weapons while they may. Although the Burgundians now slay ruthlessly, mindful of the kindness shown by Dietrich and Rudiger, they refrain from attacking them or their men. When these noblemen therefore beg permission to pass out safely with their friends, their request is at once granted. Grasping the King and Queen by the hand, Dietrich then leads them out of the hall, closely followed by Rudiger and their respective men, while the Burgundians continue the massacre until not a living foe is left in the hall.

Thirty-fourth Adventure

Weary of slaughter, the Burgundians now sit down for a moment to rest, but, finding the presence of so many corpses distasteful, they fling 700 victims down the steps, those who are merely wounded being killed by the fall. The Huns, who come to pick up their dead, now set up so loud and persistent a cry for revenge, that their monarch is compelled to prepare a force to oust the Burgundians from his banquet-hall. Seeing the aged monarch himself advance at the head of the troops, Hagen, who guards the door, loudly jeers at him, whereupon Kriemhild offers an immense reward to anyone who will bring her his head.

Thirty-fifth Adventure

The first to try to earn this guerdon is a Dane, who not only succeeds in entering the hall but in effecting a retreat. When, emboldened by this first success, he advances a second time with a new force, he is killed as are his men.

Thirty-sixth Adventure

After a second brief rest, the Burgundians prepare to meet a new assault directed by Kriemhild, whose wrath now involves all her kinsmen, although at first she meditated the death of Hagen alone. The murder of his child has incensed even Etzel, and the Huns plan a general massacre to avenge their slain. Although the Burgundians offer to meet Etzel's forces in fair fight, provided they can return home unmolested if victorious, Kriemhild urges her husband to refuse unless Hagen is delivered up. Deeming it dishonourable to forsake a companion, the Burgundians reject these terms, whereupon Kriemhild, in a frenzy of rage, orders the hall to be set on fire.

The Queen expects the Burgundians to be roasted alive, but the hall, being built of stone, offers them a place of refuge, and, as they quench in blood all the sparks that enter, they succeed in maintaining their position.

'Twas well for the Burgundians that vaulted was the roof;
This was, in all their danger, the more to their behoof.
Only about the windows from fire they suffer'd sore.
Still, as their spirit impell'd them, themselves they bravely bore.

The intensity of the heat causes such thirst, however, that Hagen bids his companions quench that too in the blood of the slain. Thus, 600 Burgundians are found alive when a new Hungarian force bursts into the hall.

Thirty-seventh Adventure

Having failed in this third attempt, Kriemhild reminds Rudiger of his solemn oath, and bids him redeem his promise by slaying the Burgundians. Although this nobleman pleads with the Queen, offering instead to relinquish all he owns and leave her land a beggar, she insists upon his obedience to her commands. Fully armed, Rudiger, therefore, finally marches toward the hall and, arriving at the foot of the staircase, explains his position to the Burgundians. Knowing his generosity, Hagen, whose shield has been cut to pieces, begs for the one Rudiger carries, and, after receiving it, declares he will give a good account of himself before he yields. The signal for battle is then given, and Rudiger and his men enter the hall, where, after many have fallen on both sides, Gernot, one of Kriemhild's brothers, and Rudiger slay each other.

Thirty-eighth Adventure

A new batch of corpses having been flung down the stairs, such a lament arises among the Huns that Dietrich of Bern inquires what it may mean. On learning that Rudiger has been slain, Dietrich bids Hildebrand go and claim his corpse, but, instead of acting merely as ambassador, this warrior first bandies words with Volker and then slays him. Hagen drives him down the stairs, but all the Burgundians have now been slain, and he and Gunther alone remain alive in the hall. Meantime Hildebrand having reported to Dietrich all that has occurred, this chief, hearing that most of his men have perished, sallies forth to avenge them.

Thirty-ninth Adventure

On approaching the hall, Dietrich summons Hagen and Gunther to surrender, promising to use his influence to secure their safe return home; but the two Burgundians, feeling sure that Kriemhild will show no mercy, refuse to yield. A duel, therefore, takes place between Dietrich and the exhausted Hagen, in the course of which, by means of a sudden feint, Dietrich seizes and binds his foe. Then, leading him to Kriemhild, he implores her to be merciful to this prisoner, while he returns to secure Gunther also.

> "Fair and noble Kriemhild," thus Sir Dietrich spake,
> "Spare this captive warrior who full amends will make
> For all his past transgressions; him here in bonds you see;
> Revenge not on the fetter'd th' offences of the free."

While Dietrich is securing Gunther, the Queen, left alone with Hagen, again demands her treasures. Hagen rejoins that, having promised never to reveal their hiding-place as long as his lords live, he cannot reveal the secret to her. Kriemhild, whose rage now knows no bounds, orders Gunther—her last brother—to be slain, and herself carries his head to Hagen, as proof that there is no more reason for keeping the secret. Exultantly informing her that since it now rests with him alone, it will remain unrevealed for ever, Hagen so exasperates Kriemhild that, drawing from its scabbard the sword which once belonged to Siegfried, she hews off her prisoner's head with one revengeful stroke! Although neither her husband nor Hildebrand have been quick enough to forestall this crime, the latter is so exasperated by Kriemhild's cruelty that he now slays her in his turn.

Hildebrand the aged, fierce on Kriemhild sprung;
To the death he smote her as his sword he swung.
Sudden and remorseless he his wrath did wreak.
What could then avail her her fearful thrilling shriek?

It is over her corpse that Dietrich and Etzel utter the loud lament with which the *Nibelungenlied* closes.

There is, however, another poem called the *Nibelungenklage*, or the Lament of the Nibelungs, wherein Etzel, Dietrich, Hildebrand, Bishop Pilgrin, and the rest utter successive laments over the slain. Then the spoil of the Burgundians is sent back to Worms, where these lamentations are continued, each mourner reciting the deeds of the man whose fate he bewails. This poem is, however, greatly inferior to the real *Nibelungenlied*, and was evidently not composed by the same bard.

'Tis more than I can tell you what afterward befell,
Save that there was weeping for friends belov'd so well;
Knights and squires, dames and damsels, were seen lamenting all.
So here I end my story. This is the Nibelungers' Fall.

THE STORY OF THE HOLY GRAIL

The Anglo-Norman *trouvères* rightly considered the *Story of the Holy Grail* the central point of interest of the Arthurian Cycle.

So many versions of the tale have been written by poets of different nationalities and different ages—all of whom have added characteristic touches to the story—that, instead of following the text of any one particular version, a general outline of the two principal Holy Grail legends will be given here. Although all the poets do not mention the origin of the Holy Grail, or sacred vessel, a few trace its history back to the very beginning. They claim that when Lucifer stood next to the Creator, or Father, in the heavenly hierarchy, the other angels presented him with a wonderful crown, whose central jewel was a flawless emerald of great size.

The advent of the Son, relegating Lucifer to the third instead of the second place, occasioned his apostasy, which, as Milton explains, was followed by war in Heaven and by the expulsion of the rebel angels. During his fall from the heights of heaven to the depths of hell, the emerald, dropping out of Satan's crown, fell upon earth. There it was fashioned into the cup or dish which Our Lord used during the Last Supper, and in which Joseph of Arimathea caught a few drops of blood which flowed from His side. After the Crucifixion the Jews walled Joseph alive in a prison, where he was sustained in good health and spirits by the Holy Grail (' Cup '), which he had taken with him. In this prison Joseph lingered until Vespasian, hearing the story of Christ's passion, sent messengers to Palestine for relics, hoping they might cure his son Titus of leprosy. Restored to health by the sight of St Veronica's handkerchief—which had wiped away the bloody sweat from Our Lord's brow and bore the imprint of His features—Titus proceeded to Jerusalem, where he summoned the Jews to produce the body of Christ. Not being able to comply, they accused Joseph of having stolen it. Thereupon Titus, continuing his investigations, found Joseph alive and well in the prison where he was supposed to have perished. Free once more, yet dreading further persecution, Joseph embarked, with his sister and brother-in-law Brons, in a vessel bound for Marseilles, the Holy Grail supplying all their needs during the journey. On landing in France, Joseph was divinely instructed to construct a table, round which he and his companions could be seated, and where the Holy Grail supplied each guest with the food he preferred. But one seat at this table, in memory of Judas, was to remain empty until a sinless man came to occupy it. A sinner, once attempting to seat himself in it, was swallowed up by the earth, and Joseph was informed that the enchanter Merlin would in time make a similar table, where a descendant of Brons would have the honour of occupying this 'Siege Perilous.' From Marseilles, by gradual stages, and meeting with every kind of adventure on the way, Joseph, or his descendants, conveyed the Holy Grail to Glastonbury, in England, where it remained visible until people became too sinful for it to dwell any more in their midst. It was then borne off to Sarras, an island city—presumably located in the Mediterranean—where, according to one legend, King Evelake mounted guard over the treasure.

According to another legend, a pilgrim knight laid a golden cross on the Holy Sepulchre, ardently praying for a son, whom at his birth he named Titurel and dedicated to the service of the Lord. When Titurel had spent many years in warfare against the Saracens and in doing good to the poor, an angel appeared to him and announced that he had been chosen to guard the Holy Grail, which was about to descend once more to earth, and take up its abode on Montsalvatch. This vision impelled Titurel to set out on a quest for the Holy Mountain, which some authorities identify with the place of the same name on the east coast of Spain, whither he was safely led by a guiding cloud.

After ascending the steep mountain, Titurel was favoured with a glimpse of the Holy Grail, and he and a number of knights—also brought thither by miraculous means—erected a marvellous temple, whose foundations were laid by the angels, who laboured at the edifice while the volunteer builders were at rest. In a marvellously short time a temple of transcendent beauty was thus finished, and, as soon as it was consecrated, the Holy Grail stole down from Heaven on a beam of celestial light, to abide in its midst. Titurel, king and guardian of the Holy Grail, always presided at the table round which his knights gathered, and where one and all were miraculously fed. From time to time there appeared on the edge of the sacred vase, in letters of fire, instructions bidding a knight go out into the world to defend some innocent person or to right some wrong. The Knights of the Holy Grail, or Templars, as they were indifferently styled, then immediately sallied forth to fulfil this behest, which, according to their vows, they must accomplish without revealing their name or origin. In this way Titurel received the divine instruction to marry, whereupon he wooed a Spanish maiden, by whom he had a son and daughter. This son, marrying in the same way, had in time two sons and three daughters, one of whom became the mother of Parzival.

Old and weary of reigning, Titurel finally resigned the care of the Holy Grail, first to his son, who was slain in war, and then to his grandson Amfortas. But the latter proved restless also, and went out into the world, where, instead of serving the Holy Grail, he lived a life of pleasure and adventure. Wounded by a thrust from a poisoned lance—some authors claim it was the one which wounded the Saviour's side—

Amfortas sadly returned to Montsalvatch, where the mere thought of the veiled Holy Grail increased his pain by intensifying his remorse. There, one day, he read on the rim of the cup, that his wound was destined to be healed by a guileless fool, who would accidentally climb the mountain and, moved by sympathy, would inquire the cause of his suffering and thereby make it cease.

We have already mentioned the fact that Parzival was a great-grandson of Titurel; his mother, fearing he would die young, like his father, were he to become a knight, brought him up in seclusion, telling him nothing about knights, fighting, or the world. Straying in the forest one day this youth encountered a couple of knights, whom he mistook for angels, owing to their bright array, and offered to worship. The knights, however, refused his homage, and good-naturedly advised him to hasten to Arthur's court and learn to become a knight too.

Parzival now left his mother, who died of grief, went to court (meeting with many adventures on the way), and there asked to be knighted. He was told that he must first procure a horse and armour, whereupon he followed and slew an insolent knight who defied King Arthur. But Parzival did not know how to remove the armour from his dead foe, until a passing knight obligingly instructed him.

Parzival now spent a time of apprenticeship at court, where he learned, among other things, that a knight should never be unduly inquisitive; then he went to the rescue of a persecuted and virtuous queen, whom he wooed and married. He soon left her, however, to visit his mother, of whose death he was not aware. On his way home Parzival came to a lake, and a richly-dressed fisherman informed

Parzival at the Court of Arthur
Evelyn Paul

428

him that he might find a night's lodging in the castle on the hill, whither he offered to conduct him. Thus Parzival penetrated into the castle on Montsalvatch and was duly led into the banqueting hall. Awed by the splendour of his surroundings, the young candidate for knighthood silently noted that his host seemed to be suffering from a secret wound, and perceived that all the other guests were oppressed by overwhelming sadness. Then suddenly the doors opened wide, and a strange procession entered the hall, slowly circled around the table, and again passed out! In this procession marched a servant bearing a bloody lance, at the sight of which all present groaned, then came maidens carrying the stand for the Holy Grail, which was reverently brought in by Titurel's grand-daughter. The vase was, however, closely veiled, and it was only after repeated entreaties from the knights present that the host unveiled it, uttering the while heart-rending groans.

All present were now served with the food which they most desired, and ate in silence, after which the knights marched out of the hall, gazing reproachfully at Parzival, who silently wondered what all this might mean. His hunger sated, Parzival was conducted to luxurious sleeping apartments, but, when he was ready to leave on the morrow, all the castle seemed deserted, and it was only when he had crossed the drawbridge and it had been raised behind him, that a harsh voice was heard vehemently cursing him. Shortly after, on learning that a sympathetic inquiry would have dispelled the gloom in the palace which he had just left, Parzival attempted to return, but the mysterious castle was no longer to be found. Such was our hero's remorse for his sin of omission that he continued the quest for years, doing meanwhile all manner of noble and heroic deeds. In reward, he was knighted by Arthur himself, and bidden by Merlin occupy the 'Siege Perilous,' where his name suddenly appeared in letters of gold.

One version of the story explains that, just as he was about to sit down in the Siege Perilous, the witch Kundrie arrived, and hotly denounced him as an unfeeling wretch, whereupon Parzival immediately renewed his quest. Adequate penance having been done at last, and the young knight having stood every test without losing his purity, Parzival was finally allowed to atone for his unconscious fault. Once more he arrived at the castle, once more entered the banquet hall, and once more beheld the mystic procession. Strengthened by silent prayer, Parzival then asked the momentous question, whereupon Amfortas' wound was instantly healed, the aged Titurel released from the pain of living, Kundrie baptized, and Parzival unanimously hailed as future guardian of the Grail, an office which he humbly yet proudly assumed.

Another legend claims that his son Lohengrin, ordered by the Holy Grail to go and defend Elsa of Brabant, received from his father a magic horn, by means of which he was to announce his safe arrival at his destination, and to summon help whenever he wished to return. Instead of riding a charger, Lohengrin was conveyed in a swan-drawn skiff to Brabant, where he found Elsa praying for a champion to defend her against Frederick of Telramund's accusation of having slain her little brother, who had mysteriously disappeared.

Lohengrin, having proved the falsity of the charge by defeating the accuser in a judicial duel, married Elsa, warning her that she must never seek to discover his name or origin, under penalty of seeing him depart as suddenly as he had arrived. The machinations of Frederick of Telramund, and of his artful wife, finally drove Elsa to ask the fatal question, and, as soon as Lohengrin had sorrowfully answered it, the swan appeared and bore him away! But, as Lohengrin departed, Elsa's brother reappeared to serve as her protector.

This—mostly German—version of the Grail legend was embodied by Wolfram von Eschenbach in a long and famous epic, and by Wagner in his operas *Parzival* and *Lohengrin.* In the French and particularly in the English versions of the *Quest for the Holy Grail*, or Sangreal, Percival (in German Parzival) is with the other knights of Arthur's Round Table when they take this vow. He seeks for it, perceives it through a veil, but never entirely achieves the quest, since that privilege is reserved for the peerless Galahad.

The version of the Holy Grail Story of which Galahad is the hero runs as follows: Galahad is the son of Launcelot and Elaine, the latter's nurse having, by means of enchantment, made her to appear as Guinevere—whom Launcelot loved. Deserted by the accidental father of her coming child, this Elaine—daughter of King Pelles—took refuge in a nunnery, where she gave birth to Galahad, whom when dying she entrusted to the nuns. Brought up by those holy women and strengthened in early infancy by frequent glimpses of the Holy Grail—whose light was blinding to all but the perfectly pure—Galahad reached manhood as pure as when he was born. One day Sir Launcelot and Sir Bors were summoned from Camelot to a small church near by, to act as sponsors for a young candidate for knighthood, who was presented to them by some nuns. Launcelot and

Bors, having thus heard Galahad take his vows, were not surprised to see him brought into their midst on a gala day, by Merlin or by the spirit of Joseph, and to hear him warmly welcomed by Arthur. Some versions claim that Galahad, led to the Siege Perilous, found his name miraculously inscribed on it in letters of gold, and was told that he alone should occupy that place at the Round Table.

According to some accounts, it was while all the knights were thus seated round Arthur's board on this occasion, that the Holy Grail suddenly appeared in their midst, its radiance so veiled by its coverings that one and all vowed—when it had disappeared—never to rest until they had beheld it unveiled. Arthur, knowing that this boon would be granted only to the absolutely pure, and that, with one exception, they were all sinful men in various degrees, keenly regretted they should have made a vow which would entail a hopeless quest, and would at the same time leave him bereft of the very knights who had hitherto helped him to right the wrong and keep the pagans at bay. The knights hastened to church to receive a blessing before they departed, and then went off singly or in small groups, to seek the Holy Grail.

When Galahad arrived at Arthur's court, he was fully armed, save that an empty scabbard hung by his side and that he bore no shield. Soon after his arrival, a servant breathlessly announced that he had just seen a large block of stone floating down the river, into which a beautiful sword was thrust to the hilt. Arthur and his knights hurried down to the landing-place, but, although the stone paused there, neither the King nor any of the nobles at his court were able to draw out the sword. It became evident that it was intended for Galahad only, when he easily drew it out of the stone. It was then, according to this version, that the other knights pledged themselves to go in quest of the Holy Grail. Riding off alone, Galahad came to an abbey, where hung a white shield bearing a red cross, which he learned had once belonged to the King of Sarras, who had been converted by Joseph's son. The red cross was drawn with blood, and had remained undimmed for its future bearer, Galahad.

The young champion, thus completely equipped, rode off and next arrived at the enchanted Castle of the Holy Grail. There he saw Titurel, the sleeping king, and Amfortas, the acting king, before whom the Grail passed unseen because he had sinned. Silently Galahad watched the mystic procession of bleeding spear, miraculous dish or cup, and Seven-branched Candlesticks. Like Parzival he hesitated to ask any questions, and failed to achieve the Holy Grail, because, although possessing all other virtues, he could not entirely forget himself for the sake of others, and thus lacked true sympathy or altruism. Thrust out of the castle—like Parzival—he wandered through a blighted country, where he met the Loathley Damsel, who in punishment for her sins was turned loose into the world to work evil on men. She hotly reviled Galahad for not having asked the momentous question, and the youth, learning thus in what way he had been wanting, solemnly vowed to return to the castle and atone for his omission.

But the enchanted castle had vanished, and Galahad, the Champion of Purity, whose red colour he always wears, travelled through the world, righting the wrong. He thus arrived at the gate of a castle defended by seven knights—the Seven

Deadly Sins—with whom he struggled to such good purpose that he defeated them, and was free to enter into the Castle of the Maidens, or place where the Active Virtues have long been kept in durance vile. But, the door still being locked, Galahad was glad to receive the key proffered by an old monk, who, in the legend, personified Righteousness.

Galahad, the emblem of a pure soul, now penetrated into the castle, where the maidens blessed him for setting them free, and where he modestly received their thanks. Among these maidens was Lady Blanchefleur, Galahad's match in purity, to whom he bade farewell as soon as their nuptials were solemnized, for he realized that The Quest could be achieved only by a virgin knight.

Once more Galahad rides through the world, and this time he again finds and enters into the Castle of the Grail, where he once more beholds the Sacred Mysteries. His heart full of sympathy for the suffering Amfortas, he now overlooks the rules of formal politeness in his desire to help, and asks the decisive question. Immediately a refulgent light shines forth from the veiled Grail in all its life-giving radiance, and King Amfortas, healed of his sin, and hence able to see the vessel, dies of joy, just as an angel bears the priceless treasure away from the Enchanted Castle, where it is no longer to sojourn.

Longing for the time when he too can see the Grail unveiled, Galahad again mounts his milk-white steed and rides through the world, where everybody thanks him for freeing the world of the pall of darkness and sin which has rested upon the land ever since Amfortas, titular guardian of the Holy Grail, sinned so grievously. Riding thus,

Galahad comes at last to the sea, where King Solomon's ship awaits him. This vessel has been miraculously preserved for this purpose, and sent here to convey him safely to Sarras, " the spiritual place." It is the present home of the Holy Grail, which had already sojourned there after the death of Joseph of Arimathea.

The ship in which Galahad embarks is steered by an angel, one of the Guardians of the Holy Grail, and the cup which it holds, although closely veiled from profane glances, casts beams of refulgent light upon Galahad and his companions Sir Percival and Sir Bors. These two, however, not being perfectly pure, cannot clearly distinguish the Grail, the sight of which fills the soul of Galahad with ineffable rapture. Before long the ship arrives at Sarras, the fabulous city, where Galahad can hang up his sword and shield and take his well-earned rest, for the Quest is at last achieved! The travellers are welcomed by an old man, and when the King of Sarras dies, the people unanimously elect Galahad as their ruler.

After governing them wisely for a year, Galahad —who prayed in King Solomon's ship that he might pass out of the world whenever he should so desire —begged for the death of the body, that he might find the eternal life of the soul.

When he died, the Holy Grail, which had been piously guarded in Sarras, returned to heaven, for Galahad's work was finished on earth.

EPICS OF THE NETHERLANDS

IN searching among Dutch masterpieces of literature, we find that their greatest epic is *Joannes Boetgezant*, or John the Messenger of Repentance. This epic, in six books, on the life of John the Baptist, was written in 1662 by Vondel, and bears many traits of resemblance to Milton's great epic.

It has been conjectured that the most famous of all the animal epics or beast fables originated in Flanders or Luxembourg, which for a time was included in the Low Countries. This epic, which has been translated into every European language, and has even found its way into the Far East, has been frequently remodelled. The oldest extant MS. in Latin dates back to the eleventh or twelfth century. Among modern versions the most clever, finished, and popular is Goethe's *Reinecke Fuchs*.[1]

In this poem he describes how the animals assemble at Whitsuntide to complain to their king, Noble the Lion, about the dark deeds of Reynard the Fox. The main grievance is that of Isegrim the Wolf, who asserts that Reynard has blinded three of his offspring and insulted his wife. Speaking in French, the Lapdog Wackerlos next pathetically describes how he was robbed of a sausage, which the Tom-cat vehemently declares was his.

Having heard the depositions of the Wolf, the Dog, the Cat, the Panther, and the Hare, Noble is about to sentence the delinquent when Grimbart the Badger, uncle of Reynard, rises to defend the accused. Artfully he turns the tables on the plain-

[1] See the author's *Myths and Legends of the Middle Ages*.

tiffs, and winds up his plausible peroration with the statement that Reynard, repenting of all past sins, has turned hermit, and is now spending his time in fasting, alms-giving, and prayer!

Just as Noble is about to dismiss the case as non-proven, Henning the Cock appears, followed by his sons, who bear on a litter the mangled remains of a hen, strangled by Reynard, who slipped into the chicken-yard in the guise of a monk.

The King immediately dispatches Brown the Bear to Malepartus to summon Reynard to appear at court. On arriving at his destination, the Bear, although still resenting the King's recommendations to be wary, allows himself to be led to a half-split tree-trunk, within which Reynard assures him he will find stores of honey to refresh himself. As soon as the Bear's nose and forepaws are greedily inserted into the crack, Reynard slyly removes the wedges and decamps, leaving the Bear a prisoner and howling with pain.

His roars soon attract the peasant and his son, who beat the captive until he wrenches himself loose, at the cost of some patches of skin and of a few claws. The Bear, returning to court in this plight, is taxed with stupidity and greed, and Hintze the Cat is now sent to summon Reynard to court. The Cat, hungry also, is led to a small opening in a barn which Reynard declares is swarming with mice, but where the poor Tom-cat is caught in a trap, whence he escapes only after having received a beating and lost one eye.

His woeful report decides the King to send Grimbart the Badger to summon his nephew to court. Reynard receives this emissary most courteously, and, on hearing that the King will raze his fortress if he does not obey, sets out for court. On the way Reynard begs Grimbart to act as his confessor, and, having unburdened his conscience, does penance and receives absolution. But scarcely has this ceremony been completed when Reynard, spying some fat hens, begins to chase them, and is only with difficulty recalled to a sense of what is fitting.

On arriving at court, Reynard hypocritically regrets that so many people have slandered him to the King, and tries to refute every charge. He is, however, sentenced to the gallows, but even on the road thither devises a plan of escape. Pretending regret for his past, he humbly begs the King's permission to address the spectators, and in a lengthy speech describes how he was led astray in his youth by Isegrim the Wolf. He also declares that his only regret is to die before he can reveal to the King the hiding-place of a vast treasure, which would enable him to outwit the plots of some rebels who are even now conspiring to kill him. The King immediately orders a reprieve, and, questioning the Fox in secret, learns that the conspirators are Brown the Bear, Isegrim the Wolf, and others. To reward the Fox for saving her husband's life, the Queen now obtains his pardon, which Noble grants in exchange for information in regard to the treasure.

Having given these indications, the Fox sets out on a pilgrimage to Rome, escorted by the Ram and the Hare, which latter is slain as soon as they arrive at Malepartus, where Reynard wishes to bid his family farewell. After feasting upon the flesh of this victim, Reynard puts his bones into a wallet and ties it on the Ram's back, bidding him hasten back to court with this present and receive his reward! Although the circumstantial evidence is enough to convict the poor

Ram of murder, a few days later new complaints are made against Reynard by a Rabbit and a Crow. Noble, roused again, prepares to batter down the walls of Malepartus, and Grimbart, perceiving Reynard's peril, hurries off to give him warning.

He finds Reynard contemplating some young doves, upon which he intends to dine. On hearing what Grimbart has to say, Reynard declares that he would easily acquit himself could he only gain the King's ear long enough to explain the real state of affairs. Then he again begs Grimbart to act as his father confessor, and, resuming his confession where he left off, makes a clean breast of all his misdeeds. Shortly after this, Reynard meets the Ape, who tells him that should he ever be in a quandary he must call for the aid of this clever ally or of his wife.

At his second appearance at court, the Fox openly regrets that there are so many vile people in the world ready to accuse innocent persons, and proceeds to set all his doings in such a plausible light, that the King, instead of sentencing him again to death, allows him to settle his case by fighting a judiciary duel with the Wolf. The preparations for the duel are ludicrous, because the Fox, advised by the Ape, is shaven smooth, greased until too slippery to be held, and duly strengthened by advice and potations. Blinded by the sand continually whisked into his eyes by the Fox's tail, unable to hold his all too slippery opponent, the Wolf is beaten and the Fox acquitted by the Judgment of God!

Although Noble now offers to make Reynard his privy counsellor, the Fox returns home, where his admiring wife and children welcome him rapturously.

In some versions of the tale Reynard further avenges himself by suggesting, when the King is taken ill, that he can be cured if he eats the head of a wolf just seven years old, knowing that the only wolf of that age is Isegrim, who throughout the epic is fooled by the clever Fox, the hero of endless adventures which have delighted young and old for centuries.

SCANDINAVIAN EPICS

THE different Scandinavian dialects formed but one language until about A.D. 1000, when they split up into two great groups, the East Northern including the Danish and Swedish; and the West Northern including the Icelandic, Norwegian, and Faroese. Danish literature boasts of some five hundred chivalric ballads (*Kjaempeviser*), on partly historical and partly mythical themes, which were composed between the fourteenth and sixteenth centuries. It was the Danish translator of the Bible who introduced his countrymen to Charlemagne and Ogier, whose legends received their finished forms at his hands. In 1555 *Reynard the Fox* was translated into Danish from the French, in 1663 the *Heimskringla* from the Icelandic, but it was in 1641 that Arrebo composed the *Hexaemeron* or first real Danish epic. In the nineteenth century Paludan Müller also wrote epics, which, however, are not very popular outside his own country. The runes of Sweden bear witness to the existence of several ancient sagas or epics which perished when Christianity was introduced into the land. In the Middle Ages, a gleeman at the court of Queen Euphemia (1303-12) composed the *Euphemiaviser*, or romances of chivalry done into Swedish verse. The greatest epic work of Sweden is, however, Tegner's *Frithjof's Saga* (1846), relating the adventures and courtship of an old Scandinavian hero, a work of which a complete synopsis is given in the author's *Legends of the Middle Ages*.

The *élite* of the Norwegians emigrated to Iceland for political reasons during the twelfth and thirteenth centuries. Owing to their geographical isolation and to the long winters, these people were thrown entirely on their own resources for amusement. The hours of darkness were beguiled by tales and songs, so young and old naturally delighted in the recitations of the skalds. Thus arose an oral literature of great value, and, although many of the works of the skalds have perished, the Icelanders fortunately recovered in 1643, after centuries of oblivion, the *Elder Edda*, an eleventh-century collection of thirty-three poems on mythical and heroic subjects by Saemunt the Wise.

There is also a similar work in prose known as the *Younger Edda*, by Snorro Sturluson, which contains tales of Scandinavian mythology, and this writer also collected many of the old hero tales in his *Heimskringla*.

Many of the old sagas have been preserved in more or less perfect forms. They are generally divided into three groups, the first including sagas on historical themes, such as the *Egilssaga*, the *Eyrbyggjasaga*, the *Njalssaga*, the *Laxdaelasaga*, and the already mentioned *Heimskringla*.

The second, mythical, or heroic group comprises the *Grettis* saga and the *Volsunga*, the finest of all the sagas, and one of the main sources of the *Nibelungenlied* and of Wagner's Trilogy. This epic has been wonderfully rendered into modern English by William Morris.

In the third and last group are massed together the romantic epics, translations or imitations of the Latin, French, and German epics and romances, relating to Alexander, Charlemagne, Percival, etc. The finest saga in this group is the *Gunnlaugssaga*.

Norwegian literature goes back to the skald Bragi (*c.* 800), whose principal poem, *Ragnarsdrapa*, relates the marvellous adventures of the national hero Ragnar Lodbrog. This poem was incorporated by Snorro Sturluson in what is known as the *Snoror Edda.* Most of the poems in the *Elder Edda* are also of Norwegian origin, as well as Hvin's *Haustlöng* or account of a famous warrior. In the thirteenth century prose sagas were plentiful among the Danes, who took special pleasure in the *Thidrekssaga* (1250), or life and adventures of Dietrich von Bern; in the *Karlamagnussaga*, or story of Charlemagne; and in the *Barlaamssaga ok Josaphats*, or Hebrew tale of Barlaam and Josaphat.

Norway also possesses a rich fund of folk tales, which have been collected by Asbjörnsen, and which, having many of the qualities of prose epics, have delighted many generations.

THE VOLSUNGA SAGA[1]

The Second Part of the *Edda* contains the famous *Volsunga Saga*, or Epic of the Volsungs, which inspired not only the *Nibelungenlied* and Wagner's famous Trilogy of operas, but also William Morris' *Sigurd the Volsung.* The plot of this, the most characteristic and famous of the Scandinavian sagas, is as follows:

Volsung, a lineal descendant from Odin, built his dwelling around the trunk of a mighty oak, the Branstock, whose branches overshadowed his whole dwelling. When Signy, Volsung's only daughter, was married against her will to Siggier, King of the Goths, a one-eyed stranger (Odin) suddenly appeared among the wedding guests, and thrust a

[1] See the author's *Myths of the Norsemen.*

priceless sword (Balmung) deep into the bole of the homestead oak. Before departing, as abruptly as he had come, the stranger proclaimed that the weapon should belong to the man who pulled it out, and prophesied that it would assure him the victory in every fight.

> "Now let the man among you whose heart and hand may shift
> To pluck it from the oak-wood e'en take it for my gift.
> Then ne'er, but his own heart falter, its point and edge shall
> fail
> Until the night's beginning and the ending of the tale."[1]

Although conscious that Odin had been in their midst, Volsung courteously invited the bridegroom to try his luck first, then himself attempted to draw out the divine sword before he bade his ten sons exert their strength in turn. Only the youngest, Sigmund, was at last able to perform the required feat, and when Siggier eagerly offered to purchase his trophy from him, he firmly refused to part with it. Full of anger at this refusal, the Goth departed on the morrow, but although Signy loyally warned her kinsmen that her husband was plotting revenge, the Volsungs accepted his invitation to visit them soon.

When Volsung and his ten sons arrived in Gothland, Signy again bade them beware of coming treachery, but all in vain. The brave Volsungs, drawn into an ambush by their wily foe, were seized and bound fast to a fallen tree in a lonely forest, where every night a wild beast devoured one of these helpless men. Closely watched by her cruel husband, Signy could lend no aid to the prisoners, but when none but Sigmund, the youngest, was left, she directed a slave to smear his face with honey. The

[1] All the quotations are from William Morris's *Sigurd the Volsung*, by permission of the trustees of the late William Morris.

wild beast, attracted by the sweet odour, licked the face of the last prisoner, who, thus enabled to catch its tongue between his teeth, struggled with the beast until his bonds broke and he was free!

When Siggier sent to investigate as usual the next morning, his messenger reported that no prisoners were left bound to the tree and that only a heap of bones was visible. Sure that his foes were all dead, Siggier ceased to watch his wife, who, stealing out into the forest to bury the remains of her kin, discovered Sigmund in a thicket, and promised to aid him to obtain his revenge. To redeem this promise she sent to her brother, one after another, two of her sons to be trained as avengers, but, as both of these children proved deficient in courage, she came to the conclusion that none but a pure-blooded Volsung would prove worthy. To secure a son of this house, Signy, disguised as a gipsy, secretly visited her brother's hut, and when their child, Sinfiotli, was older, sent him to Sigmund to foster and train.

With a youthful helper whom nothing could daunt, Sigmund, after achieving many adventures, lay in wait in Siggier's cellar, but, warned by two of his young children that murderers were hiding behind his casks, Siggier had them seized and cast into separate cells. There he decreed that they should starve to death. But, before their prison was closed, Signy cast into it a bundle of straw, wherein she had concealed Balmung, the magic sword. Thanks to this weapon, Sigmund and Sinfiotli not only hewed their way out of their separate prisons, but slew all the Goths who attempted to escape from Siggier's dwelling, which they set aflame. But, although both proposed to save Signy, she merely stepped out of the house long enough to reveal Sinfiotli's origin and bid them farewell, ere she plunged back into the flames!

And then King Siggier's roof-tree upheaved for its utmost fall,
And its huge walls clashed together, and its mean and lowly things
The fire of death confounded with the tokens of the kings.
A sign for many people on the land of the Goths it lay,
A lamp of the earth none needed, for the bright sun brought the day.

Having done his duty by avenging his father's and brothers' deaths, Sigmund now returned home, where in his old age he was slain in battle shortly after his marriage to a young wife. Finding him dying on the battle-field, his wife bore off the fragments of his magic sword as sole inheritance for his child, who she hoped would prove a boy who could avenge him. One version of the story relates that to escape the pursuit of Sigmund's foes this expectant mother plunged into the woods and sought help and refuge in the smithy of Mimer, a magician as well as a blacksmith. Here she gave birth to Sigurd, who, as she died when he was born, was brought up by Mimer, who marvelled to find the boy absolutely fearless.

Another version claims that, discovered by a Viking, mourning over her dead spouse, the widow was carried off by him, and consented to become his wife on condition that he would prove a good foster-father to Sigmund's child. In this home Sigurd was educated by the wisest of men, Regin, who taught him all a hero need know, and advised him in the choice of his wonderful steed Grane or Greyfell (a descendant of Odin's Sleipnir), from a neighbouring stud.

Seeing the youth ready for adventure, Regin now told him how the gods Odin, Hoenir, and Loki, wandering upon earth in the guise of men, once slew an otter, which they carried to a neighbouring hut, asking to have its meat served for their dinner. Their host, however, exclaiming that they had killed his eldest son, who often assumed the form of an otter, seized and bound them fast, vowing they should not be free until they gave as ransom gold enough to cover the huge otter-skin.

The gods, knowing that none but a magic treasure would suffice, bargained for the release of Loki, who departed in quest of the dwarf Andvari, the collector of an immense hoard of gold. The wily Andvari could not easily be found, and it required all the astuteness of the god of evil to discover him in the guise of a fish at the source of the Rhine, and to catch him by means of the sea-goddess's infallible net.

Having the dwarf in his power, Loki wrung from him his huge treasure, his Helm of Dread, or cap of invisibility, and even tore from his very finger a magic ring of gold, thus incurring the dwarf's curse.

"For men a curse thou bearest; entangled in my gold,
Amid my woe abideth another woe untold.
Two brethren and a father, eight kings my grief shall slay;
And the hearts of queens shall be broken, and their eyes shall
loathe the day.
Lo, how the wilderness blossoms! Lo, how the lonely lands
Are waving with the harvest that fell from my gathering hands!"

Scorning this prediction, Loki hastened to the rescue of his fellow-gods; but, as the otter-skin stretched further and further, it required not only all the treasure, but even the helmet and the serpent ring of gold, to cover it and thus complete the required ransom.

The new owner of the treasure now gloated over his gold until his very nature changed, and he was transformed into a hideous dragon. One of his two remaining sons, Fafnir, entering the hut, slew the dragon before he realized that it was his father, and then, fascinated by the treasure and ring, bore them off to a lonely heath, where in the guise of a dragon he too mounted guard over them. The appropriation of these treasures was keenly resented by his brother Regin, who, unable to cope with the robber himself, now begged Sigurd to help him. Like Mimer in the other version of the tale, Regin was an experienced blacksmith, but, notwithstanding all his skill, Sigurd broke every blade that he forged for this task. Finally the young hero hammered out of the fragments of his dead father's blade a weapon which sheared the anvil in two, and could neatly divide a number of fleeces floating down a stream.

Properly mounted and armed, Sigurd was guided by Regin to the Glittering Heath, the place where Fafnir guarded his gold. A one-eyed ferryman (Odin) conveyed the youth across the river, advising him to dig a pit in the track which the dragon had worn in his frequent journeys to the river to drink. Hidden in this pit—the ferry-man explained—the youth could mortally wound the dragon while he crawled over his head.

This advice being too pertinent to be scorned, Sigurd faithfully carried out the plan and slew the dragon, whose fiery blood poured down upon him and made every part of his body invulnerable, save a tiny spot between his shoulders, where a lime-leaf stuck so closely that the dragon blood did not touch the skin.

While Sigurd was still contemplating the fallen monster, Regin joined him, and, fearing lest he might claim part of the gold, plotted to slay him. First, he bade Sigurd cut out the heart of the dragon and roast it for him, a task which the youth obediently performed, but in the course of which he stuck a burnt finger in his mouth to allay the smart. This taste of Fafnir's heart-blood then and there conferred upon Sigurd the power to understand the language of some birds near by, who exclaimed that Regin was coming behind him to slay him with his own sword! Enraged at such ingratitude and treachery, Sigurd now slew Regin, and after piling up most of the treasure in a cave—where it continued to be guarded by the dragon's corpse—Sigurd rode away, taking with him his sword, the magic helmet, and the ring.

Still guided by the birds, Sigurd next rode up a mountain, crowned by a baleful light, which he presently discovered emanated from a fire forming a barrier of flame around a fortress. Setting spurs to his divine steed, Sigurd rode right through these flames, which then flickered and died out, and discovered in the centre of the fortress a mound whereon lay an apparently lifeless warrior. Using his sword to cut the armour fastenings, Sigurd discovered, beneath this armour, the Valkyr or battle-maiden Brynhild, who, on recovering consciousness, hailed her return to life and light with rapture and warmly thanked her deliverer. Then the two, having fallen in love with each other at first sight, explained to each other who they were; and Sigurd, after relating his own origin and adventures, learned that Brynhild, a Valkyr, having defied Odin by saving a man whom he had doomed to death, had been condemned to mate with any mortal who should claim her hand. Dreading to become the prey of a coward, Brynhild implored Odin to surround her with a barrier of fire which none save a brave man could cross. Although a goddess, she admits that she loves her rescuer, gladly accepts the magic ring he tenders, and promises to be his wife.

> Then he set the ring on her finger and once, if ne'er again,
> They kissed and clung together, and their hearts were full and fain.

The hero, however, doomed to press on in quest of further adventures, soon left Brynhild in the castle where he had found her, still protected by the barrier of flame, and rode off to Burgundy, the land of the Niblungs. Here reigned Guiki, whose fair daughter Gudrun once dreamt that a falcon, after hovering for some time over her house, nestled in her bosom, which she soon beheld dyed red by its life-blood. Disturbed by this ominous dream, Gudrun visited Brynhild and besought her interpretation, only to learn that she would marry a king who would in time be slain by his foes.

Shortly after this occurrence, Sigurd reached the land of the Niblungs and challenged Gunnar, brother of Gudrun, to fight. But, rather than cross swords with the slayer of a dragon, Gunnar offered the stranger his hand in friendship and sent for his sister to give him the cup of welcome. While sojourning here with the Niblungs, Sigurd distinguished himself by athletic feats and, when war broke out, by conquering their foes. These proofs of strength and daring captivated the heart of Gudrun, who, as Sigurd paid no attention to her, prevailed upon her mother to give her a love potion, which she offered to him on his return from one of his adventures.

Odin and Brynhild

Ferd. Lecke

He laughed and took the cup: but therein with the blood of the earth
Earth's hidden might was mingled, and deeds of the cold sea's birth,
And things that the high gods turn from, and a tangle of strange love,
Deep guile, and strong compelling, that whoso drank thereof
Should remember not his longing, should cast his love away,
Remembering dead desire but as night remembereth day.

No sooner has this potion been quaffed than our hero, utterly oblivious of earlier promises to Brynhild, sued for Gudrun's hand, and received the promise she should be his bride if he would help Gunnar to secure Brynhild.

In behalf of his future brother-in-law—whose form he assumed—Sigurd once more rode through the flames, and, although haunted by vague memories of the past, wrested from Brynhild the magic betrothal ring he had given her, and claimed her as bride. Compelled by fate to wed any man who rode through the flames to claim her, Brynhild reluctantly obeyed Sigurd—whom she did not recognize—and was duly married to Gunnar, King of the Niblungs. But, on perceiving Sigurd at his court, she vainly strove to make him remember her and his vows, and was filled with bitter resentment when she witnessed his entire devotion to Gudrun, his present bride.

Meanwhile, although Gunnar had secured the wife whom he coveted, he was anything but a happy man, for Brynhild would not allow him to approach her. Sigurd, to whom he finally confided this unsatisfactory state of affairs, volunteered to exert his fabulous strength to reduce to obedience the rebellious bride, whom he turned over to his brother-in-law in a submissive mood, after depriving her of her girdle and ring, which he carried off as trophies and gave to Gudrun.

Brynhild's resentment, however, still smouldered, and when Gudrun, her sister-in-law, attempted to claim precedence when they were bathing in the river, she openly quarrelled with her. In the course of this dispute, Gudrun exhibited the magic ring, loudly proclaiming that her husband had wooed and won Gunnar's bride! Two distinct parties now defined themselves at court, where Högni, a kinsman of the Niblungs, vehemently espoused Brynhild's cause. By some secret means—for his was a dark and tortuous mind, ever plotting evil—Högni discovered the trick of the magic potion, as well as Brynhild's previous wooing by Sigurd, and proposed to her to avenge by blood the insult she had received.

According to one version of the tale, Högni, who discovers in what spot Sigurd is vulnerable, attacks him while he is asleep in bed and runs his lance through the fatal spot. The dying Sigurd therefore has only time to bid his wife watch over their children ere he expires. By order of Gudrun, his corpse is placed on a pyre, where it is to be consumed with his wonderful weapons and horse. Just as the flames are rising, Brynhild, who does not wish to survive the man she loves, either plunges into the flames and is consumed also, or stabs herself and asks that her corpse be burned beside Sigurd's, his naked sword lying between them, and the magic ring on her finger.

"I pray thee a prayer, the last word in the world I speak,
That ye bear me forth to Sigurd and the hand my hand would
    seek;
The bale for the dead is builded, it is wrought full wide on the
    plain,
It is raised for Earth's best Helper, and thereon is room for
    twain:

Ye have hung the shields about it, and the Southland hangings spread,
There lay me adown by Sigurd and my head beside his head:
But ere ye leave us sleeping, draw his Wrath from out the sheath,
And lay that Light of the Branstock and the blade that frighted Death
Betwixt my side and Sigurd's, as it lay that while agone,
When once in one bed together we twain were laid alone:
How then when the flames flare upward may I be left behind?
How then may the road he wendeth be hard for my feet to find?
How then in the gates of Valhall may the door of the gleaming ring
Clash to on the heel of Sigurd, as I follow on my king?"

Another version of the tale relates that Sigurd was slain by Högni while hunting in the forest, as the story runs in the *Nibelungenlied*. Next we are informed that Atli, King of the Huns, demanded satisfaction from Gunnar for his sister Brynhild's death, and was promised Gudrun's hand in marriage. By means of another magic potion, Sigurd's widow was induced to marry the King of the Huns, to whom she bore two sons. But, when the effect of the potion wore off, she loathed this second marriage and dreamed only of avenging Sigurd's death and of getting rid of her second spouse.

As in the *Nibelungenlied*, Atli invited her kin to Hungary, where they arrived after burying the golden hoard in a secret spot in the Rhine, a spot which they pledged themselves never to reveal. Once more we have a ride to Hungary, but Gudrun, seeing that her husband means treachery, fights by her brother's side. Throughout this battle Gunnar sustains the courage of the Niblungs by playing on his harp, but, when only he and Högni are left, they are overpowered and flung into prison. There Atli vainly tries to make them confess the hiding-place of the hoard, and, hearing that Gunnar will not speak as long as Högni lives, finally orders that this warrior be slain and his heart brought into Gunnar's presence.

Convinced at last that the momentous secret now lies with him alone, Gunnar flatly refuses to reveal it.

> Then was Gunnar silent a little, and the shout in the hall had died,
> And he spoke as a man awakening, and turned on Atli's pride.
> "Thou all-rich King of the Fastlands, e'en such a man might I be
> That I might utter a word, and the heart should be glad in thee,
> And I should live and be sorry: for I, I only am left
> To tell of the ransom of Odin, and the wealth from the toiler reft.
> Lo, once it lay in the water, hid deep adown it lay,
> Till the gods were grieved and lacking, and men saw it and the day;
> Let it lie in the water once more, let the gods be rich and in peace!
> But I at least in the world from the words and the babble shall cease."

In his rage Atli orders the bound prisoner to be cast into a pit full of venomous serpents, where, his harp being flung after him in derision, Gunnar twangs its strings with his toes until he dies. To celebrate this victory, Atli orders a magnificent banquet, where he is so overcome by his many potations that Gudrun either stabs him to death with Sigurd's sword, or sets fire to the palace and perishes with the Huns, according to different versions of the story.

A third version claims that, either cast into the sea or set adrift in a vessel in punishment for murdering

Atli, Gudrun landed in Denmark, where she married the King and bore him three sons. These youths, in an attempt to avenge the death of their fair step-sister Swanhild, were stoned to death. As for Gudrun, overwhelmed by the calamities which had visited her in the course of her life, she finally committed suicide by casting herself into the flames of a huge funeral pyre.

This saga is evidently a sun myth, the blood of the final massacres and the flames of the pyre being emblems of the sunset, and the slaying of Fafnir representing the defeat of cold and darkness which have carried off the golden hoard of summer.

> Ye have heard of Sigurd aforetime, how the foes of God he slew;
> How forth from the darksome desert the Gold of the Waters he drew;
> How he wakened Love on the Mountain, and wakened Brynhild the Bright,
> And dwelt upon Earth for a season, and shone in all men's sight.
> Ye have heard of the Cloudy People, and the dimming of the day,
> And the latter world's confusion, and Sigurd gone away;
> Now ye know of the Need of the Niblungs and the end of broken troth,
> All the death of kings and of kindreds and the Sorrow of Odin the Goth.

RUSSIAN & FINNISH EPICS

THERE is strong evidence that the Finns, or some closely allied race, once spread over the greater part of central Europe. The two or more million Finns who now occupy Finland, and are subject—much against their will—to the Czar, are the proud possessors of an epic poem—the *Kalevala*—which until last century existed only in the memory of a few peasants. Scattered parts of this poem were published in 1822 by Zacharias Topelius, and Elias Lönnrot, who patiently travelled about to collect the remainder, was the first to arrange the 22,793 verses into fifty runes or cantos. The *Kalevala* attracted immediate attention, and has already been translated into most modern languages. Like most epics, its source is in the mythology and folk-lore of the people, and its style has been closely imitated by Longfellow in his *Hiawatha.* The latest English adaptation of this great epic is Baldwin's *Sampo.*

Although Russian literature is rich in folk poetry and epic songs, none of the latter had been written down until lately, with the exception of the twelfth-century *Song of Igor's Band.* The outline of this epic is that Igor, Prince of Southern Russia, after being defeated and made prisoner, effected his escape with the help of a slave. Among the fine passages in this work we note Nature's grief over the Prince's capture and the lament of his faithful consort.

It was only in the nineteenth century, after Zhukovski and Batyushkoff had translated into Russian some of the world's great masterpieces, such as Tasso's *Jerusalem Delivered* and Homer's *Odyssey*, that Puskhin wrote (1820) the epic *Ruslan and Lyudmila*, drawing the materials for this poem from Russian antiquity and from popular legends.

There are in Russia and Siberia any number of epic songs or *bylinas*, dating from legendary times to the present day, which have recently been collected by Kireyevski and others, and which already fill some ten volumes. The heroes of these songs are either personifications of the forces of nature or favourite historical personages. They form great cycles, one clustering, for instance, round Vladimir and the ancient capital of Russia, Kiev, another round the free city of Novgorod, and a third belonging to the later Moscow period. The principal hero of many of the Russian folk-tales, and of the epic songs most frequently sung by wandering bards, is Ilya Muromets, who nobly protects widows and orphans and often displays his fabulous strength by reducing mighty oaks to firewood with a few blows.

THE KALEVALA, OR THE LAND OF HEROES

The national epic of the Finns was rescued from oblivion by Topelius and Lönnrot, two physicians, who took it down from the mouth of the people and published it in the first half of the nineteenth century. It consists of 22,793 verses, divided into fifty runes, and is considered by a great German authority—Steinthal—as one of the four great national epics of the world.

Not only does it relate "the ever-varying contests between Finns and Laplanders," but that between Light and Darkness, Good and Evil, for in the poem the Finns personify Light and Good, while the Lapps are emblems of Darkness and Evil. The Sampo, which is mentioned in this poem, and which seems to have been some sort of a magic grist-mill, holds the same place in Finn mythology as the Golden Fleece in that of the Greeks. Many of the poems incorporated in this epic date back some three thousand years, and the epic itself is composed in alliterative verse, although it also contains rhythm of line and sound, as the following introductory lines prove.

Mastered by desire impulsive,
By a mighty inward urging,
I am ready now for singing,
Ready to begin the chanting
Of our nation's ancient folk-song
Handed down from bygone ages.
In my mouth the words are melting,
From my lips the tones are gliding,
From my tongue they wish to hasten;
When my willing teeth are parted,
When my ready mouth is opened,
Songs of ancient wit and wisdom
Hasten from me not unwilling.[1]

The proem then invites all people to listen to legends of bygone times and to the teachings of the wizard Wainamoinen, to admire the works of Ilmarinen and the doings of Youkahainen in the pastures of the Northland and in the meads of Kalevala. It adds that these runes were caught from the winds, the waves, and the forest branches, and have been preserved in the Northland ever since.

Rune I

In the first rune we are informed that Ilmater, daughter of the air, weary of floating alone in space,

[1] All the quotations from the *Kalevala* are from Crawford's translation (G. P. Putnam's Sons, 1889).

finally descended to the ocean, where she was rocked in the cradle of the deep for 700 years. She made use of this time to create, out of the eggs of a wild duck, the canopy of the heavens, and the spherical earth, with its islands, rocks, and continents. At the end of these 700 years, Ilmater gave birth to Wainamoinen, having waited all this time to be delivered of him, and having vainly called all living creatures to her aid. After coming into the world, this wonderful child floated about on the ocean for eight years, and then drew himself up on a barren promontory to admire the sun, moon, and starry skies.

Rune II

After living alone for some time on this promontory or island, Wainamoinen summoned Pellerwoinen, " first-born of the plains and prairies," and bade him scatter broadcast seeds for the trees which were destined to clothe both vale and hillsides. In a twinkling of an eye, every variety of forest growth waved its branches hither and thither, and, although Wainamoinen rejoiced to see the forest, he soon discovered that the oak, the " tree of heaven," was lacking in it. Because the oak still slept within an acorn, Wainamoinen wondered how to conjure it out of its hiding-place, and, after consulting five water-maidens, called the giant Tursus out of the depths of the ocean. After burning the hay which the water-maidens raked together, this giant planted in the ashes an acorn, which quickly sprouted, and whence arose a tree of such mighty proportions that its branches hid the rays of the sun and blotted out the starlight.

Terrified by what he had done, Wainamoinen wondered how to get rid of the oak, and implored his mother to send some one to help him. Immediately there rose from the sea a pygmy, armed in copper, whom Wainamoinen deemed incapable of coping with so large a tree, until the dwarf suddenly transformed himself into a giant of such proportions that four blows from his copper axe felled the oak, scattering its trunk to the East, its top to the West, its leaves to the South, and its branches to the North. The chips from the fallen oak were collected by a Northland maiden to make enchanted arrows for a magician, and the soil which it had overshadowed immediately began to bear vegetation of various kinds.

Gazing at this new growth Wainamoinen discovered every kind of seed sprouting there save barley. Soon after, he found seven grains of this cereal on the seashore and consulted the birds how best to plant them. They advised him to fell the forests, burn the branches, and plant the barley in the land thus cleared. While obeying these directions in the main, Wainamoinen allowed the birch to stand, declaring that there must be some place where the cuckoo and the eagle could build their nests. These two birds, greatly pleased by this attention, watched Wainamoinen as he sowed his seed, and heard him chant a prayer to Ukko, Father of Heaven, to send down rain to help it to germinate. This prayer was answered to such good purpose that eight days later Wainamoinen found a crop of barley ready to harvest, and heard the cuckoo's notes as it perched in the birch trees.

> Therefore I have left the birch-tree,
> Left the birch-tree only growing,
> Home for thee for joyful singing.
> Call thou here, O sweet-voiced cuckoo,

Sing thou here from throat of velvet,
Sing thou here with voice of silver,
Sing the cuckoo's golden flute-notes;
Call at morning, call at evening,
Call within the hour of noontide,
For the better growth of forests,
For the ripening of the barley,
For the richness of the Northland,
For the joy of Kalevala.

Rune III

In the beautiful Land of the Heroes—Kalevala—Wainamoinen sang songs so wonderful that their fame spread northward to the land of the Lapps, and prompted Youkahainen to journey southward and challenge the "ancient minstrel" to a singing contest. In vain Youkahainen's parents strove to dissuade him from this undertaking; the bold youth harnessed his sledge and drove rapidly southward, colliding with Wainamoinen, who was also out in his sledge that day. Although Wainamoinen was modest, his opponent was boastful and boldly proposed that they should show their skill by singing. Invited to sing first, Wainamoinen chanted a set of commonplace axioms; but when Youkahainen imitated him, the ancient minstrel challenged his guest to sing of creation or philosophy. Although Youkahainen now claimed he and seven other primeval heroes saw how the earth was fashioned, how the sky was arched, and how the silvery moon and golden sun were set in position, Wainamoinen termed him prince of liars and averred he was not present at the Creation as he claimed. This contradiction so enraged Youkahainen that he offered to fight, but, instead of accepting this challenge, Wainamoinen sang a magic song of such power that it resolved Youkahainen's sledge and harness to their primitive components, and caused him to sink into quicksands which finally rose to his very lips. Realizing his desperate plight, Youkahainen implored Wainamoinen to cease his enchantments, offering as a ransom for his life all manner of magic gifts which Wainamoinen scorned. In fact, it was only when the culprit promised him the hand of his sister Aino that the ancient minstrel reversed his spell, and not only released Youkahainen, but restored to him all his possessions.

The defeated bard now returns to Lapland, and on arriving there smashes his sledge in token of anger. His parents wonderingly question him, and on learning that he has promised his sister's hand in marriage to the magician Wainamoinen, they are delighted that she should marry so influential a man, although the maiden herself mourns because all pleasures are to be taken from her for ever.

Rune IV

While out in the forest gathering birch shoots for brooms, this maiden soon after is seen by Wainamoinen, who bids her adorn herself for her wedding, whereupon she petulantly casts off the ornaments she wears and returns home weeping without them. When her parents inquire what this means, Aino declares that she will not marry the old magician, until her mother bribes her by the offer of some wonderful treasures, bestowed by the Daughter of the Sun and Moon, and which until now have lain hidden in the depths of the earth.

Although decked in these magnificent adornments, the girl wanders round the fields, wishing she were dead, for marriage has no attractions for her and she is not anxious to become an old man's bride. Stealing down to the seashore, she finally lays aside her garments and ornaments and swims to a neighbouring rock, on which she no sooner perches than it topples over, and she sinks to the bottom of the sea! Such is the death of Aino, and the water is formed of her blood, the fish from her flesh, the willows from her ribs, and the sea-grass from her hair! Then all nature wonders how the news of her drowning shall be conveyed to her parents, and when the bear, wolf, and fox refuse to transmit so sad a message, the sea-maidens depute the hare, threatening to roast him unless he does their bidding. On learning that her daughter has perished thus miserably, the mother of Aino recognizes that parents should not compel daughters to marry against their will.

> "Listen, all ye mothers, listen,
> Learn from me a tale of wisdom:
> Never urge unwilling daughters
> From the dwellings of their fathers,
> To the bridegrooms that they love not,
> Not as I, inhuman mother,
> Drove away my lovely Aino,
> Fairest daughter of the Northland.

Her sorrow is such that three streams of tears flow from her eyes and, increasing as they flow, form cataracts, between which rise three pinnacles of rock, whereon grow birches, upon which cuckoos for ever chant of " love, suitors, and consolation!"

Rune V

The news of Aino's death travels swiftly southward, and Wainamoinen, hearing that his bride has perished, is plunged in grief. When he seeks consolation from the water-maidens they bid him go out fishing. After angling for many days, he finally secures a salmon, larger and more beautiful than any fish ever seen. He is unsheathing his knife to cut the salmon open, when it suddenly springs back into the deep, informing him that it was Aino who had come to join him, but who now escapes in punishment for his cruelty. Not discouraged by this first failure, Wainamoinen fishes on, until the spirit of his mother bids him travel northward and seek a suitable wife among the Lapps.

> " Take for thee a life companion
> From the honest homes of Suomi,
> One of Northland's honest daughters ;
> She will charm thee with her sweetness,
> Make thee happy through her goodness,
> Form perfection, manners easy,
> Every step and movement graceful,
> Full of wit and good behaviour,
> Honour to thy home and kindred."

Rune VI

Preparing for a journey northward, Wainamoinen bestrides his magic steed, and galloping over the plains of Kalevala crosses the Blue Sea as if it were land. The bard Youkahainen, foreseeing his coming, lies in wait for him and prepares arrows to shoot him, although his mother warns him against the attempt. The third poisoned arrow from Youkahainen's bow strikes Wainamoinen's horse, which immediately sinks to the bottom of the sea, leaving its rider to struggle in the water some eight years. Meantime Youkahainen exults because his foe is dead, although his mother maintains that her son has merely brought woe upon the earth.

Rune VII

Instead of treading the waves, Wainamoinen swims about until an eagle—grateful because he left birch-trees for birds to perch upon—swoops down, invites him to climb upon its back, and swiftly bears him to the dismal northland Sariola. There Wainamoinen is discovered by the Maid of Beauty, who sends her mother, toothless Louhi, to invite him into the house, where she bountifully feeds him. Next Louhi promises to supply Wainamoinen with a steed for his return, and to give him her daughter in marriage, provided he will forge for her the Sampo, or magic grist-mill. Although Wainamoinen cannot do this, he promises that his brother, the blacksmith Ilmarinen, shall forge it for her, and thus secures the promise of the hand of the Maid of Beauty. This bargain made, Wainamoinen drives away in a sledge provided by his hostess, who cautions him not to look up as he travels along, lest misfortune befall him.

Rune VIII

Instead of obeying these injunctions, Wainamoinen gazes upward on his way home, and thus discovers the Maid of Beauty, or Maiden of the Rainbow, weaving "a gold and silver air-gown." When he invites her to come with him, she pertly rejoins that the birds have informed her that a married woman's life is unenviable, for wives "are like dogs enchained in kennel." When Wainamoinen insists that wives are queens, and begs her to listen to his wooing, she retorts that when he has split a golden hair with an edgeless knife, has snared a bird's egg with an invisible snare, has peeled a sandstone, and made a whipstock from ice without leaving any shavings, she may consider his proposal.

These impossible tasks are quickly accomplished by the wizard, but, while fulfilling the Rainbow Maiden's last order—to fashion a ship out of her broken spindle—Wainamoinen accidentally cuts his knee, and the blood flows so fast that no charm can stop it. In vain different remedies are tried, in vain Wainamoinen seeks help at many houses, the blood continues to pour out of his wound until he is in danger of death.

Rune IX

Wainamoinen finally enters a cottage where an old man informs him that he can be healed if he will only "sing the origin of iron." Thereupon Wainamoinen chants that Ukko, Creator of Heaven, having cut air and water asunder, created three lovely maidens, whose milk, scattered over the earth, supplied iron of three different hues. He adds that Fire then caught Iron, and carried it off to its furnace, where Ilmarinen discovered a way to harden it into steel by means of venom brought to him by the bird of Hades.

This song finished, the old man checks the flow of blood, and sends his daughters to collect various herbs, out of which he manufactures a magic balsam which heals the cut immediately.

Runes X and XI

Wainamoinen now hastens back to Kalevala and interviews his brother Ilmarinen, who refuses to journey northward or to forge the magic Sampo. To induce the smith to do his will, Wainamoinen persuades him to climb a lofty fir-tree, on whose branches he claims to have hung the moon and the Great Bear. While Ilmarinen is up in this tree, the wizard Wainamoinen causes a violent storm to blow his brother off to the Northland, where, welcomed by Louhi, Ilmarinen sets up his forge, and after four days' arduous work produces the magic Sampo.

> "I will forge for thee the Sampo,
> Hammer thee the lid in colours,
> From the tips of white-swan feathers,
> From the milk of greatest virtue,
> From a single grain of barley,
> From the finest wool of lambkins,
> Since I forged the arch of heaven,
> Forged the air a concave cover,
> Ere the earth had a beginning."

The sorceress is so pleased with the Sampo—by means of which she daily grinds out treasures untold—that, after hiding it away safely in a mountain, she authorizes Ilmarinen to woo the Maid of Beauty, who assures him also that she never will marry. Saddened by this refusal, Ilmarinen longs for home, whither he is wafted in Louhi's magic boat of copper.

Meanwhile Wainamoinen has been building a magic boat in which to sail northward. He is aided in this work by Lemminkainen, who, on meeting the Maid of Beauty, boldly kidnaps her. But the maiden consents to be his spouse only if he will promise never to fight, a pledge which he readily gives in exchange for hers to forego all village dances. These vows duly exchanged, the young couple are united, and all goes well as long as both scrupulously keep their promise.

Rune XII

The time comes, however, when Lemminkainen goes fishing, and during his absence his wife secretly attends a village dance. When the husband returns, his sister informs him that his bride has broken her promise, whereupon Lemminkainen vows it is time he too should break his, and, harnessing his sleigh, starts off for Lapland to fight. On arriving there he enters several houses, and finally meets in one of them a minstrel, whose song he roughly criticises. Then, seizing the man's harp, Lemminkainen chants all sorts of spells, until all present are under their influence save a blind shepherd, whom Lemminkainen allows to go, and who hastens down to the River of Death, declaring he will there await the singer's arrival.

Runes XIII and XIV

Lemminkainen now asks Louhi for her second daughter, whom she refuses to give him, declaring that after deserting her first daughter he can obtain her second only by catching the wild moose ranging in the fields of Hisi (Death), by bridling his fire-breathing steed, and by killing with his first arrow the great swan swimming on the River of Death. The first two tasks, although bristling with difficulties, are safely accomplished by Lemminkainen, but when he reaches the River of Death, the blind shepherd ruthlessly slays him, chops his body into pieces, and casts them into the stream.

Rune XV

After vainly awaiting Lemminkainen's return, his aged mother, seeing blood drip from his hair-brush, concludes that evil must have befallen her son.

She therefore hastens northward, and threatens to destroy Louhi's magic Sampo unless the sorceress will reveal what has become of Lemminkainen. Louhi then confesses that she sent him down to Hades to hunt the Death swan, so Lemminkainen's mother hastens down to the River of Death, only to learn that her son has perished. Hastening back to the blacksmith Ilmarinen, the frantic mother beseeches him to make her a rake with a handle five hundred fathoms long, and armed with this implement she begins to dredge the river. Presently she fishes out one by one the garments and various fragments of her son! Thanks to powerful incantations she restores Lemminkainen to life, speech, and motion, whereupon the youth thanks her, and graphically relates how he came to his death. But, although he is home once more, Lemminkainen is always thinking of the beautiful maiden whom he wooed, and he still longs to kill the swan swimming on the River of Death!

Runes XVI and XVII

Leaving Lemminkainen, the poem now relates how Wainamoinen built a boat, asking the God of the Forest to supply him with the necessary material for its different parts. When questioned, the trees one after another declare they are unfit for shipbuilding, until the oak proffers its strong trunk. Wainamoinen now constructs his vessel, but discovers that he lacks three "master words" to finish it properly. After vainly seeking these words among birds and animals, he crosses the River of Death in a boat, only to find that the magic formula is unknown even to the angel of Death! The words are, however, well known to Wipunen, a giant of whom he goes in quest. Prising open the monster's lips to force him to speak, Wainamoinen stumbles, falls into the huge maw and is swallowed alive. But, unwilling to remain indefinitely in the dark recesses of the giant's body, Wainamoinen soon sets up a forge in the entrails of the colossus, causing him such keen discomfort that the monster endeavours to eject his guest, who flatly refuses to be dislodged until he learns the magic words. Having thus cleverly secured what he is seeking, Wainamoinen returns home and completes his boat, which proves self-propelling, and speedily bears him to the Northland to woo the Maiden of the Rainbow.

Thus the ancient Wainamoinen
Built the boat with magic only,
And with magic launched his vessel,
Using not the hand to touch it,
Using not the foot to move it,
Using not the knee to turn it,
Using nothing to propel it.
Thus the third task was completed,
For the hostess of Pohyola,
Dowry for the Maid of Beauty
Sitting on the arch of heaven,
On the bow of many colours.

Rune XVIII

Wainamoinen's departure in the magic vessel is noted by Ilmarinen's sister, who immediately informs her brother that a suitor is starting to woo the maid he covets. Jumping into his sledge, Ilmarinen drives off, and both suitors approach the maiden's dwelling from different points at the same moment. Seeing them draw near, the witch Louhi bids her daughter accept the older man because he brings a boat-load of treasures, and refuse the empty-handed youth. But the daughter, who prefers a young bridegroom, declares that the smith who fashioned the incomparable Sampo cannot be an undesirable match. When Wainamoinen therefore lands from his ship and invites her to go sailing with him, she refuses his invitation. Heavy-hearted, Wainamoinen is obliged to return home alone, and, on arriving there, issues the wise decree that old men should never woo mere girls or attempt to rival young men.

Rune XIX

In his turn Ilmarinen now woos the Rainbow Maiden, and is told by Louhi that ere he can claim his bride he must plough the serpent-field of Hades, bring back from that place the Tuoni-bear safely muzzled, and catch without a net a monster pike swimming in the River of Death. Helped by the maiden, Ilmarinen accomplishes these three difficult feats, by first forging the plough and noose required, and also a fishing eagle which seizes the pike in its beak.

Runes XX, XXI, XXII, XXIII, and XXIV

Extensive preparations are now made for the marriage of Ilmarinen and the Maiden of the Rainbow. Not only is the mighty ox of Harjala slain and roasted, but beer is brewed for the first time in the Northland, and many verses are devoted to the description of the processes by which this national drink was brought to its state of perfection! When at last Ilmarinen appears to take away his bride, the Rainbow Maiden seems unwilling to go, and objects that a wife is her husband's slave, and must spend all her days in pleasing him, his father, and his mother. Although her lament is touching indeed, the bride-adviser directs her to please her new relatives, admonishes Ilmarinen to treat her kindly, and watches the two set off, the Rainbow Maiden shedding bitter tears at leaving her beloved home.

Rune XXV

The bride and bridegroom are next warmly welcomed by Ilmarinen's family, old Wainamoinen himself singing at their bridal feast, and again instructing the bride to be all love and submission and to expect nothing save bitterness and hardship from marriage. Having concluded his song by praising the father who built the house, the mother who keeps it, and having blessed bridegroom and bride, Wainamoinen departs for the Land of the Dead, to borrow an auger to repair his sledge, which has fallen to pieces while he sang.

Rune XXVI

Meanwhile Lemminkainen, angry because he alone has received no invitation to the wedding banquet, decides, in spite of his mother's advice, to go forth and take his revenge. Although he has to overcome a flaming eagle, pass through a pit of fire, slay a wolf and a bear, and destroy a wall of snakes mounting guard at the entrance of Lapland before he can reach his destination, his spells and incantations safely overcome these and other dire perils.

Rune XXVII and XXVIII

Reaching Northland at last, Lemminkainen slays the husband of Louhi, from whom he escapes before she can attack him. His mother now warns him that his foes will pursue him, and advises him to go to the Isle of Refuge, situated in the centre of the

Tenth Ocean, and abide there for three years, pledging himself not to fight again for sixty summers.

Rune XXIX

We now have a description of the Isle of Refuge, where Lemminkainen tarries three whole years with the sea-maidens, who bid him a tender farewell when he sails away again. He has, however, proved neglectful toward one of them, a spinster, who curses him, vowing he will suffer many things in return for his neglect. True to her prediction, he encounters many dangers on the homeward journey, and finds his house reduced to ashes and his parents gone! But, although he mourns for them as dead, he soon discovers them hiding in the forest, to escape the fury of the Lapps.

Rune XXX

To punish these foes, Lemminkainen now sets out for the North, taking with him Tiera, hero of the broadsword, who is to help him. Aware of his coming, Louhi bids her son Frost stop them by holding their vessel fast in the ice, but Lemminkainen trudges over the ice, hurls the Frost-god into the fire, and, somewhat discouraged, returns home.

Runes XXXI, XXXII, and XXXIII

During this time a slave, Kullerwoinen, the son of Evil, has been sold to Ilmarinen to serve as his shepherd. The Rainbow Maiden therefore sends him forth with her cattle, giving him a loaf of bread as sole sustenance. When the son of Evil attempts to cut this bread, he breaks his knife, for the housewife has baked a flint-stone in it. In his anger the shepherd conjures up wolves and bears, which devour the cattle, and which he drives home in their stead after dark. When the Rainbow Maiden therefore unsuspectingly tries to milk them, she is instantly devoured by these wild beasts.

Runes XXXIV and XXXV

Having thus effected his revenge, the Spirit of Evil hurries away to his tribe folk, who bid him perform various tasks, in the course of which he crowns his evil deeds by assaulting a sister who was lost in infancy, and whom he fails to recognize. On discovering the identity of her ravisher, the unhappy girl throws herself into the river, where she perishes.

Rune XXXVI

Forbidden by his mother to commit suicide in punishment for his crime, Kullerwoinen decides to seek death on the field of battle. Although the various members of his family see him depart without regret, his mother assures him that nothing can destroy her love for her son.

"Canst not fathom love maternal,
Canst not smother her affection;
Bitterly I'll mourn thy downfall,
I would weep if thou shouldst perish,
Shouldst thou leave my race for ever;
I would weep in court or cabin,
Sprinkle all these fields with tear-drops,
Weep great rivers to the ocean,
Weep to melt the snows of Northland,
Make the hillocks green with weeping,
Weep at morning, weep at evening,
Weep three years in bitter sorrow
O'er the death of Kullerwoinen!"

Kullerwoinen, armed with a magic sword, does great slaughter among his foes, and returns home only to find that all his kin have perished. While he mourns their death, his mother's spirit bids him follow his watch-dog—the only living creature left him. During this strange journey, coming to the spot where he assaulted his sister, Kullerwoinen falls upon his magic sword and dies, an episode which inspires Wainamoinen with these words of wisdom:

> "If the child is not well nurtured,
> Is not rocked and led uprightly
> Though he grow to years of manhood,
> Bear a strong and shapely body,
> He will never know discretion,
> Never eat the bread of honour,
> Never drink the cup of wisdom."

Runes XXXVII and XXXVIII

Ilmarinen, after grieving three months for the loss of the Rainbow Maiden, proceeds to fashion himself a wife out of gold and silver, but, as she is lifeless and unresponsive, he offers her to Wainamoinen—who refuses her—and travels northward once more to woo a sister of his former bride. On arriving at Louhi's house—undeterred by many evil omens which have crossed his path—Ilmarinen sues for a bride. Louhi reproaches him for the treatment her first daughter has undergone, but, although the second maiden refuses to follow him, he boldly carries her off by force. She is, however, so unhappy with him that the blacksmith finally changes her into a sea-gull.

> "I have changed the hateful virgin
> To a sea-gull on the ocean;
> Now she calls above the waters,
> Screeches from the ocean-islands,
> On the rocks she calls and murmurs,
> Vainly calling for a suitor."

Runes XXXIX, XL, and XLI

To comfort himself, Ilmarinen determines to obtain possession of the Sampo, and persuades Wainamoinen and Lemminkainen to accompany him northward. They sail in a magic ship, which is stranded on the shoulders of a huge pike. Wainamoinen kills this fish, and from its bones and sinews fashions the first harp, an instrument so wonderful that none but he can play it, but, whenever he touches its strings, trees dance about him, wild animals crouch at his feet, and the hearts of men are filled with rapture.

All of Northland stopped and listened.
Every creature in the forest,
All the beasts that haunt the woodlands,
On their nimble feet came bounding,
Came to listen to his playing,
Came to hear his songs of joyance.

The music which he makes is so touching that it draws tears even from the player's eyes, tears which drop down into the sea, where they are transformed into pearls, which are brought to him by a duck.

Gathered Wainamoinen's tear-drops
From the blue sea's pebbly bottom,
From the deep, pellucid waters;
Brought them to the great magician,
Beautifully formed and coloured,
Glistening in the silver sunshine,
Glimmering in the golden moonlight,
Many-coloured as the rainbow,
Fitting ornaments for heroes,
Jewels for the maids of beauty.
This the origin of sea-pearls
And the blue-duck's beauteous plumage.

Runes XLII and XLIII

Having lulled the Spirits of Evil to sleep with magic music, Wainamoinen and Ilmarinen go in quest of the Sampo, which they find hidden in the bosom of a magic mountain, and bear away in triumph. The spell they have laid upon all living creatures is broken only when Louhi discovers her loss and sets out in pursuit of the robbers of her treasure.

In various guises she attacks them, finally transforming herself into a huge eagle and pouncing down upon the Sampo, which she tries to bear away in her talons. But Wainamoinen fights this aggressor to such good purpose that it drops the Sampo into the sea, where it is dashed to pieces! Not only has Wainamoinen lost the Sampo, whose fragments he collects and buries so that they may bring prosperity to his people, but his magic harp has also fallen overboard during his fight with Louhi.

Runes XLIV and XLV

Wainamoinen therefore proceeds to construct a second harp from the wood of the birch, while Louhi, who has returned northward, but who still owes him a grudge, sends down from the north nine fell diseases—colic, pleurisy, fever, ulcer, plague, consumption, gout, sterility, and cancer—all of which Wainamoinen routs by means of vapour baths which he discovers.

Rune XLVI

Hearing that Wainamoinen prospers in spite of all she can do, Louhi is so disappointed that she sends a magic bear to devour both him and his brother. But, hearing that this monster is coming, Wainamoinen directs the blacksmith to make him a wonderful spear, with which he slays the bear, whose skin and flesh prove a boon to his people.

Runes XLVII and XLVIII

Still angry, Louhi steals from Wainamoinen the sun, moon, and fire, and thus all the homes in Kalevala are cold, dark, and cheerless. Gazing downward, Ukko, King of the Heaven, wonders because he sees no light, and sends down a flash of lightning, which, after striking the earth, drops into the sea and is swallowed by a pike. This fiery mouthful, however, proves so uncomfortable, that the fish swims madly around until swallowed by another. Learning that the fire-ball is now in a pike, Wainamoinen fishes until he secures that greedy denizen of the deep. Opening his quarry, he seizes the lightning, which burns his fingers so badly that he drops it, until he decides to convey it to his people in the wood of an elm.

Rune XLIX

Although fire is thus restored to mankind, the sun and the moon are still missing. Ilmarinen therefore forges a magnificent silver moon and golden sun, in the vain hope of replacing the orbs which Louhi has stolen, and which are hidden in the cave where she once treasured the Sampo. Discovering this fact by magic means, Wainamoinen starts out in quest of the sun and moon, and by changing himself into a pike to cross the river, reaches the land of Louhi, defeats her sons, and finds the orbs he is seeking guarded by a multitude of snakes. Although

Wainamoinen slays these keepers, he cannot recover the captive sun or moon until Louhi, who has meantime assumed the form of an eagle and then of a dove, sends them back to Kalevala, where their return is hailed with joy.

> "Greetings to thee, Sun of fortune;
> Greetings to thee, Moon of good-luck;
> Welcome sunshine, welcome moonlight;
> Golden is the dawn of morning!
> Free art thou, O Sun of silver,
> Free again, O Moon beloved,
> As the sacred cuckoo's singing,
> As the ring-dove's liquid cooing.
> "Rise, thou silver Sun, each morning,
> Source of light and life hereafter,
> Bring us daily joyful greetings,
> Fill our homes with peace and plenty,
> That our sowing, fishing, hunting,
> May be prospered by thy coming.
> Travel on thy daily journey,
> Let the Moon be ever with thee;
> Glide along thy way rejoicing,
> End thy journeyings in slumber;
> Rest at evening in the ocean,
> When thy daily cares have ended,
> To the good of all thy people,
> To the pleasure of Wainola,
> To the joy of Kalevala!"

Rune L

Meanwhile there had been dwelling in the Northland a happy maiden named Mariatta, who, wandering on the hillsides, once asked the cuckoo how long she would remain unmarried, and heard a magic voice bid her gather a certain berry. No sooner had she done so than the berry popped into her mouth, and soon after she bore a child, which being the offspring of a berry was to be called Flower. As her mother indignantly cast her off, Mariatta had wandered about seeking a place where she might give birth to her child. She was finally compelled to take refuge in the manger of the fiery steed of Hisi, where her infant was charitably warmed by the fire-steed's breath. But once, while the mother was slumbering, the child vanished, and the mother vainly sought it until the Sun informed her that she would find it sleeping among the reeds and rushes in Swamp-land.

Mariatta, child of beauty,
Virgin-mother of the Northland,
Straightway seeks her babe in Swamp-land,
Finds him in the reeds and rushes;
Takes the young child on her bosom
To the dwelling of her father.

Mariatta soon discovered him there, growing in grace and beauty, but priests refused to baptize him because he was considered a wizard. When Wainamoinen sentenced the mother to death, the infant, although only two weeks old, hotly reproached him, declaring that, although he himself had been guilty of many follies, his people had always forgiven him. Wainamoinen, justly rebuked, baptized the child, who in time grew up to be a hero and became the greatest warrior in the land.

Wainamoinen, having grown feeble with passing years, finally built for himself a copper vessel, wherein, after singing a farewell song, he sailed "out into the west," and vanished in the midst of the sunset clouds, leaving behind him as an inheritance to his people his wondrous songs.

Thus the ancient Wainamoinen,
In his copper-banded vessel,
Left his tribe in Kalevala,
Sailing o'er the rolling billows,

Sailing through the azure vapours,
Sailing through the dusk of evening,
Sailing to the fiery sunset,
To the higher-landed regions,
To the lower verge of heaven;
Quickly gained the far horizon,
Gained the purple-coloured harbour,
There his bark he firmly anchored,
Rested in his boat of copper;
But he left his harp of magic,
Left his songs and wisdom-sayings,
To the lasting joy of Suomi.

The poem concludes with an epilogue, wherein the bard declares that it contains many of the folk-tales of his native country, and that as far as rhythm is concerned—

Nature was my only teacher,
Woods and waters my instructors.

EPICS OF CENTRAL EUROPE & OF THE BALKAN PENINSULA

GERMAN being the language spoken in a large part of Switzerland and Austria, these countries claim a great share in the Teutonic epics, many of whose episodes are located within their borders. Both the Swiss and the Austrian nations are formed, however, of various peoples, and while some of the Swiss boast of German blood and traditions, others are more closely related to the French or Italians. To study Swiss literature one must therefore seek its sources in German, French, and Italian books. It is remarkable, however, that no great Swiss epic exists on William Tell, a national hero whose literary fame rests almost exclusively upon folk-tales and upon Schiller's great drama.

WILLIAM TELL [1]

The stewards and bailiffs of the House of Austria, encouraged by immunity, daily grew more and more cruel, until, under the slightest pretext, they thrust Swiss freemen into damp and dark prisons, keeping them there for life. Fearful stories of the heartlessness of these bailiffs were noised abroad, and no one could speak strongly enough of their greed, cruelty, and total lack of principle.

The Swiss bore this oppression as patiently as they could, until their position became so unbearable that they perceived they must assert and maintain their right to freedom, or they would soon be reduced

[1] Taken from the author's *Legends of Switzerland* (Dodd, Mead and Co., New York).

to a state of abject slavery and be deprived of all power of resistance. Walter Fürst, Arnold von Melchthal, and Werner Stauffacher, the wealthiest and most respected citizens of the cantons of Uri, Schwyz, and Unterwald, therefore met to discuss the advisability of an uprising, and, in support of their views, quoted recent acts of wanton cruelty perpetrated by Austrian bailiffs.

For instance, one of these men had grievously insulted the wife of a peaceful citizen, who, to defend her, had slain the oppressor, and was now a hunted fugitive. Next, a young man of Uri had been told he must surrender the fine team of oxen with which he was ploughing, because the bailiff wanted them. As the messenger coolly proceeded to taunt him and unyoke his oxen, the young peasant, in a frantic effort to save the cattle, had dealt a blow which raised a terrible outcry among the bailiff's servants. Knowing that such an offence would be punished by life-long imprisonment in some foul dungeon, if not by prolonged torture and cruel death, the young man had hastily fled. But the blow so thoughtlessly given had been visited upon his aged father, whose eyes had been put out by order of the vindictive bailiff.

Countless other examples of fiendish cruelty and wanton oppression were not lacking, so, when the three men parted, it was with the understanding that they were to ascertain how many of their countrymen were willing to help them. They furthermore arranged to meet again, on October 17, 1307, on the Grütli or Rütli, a plateau at the foot of the Seelisberg, close by the Mythenstein, on the Lake of Lucerne.

One moonlight night, therefore, three bands of

ten picked men, led by Fürst, Stauffacher, and Melchthal, wended their way to the Grütli, and there, beneath the open sky, and in sight of the snow-crowned mountains tipped by the first glow of dawn, the leaders, clasping hands, raised three fingers to heaven. They solemnly swore to shake off the yoke of the oppressor, their motto being, "One for all and all for one." This oath was fervently echoed by the thirty companions whom they had brought thither, and ere they parted all agreed to be ready to rise at a given signal on New Year's Day, and drive the tyrants out of the land for ever.

Among the patriots who took the oath upon the Rütli was a man named Tell, son-in-law of Walter Fürst, and noted far and wide for his skill as a marksman. Strong and sure-footed, Tell delighted in pursuing the chamois over almost inaccessible heights, and along the jagged edges of dangerous precipices, where a moment's dizziness or a single false step would have hurled him down on the rocks hundreds of feet below. Tell lived, with his wife and two little sons, in a hut at Bürglen, in Uri, on the very spot where a chapel was built in his honour in 1522.

It came to pass, shortly after the patriots had met on the Grütli, and before the time set for their uprising, that Gessler, an Austrian bailiff, determined to ascertain by a clever device how many men in Uri were loyal to his master. He therefore set up a pole in the market-place at Altorf, upon which he hung a hat—the emblem of Austrian power—bidding a herald proclaim aloud that all must do homage to it under penalty of death or lifelong imprisonment.

The freemen of Uri were justly incensed when

they heard this decree, and by common consent avoided passing through the square. When compelled to do so, they resorted to various stratagems to avoid obeying Gessler's orders without forfeiting life or liberty. One of their devices was to send their priest to take up his position with the Host directly under the obnoxious Austrian emblem. Of course, all who now passed by reverently bent the knee; but it was quite evident, even to the guards, that the homage was paid to the Sacrament only and not to the imperial hat.

Living only a short distance from Altorf, but ignorant of all that had recently happened there, Tell came down to the village one day, leading his little son by the hand. Unconscious alike of pole, hat, and guards, he strolled across the square, and was greatly surprised to find himself suddenly arrested for defying Gessler's orders. While protesting his innocence, and striving to make the guards release him, Tell saw Gessler ride by; so, turning toward him, he loudly called for justice. The bailiff immediately drew near, and, standing in the midst of the crowd, composed of his attendants and of the startled inhabitants of Altorf, he sneeringly listened to Tell's account of the offence done to him.

Now, it happened that Gessler had often heard of Tell's skill as a marksman, and that he had long wished to see an exhibition of it. He therefore seized this opportunity for gratifying both his curiosity and his cruelty, and promised to set the prisoner free, provided he shot an apple from the head of his child, at a distance of 150 paces.

At these words a murmur of indignation arose in the crowd, but such was the fear inspired by the cruel Gessler that none ventured to interfere in behalf of Tell, whose prayers and protests alike proved vain. Seeing no other means of escape, and urged by his child, who of his own accord ran to place himself against a linden-tree, on the spot where the fountain now stands, Tell tremblingly selected two arrows from his quiver. One he hastily thrust in his bosom, the other he carefully adjusted in his crossbow; but when he would fain have taken aim, the weapon fell from his nerveless hand. Still, a sneer from the bailiff, and an encouraging call from his boy, steeled Tell's heart for this awful test of skill. A moment later, the child came bounding forward, proudly exhibiting the apple transfixed by his father's arrow.

Just as Tell, still dazed by emotion, was about to turn away, Gessler called him back to inquire why he had drawn two arrows from his quiver, when only one shot was required to prove his proficiency. Tell hesitated; but when Gessler assured him that he could speak without fear for his life, he hoarsely answered:

"Had I injured my child, this arrow would have found its goal in your heart, for my hand would not have trembled a second time!"

Beside himself with rage at these bold words, Gessler now bade his guards bind Tell fast, and convey him immediately down to his waiting boat at Flüelen, adding that while he would keep his promise not to kill Tell, he would nevertheless thrust him into a dungeon where neither sun nor moon should ever shine upon him, and where snakes would prey upon his living body.

Placed in the boat, with fast-bound hands and feet, his useless weapons close beside him, Tell despairingly watched the bailiff embark, and the shore near Altorf slowly recede. But, when the rowers tried to round the Axenstein, a sudden tempest swept down on the lake, whipping its waters into foam, and bringing skiff and passengers into such imminent danger that there seemed no hope of escape. The boatman, remembering that Tell was the most clever steersman on the lakeside, now implored Gessler to let him help, so the prisoner, freed from his bonds, quickly seized the rudder.

With strong arm and fearless gaze he stood there, and boldly directed the boat toward a broad ledge of rock forming a natural landing-place at the foot of the Axenberg, at a point where the lake is nearly 700 feet deep.

As the boat drew near this place, Tell suddenly let go the rudder, and seizing his bow and arrows, sprang ashore! This spot, since known as the 'Tellsplatte,' is one of the most interesting sites on the Lake of Lucerne, and in the chapel commemorating this feat there are several paintings representing various incidents of the legend.

Gessler's boat, hurled back among the seething waves, tossed about in great danger, although his boatmen now made frantic efforts to save their own lives.

Dreading the bailiff's vengeance should he manage to escape, Tell hastened over the mountains to the 'Hohle Gasse,' or Hollow Way, a narrow road between Kussnacht and Immensee, along which Gessler would have to pass to reach home. There, crouching in the bushes on the steep bank, Tell patiently waited to see whether his enemy would escape from the perils of the storm. Before long the bailiff appeared, riding at the head of his troop, and evidently meditating in what way he could best effect his revenge upon Tell. His wicked plans were all cut short, however, for an arrow from Tell's bow put an end to his tyrannical career.

The spot where Gessler fell by Tell's hand has long been marked by a small chapel, decorated with a painting representing this scene. After ascertaining that Gessler was really dead, Tell fled, making his way back to Bürglen, where he cheered friends and family by the assurance that the tyrant could never trouble them again.

No political entity boasts of a greater mixture of races and languages than the Austro-Hungarian empire, whose literature is therefore like a many-faceted jewel. Besides the Germans, there are within the borders of the empire large numbers of Czechs or Bohemians, who in the thirteenth century delighted in translations of the *Alexandreis*, of *Tristram*, and of other epic poems and romances, and whose first printed volume in 1468 was a reproduction of the Trojan Cycle.

There are also the Hungarians, whose literary language continued to be Latin until after the Reformation, and whose earliest epics treat of such themes as the *Life of St Catherine of Alexandria*. It was, therefore, only in the seventeenth century that Zrinyi, Gyöngyösi, Liszti, and other poets began to compose Magyar epics which roused their countrymen to rebel against their foes, the Turks. In the nineteenth century patriotism was further fostered among this people by the stirring epics of Czuczzor, Petöfi (whose masterpiece is *Janes Vilez*), and of Vörösmarty; at this time also were compiled the first collections of genuine Hungarian folk-tales. Among these the adventures of the national Samson (Toldi) have served as basis for Arany's modern national epic in twelve cantos.

Part of Poland being incorporated in the Austro-Hungarian empire, it cannot be amiss to mention here the fact that Polish literature is particularly rich in folk-tales, animal epics, apologues, religious legends, and hero tales, although none of the poetical versions of these works seems to be of sufficient weight or importance to require detailed treatment in this volume.

Turkish literature having been successively under Persian, Arabic, and French influence, has no characteristic epics, although it possesses wonderful cycles of fairy- and folk-tales—material from which excellent epics could be evolved were it handled by a poet of genius. The Asiatic part of Turkey being occupied mainly by Arabians, who profess the Mohammedan religion, it is natural that the sayings and doings of Mohammed should form no small part of their literature. The most important of these collections in regard to the Prophet were made by al-Bukhari, Muslem, and al-Tirmidhi.

SERBIAN EPIC POETRY

In the Balkan Peninsula there exists a remarkable body of epic poetry common to all the Serbian people, that much-tried race whose descendants form the main population not only of Serbia, but also of Bosnia and of the northern bank of the Danube, where they are known as Serbo-Croats.

This fund of national poetry, transmitted orally by the Serbian *guslari* or national bards through five centuries of subjection to the Turk, was collected and written down at the beginning of the nineteenth century by the self-taught scholar and philologist Vuk Karadgitch, who thus raised the oral tradition of his country to the dignity of a literature.

It must be borne in mind that in the fourteenth century Serbia was a mighty empire, and that Dushan, 'Tsar of the Greeks and Serbians,' ruled over a territory which extended from the Adriatic to the Black Sea, from the Danube to the gates of Byzance. A hundred years later this empire had crumbled to pieces, unable to withstand the advance of the Turks, and Serbia had been reduced to a mere Turkish pashalik ; but its subjection was only accomplished after a long and fierce struggle, among the episodes of which stands out the ill-fated battle of Kossovo (1389), in which the Serbians suffered irreparable defeat owing to treachery in their own camp.

The Serbian people still live among these great memories of the past ; their *guslari* sing of Dushan the Great, of Tsar Lazar, who perished at Kossovo, of the Voyvoda Milosh Obilitch, who after the battle slew Sultan Amurath, of the traitor Vuk Brankovitch ; but over all these towers the figure of Prince Marko Kralyevitch, who, banished from the throne by the usurper Vukashin, gathered about him a band of free lances, and with this body of followers spent his life in the pursuit of extraordinary adventures until his death in 1394 at the age—so tradition has it—of 103 years.[1] According to many, indeed, he is not dead, but sleeps in a vault under the black mountains which overhang Prilip, his native place. His sword is planted in the rocky walls of the vault, and his horse Sharatz nibbles patiently at the over-

[1] From *Hero-Tales and Legends of the Serbians*, by W. M. Petrovitch (George G. Harrap and Co.).

growing moss. Thus, little by little, the stone is worn away and the sword-blade laid bare. A day shall come when the sword will fall to the ground; then Marko will awake, and sword in hand will reappear, mounted on Sharatz, to gather the Serbs round his banner and lead them against the Turks. Nay! on November 5, 1912, when the Serbian infantry stormed the forbidding heights under which Marko slumbered, a position which all military experts had deemed impregnable, they plainly beheld him, mounted on his charger, throwing his heavy mace aloft as high as the clouds, and waving them on to victory.

Of the great body of romantic adventure which centres round Marko, and in which Moors, giants, dragons, and *vile* or fairy-nymphs freely intermingle with Turks and Serbians, we shall give only one example, the story of

Prince Marko and a Moorish Chieftain

A powerful Moorish chieftain had built for himself a magnificent castle by the sea, with windows of the most beautiful glass; he hung all the rooms and halls with the richest silks and velvets, and then soliloquized thus: "O my castle, why have I erected thee? There is no one here to tread with gentle footsteps upon these fine rugs; I have no mother, no sister, and I have not yet found a wife. But I will assuredly go at once and seek the Sultan's daughter in marriage. The Sultan must either give me his daughter or meet me in single combat."

The chieftain forthwith wrote to the Sultan, who on reading the letter immediately sought for someone who would accept the challenge in his stead, promising untold gold to the knight who would meet the Moor. Many a bold man went forth to fight the chieftain, but not one ever returned to Istamboul.

When all the Sultan's best fighters had lost their lives, the Moor arrayed himself in all his splendour, saddled his steed Bedevia, and holding before him, defiantly, his sharpest lance, rode straight to Istamboul. He pitched his tent under the walls of the town, stuck his lance deep into the earth, bound his Bedevia to the lance, and forthwith imposed upon the inhabitants a daily tax consisting of one sheep, one batch of white loaves, two barrels of red wine, and a beautiful maiden. Each maiden, after she had been his slave for twenty-four hours, he sold again for large sums of money. This imposition went on for three months, for none could stop it. But there was yet greater evil to be met.

One day the haughty Moor mounted his steed and entered the city. He went to the palace, summoned the Sultan to give him his daughter, and as he received no answer, battered the walls of the palace with his club until the shattered glass poured down from the windows like rain. The Sultan, greatly alarmed, saw no alternative open to him but to give up his only daughter, and promised her to the Moor, who thereupon returned to his castle for fifteen days to make the necessary preparations.

The Sultana and her daughter wept bitterly when they learnt that the Sultan had yielded to the demands of the Moor; but that night the Sultana had a strange dream, in which the figure of a man appeared before her, saying: "There is within the empire of Serbia a vast plain, Kossovo; in that plain there is a city, Prilip; and in that city dwells the royal Prince Marko, who is known among all men as a truly great hero."

Marko and the Sultan's Daughter

William Sewell

And the man went on to advise the Sultana to send a message to Prince Marko, offering him an immense fortune if he would vanquish the Moor and save her daughter from a shameful fate. The next morning a letter was sent to Prince Marko, promising him three horse-loads of pure golden ducats if he would come with all speed. Twice did Marko refuse to come and meet this formidable opponent, but when the Sultan's daughter wrote to him in characters traced with her own blood, offering him seven horse-loads of pure gold, together with gems and presents innumerable, he resolved to fight the Moor, and prepared to depart. He put on his cloak and cap made of wolves' skins, girded his sabre, selected his most piercing lance, saddled Sharatz with his own hands, and taking with him a leather bottle filled with red wine and his weightiest war-club, he rode off to Istamboul, where he took up his abode in an inn.

That same evening he led his horse to a lake near by to be refreshed, and as he drew near he heard the Sultan's daughter give piteous expression to her fear and grief. Making himself known to her, he spake as follows: "Do not tell others that thou hast seen me here, but request the Sultan and thy mother to have supper prepared and sent to the inn for me, and above all things beg them to send me plenty of wine. When the Moor arrives at the palace, thy parents must welcome him graciously, and go so far as to yield thee to him in order to avoid a quarrel. And I know the spot where I shall be able to rescue thee, if my customary good luck and my strength do not desert me."

While Marko sat drinking his wine in peace, all the shops in Istamboul were closed, and the landlord of the inn also came to close his doors and windows, for the Moorish chieftain was coming to take away the Sultan's daughter, and owing to their terror of him, all were forced to close their shops. Marko, however, did not allow the man to close the door of the inn, for he wished to see the Moor and his gorgeous train pass by.

At this moment the Moor, accompanied by 500 black followers in glittering armour, trotted by on his Bedevia. He noticed with astonishment that the door of the inn was open. "There must be nobody within," he thought, "or if there is anybody inside, he is assuredly a great fool; or perhaps he is a stranger, and has not yet been told how terrible I am."

The next morning the Sultan presented his daughter to the Moorish chieftain, together with all the wedding gifts. As the wedding procession passed the inn where Marko waited, the Moor again noticed the open door, but this time he urged Bedevia right up to it to see who might be there.

Marko was seated at his ease, drinking his favourite red wine from a bowl which held twelve quarts, and each time that he filled the bowl he would drink only one half of its contents, giving the other half to his steed Sharatz. The Moor was on the point of attacking Marko, when Sharatz barred his way and kicked viciously at Bedevia. The Moor, meeting unexpected resistance, turned to rejoin the procession. Then Marko rose to his feet, and turning his cloak and cap inside out, so that he presented the terrifying appearance of a wolf, he dashed on his charger after the procession. He felled horsemen right and left, reached the leader of the bride and the second witness, and killed them both.

The Moor astride his Bedevia galloped back and

addressed Marko thus : " Ill fortune is indeed overtaking thee to-day, O stranger ! Thou must have been driven here by Satan to disturb my guests and even kill my witnesses ; thou must be either a fool, knowing nothing of to-day's events, or thou must be extremely fierce and hast gone mad ; but maybe thou art merely tired of life ? By my faith, I shall draw in the reins of my Bedevia, and shall spring over thy body seven times ; then shall I strike off thy head ! " Thereupon Marko answered : " Cease these lies, O Moor ! If God and my usual luck do but attend me now, thou shalt not even spring near to me ; still less can I imagine thee carrying out thy intention of springing over my body ! " But behold ! The Moor drew in his Bedevia, spurred her violently forward, and would indeed have sprung over Marko, had not Sharatz been the well-trained fighter that he was : in a trice he reared so as to receive the adversary against his forefeet and swiftly bit off Bedevia's right ear, from which blood gushed forth profusely. In this way Marko and the Moor struggled for four hours. Neither would give way, and when finally the Moor saw that Marko was overpowering him, he wheeled his steed Bedevia round and fled along the main street of Istamboul, Marko after him. But the Moor's Bedevia was swift as a nymph of the forest, and would certainly have escaped from Sharatz if Marko had not suddenly recollected his club, and flung it after his adversary, striking him between the shoulders. The Moor fell from his horse, and the Prince severed his head from his body. Next he captured Bedevia, returned to the street where he had left the bride, and found her alone, awaiting him, for all the retinue of the Moor had fled. Marko escorted the Princess back to the Sultan, and cast the head of the Moorish chieftain at his feet.

The hero now took his leave and started at once on his journey back to Prilip. The following morning he received the seven horse-loads of gold together with the many precious gifts which the Princess had promised him, and last of all a message thanking him for the marvellous deeds he had done, and telling him that the vast stores of gold belonging to the Sultan would for ever be at his disposal.

HEBREW & EARLY CHRISTIAN EPICS

JOB

THE Book of Job ranks as "one of that group of five or six world poems that stand as universal expressions of the human spirit." For that reason it is considered the representative Hebrew epic, and, as it depicts the conflicts of a human soul, it has also been termed the "epic of the inner life."

Written after the exile—probably in the latter part of the fourth century B.C.—it incorporates various older poems, for the theme is thought to antedate the Exodus. In the prologue we have a description of Job, a model sheik of the land of Uz, whose righteousness wins such complete approval from God that the Almighty proudly quotes His servant before His assembled council as a perfect man. 'The Adversary,' Satan, now dramatically presents himself, and, when retaunted by God with Job's virtues, sarcastically retorts that it is easy to be good when favoured with continual prosperity.

Thus challenged, and feeling sure of his subject, God allows Satan to do his worst and thus test the real worth of Job. In quick succession we now behold a once happy and prosperous man deprived of children, wealth, and health—misfortunes so swift and dire that his friends in lengthy speeches insist that he has offended God, for such trials as his can only be sent in punishment for grievous sins. The exhortations of Job's three argumentative friends, as well as of a later-comer, and of his wife, extend over a period of seven days, and cover three whole cycles ; but, in spite of all they say, Job steadfastly refuses to curse God as they advise.

Unaware of the heavenly council or of the fact that he is being tested, Job, in spite of trials and friends, patiently reiterates " The Lord gave and the Lord hath taken away," and, when his wife bids him curse God and die, pathetically inquires, " What! shall we receive good at the hand of God, and shall we not receive evil ? "

There are, besides, whole passages in the book wherein Job gives way to his overwhelming grief, these laments being evidently either fragments from another, older version of the story, or tokens that even such fortitude as his gave way under pressure of disease and of his friends' injudicious attempts at consolation. These laments exceed in pathos any other Hebrew poem, while Job's descriptions of God's power and wisdom attain to a superbly exalted strain.

Having silenced Zopher, Eliphaz, and Bildad by assuring them that he will be vindicated in heaven —if not sooner—Job watches them and his last friend depart, and is finally left alone. Then only, and in an epilogue, we are informed that, having thus been tried in the furnace of affliction and proved true gold, Job receives from God, as reward, a double measure of health, wealth, and descendants, so that all men may know that he has not sinned and that his unshaken faith found favour in the eyes of God.

Some Jewish writers quote Ecclesiastes as their best sample of didactic epic, and others would rank as epics the tales of Naomi and Ruth, of Esther and Ahasuerus, and even the idyllic Song of Songs by Solomon. Early Christian writers also see in the Revelation, or the Apocalypse, by St. John, the Seer of Patmos, a brilliant example of the mystical or prophetic epic.

ARABIAN & PERSIAN EPICS

"THE long caravan marches across the monotonous deserts, when the camel's steady swing bends the rider's body almost double, taught the Arab to sing rhymes." But the poems thus sung by camel-drivers are generally short, and never reach epic might or length. None of those older poems now exist, and it was only when travellers applied the Syrian alphabet to the Arabic tongue in the sixth century that written records began to be kept of favourite compositions. Poets were then looked upon as wise men, or magicians, and called upon, like Balaam, in times of danger, to utter spells or incantations against the foe.

The most ancient pre-Islamic poems were written in golden ink, suspended in the Kaaba at Mecca, and are known in Arabia as the *Necklace of Pearls*.

Many of these poems—which replace epics in the East—follow fixed rules, the author being bound to "begin by a reference to the forsaken camping-grounds. Next he must lament, and pray his comrades to halt while he calls up the memory of the dwellers who had departed in search of other encampments and fresh water springs. Then he begins to touch on love matters, bewailing the tortures to which his passion puts him, and thus attracting interest and attention to himself. He recounts his hard and toilsome journeying in the desert, dwells on the lean condition of his steed, which he lauds and describes, and finally, with the object of obtaining those proofs of generosity which were the bard's expected meed and sole support, he winds up with a panegyric of the prince or governor in whose presence the poem is recited."

Throughout the East, professional story-tellers still spend their lives travelling about and entertaining audiences in towns and tents with poems and legends, many of the latter treating of desert feuds and battles and forming part of a collection known as the *Arab Days*.

With the founding of Bagdad by the Abbasides, Persian influence begins to make itself felt, not only in politics but in literature also, although Arabic was the sole language of the empire of the Caliphs. The greatest literary work in this literature is the famous *Arabian Nights*, an anonymous collection of tales connected by a thread of narrative. Its purport is that an Eastern monarch, "to protect himself against the craft and infidelity of women, resolves that the wife he chooses him every day shall be put to death before the next." Two sisters devote their lives to put an end to such massacres. The eldest, who becomes the King's wife, begs that her sister may spend the last night of her life in their room. At dawn the royal bride entertains her sister with a story which is cleverly left unfinished. Such is the Sultan's curiosity to hear the end, that the bride of a night is not slain, as usual. But as soon as one tale is ended another is begun, and for one thousand and one nights the clever narrator keeps her audience of two in suspense. Most of the tales told in this collection are obviously of Persian origin, and are contained in the *Hasâr Afsâna* (Thousand Tales) which was translated into Arabic in the tenth century. But some authorities claim that these stories originated in India and were brought into Persia before Alexander's conquests. These tales are so popular that they have been translated into every civilized language and are often termed prose epics.

Arabic also boasts a romance of chivalry entitled *Romance of 'Artar,'* ascribed to Al Asmai (739–831), which contains the chief events in Arab history before the advent of Mahomet and is hence often termed the Arab *Iliad.*

The *Romance of Beni Hilal* and that of *Abu Zaid,* which form part of a cycle of thirty-eight legends, are popular in Egypt to this day.

THE SHAH-NAMEH, OR EPIC OF KINGS

This Persian epic was composed by the poet Abul Kasin Mansur, who sang so sweetly that his master termed him Firdusi, or Singer of Paradise, by which name he is best known, although he is also called the 'Homer of the East.' Mahmoud, Shah of Persia, who lived about 920 B.C., decided to have the chronicles of the land put into rhyme, and engaged Firdusi for this piece of work, promising him 1000 gold pieces for every 1000 distichs that he finished. Firdusi, who had long wished to build stone embankments for the river whose overflow devastated his native town, begged the King to withhold payment until the work was done.

At the end of thirty-three years, when the poem was completed, the grand vizier, after counting its 60,000 couplets, concluded not to pay for it in gold, and sent instead 60,000 small pieces of silver. On receiving so inadequate a reward, Firdusi became so angry that, after distributing the money among the bearers and writing an insulting poem to the King, he fled first to Mazinderan and then to Bagdad, where he lingered until shortly before his death, when he returned to Tous. Tradition claims that the Shah, hearing he had come home, and having in the meantime discovered the trickery of his minister, immediately sent Firdusi 60,000 pieces of gold, but that the money arrived only as his corpse was being lowered into the tomb. As the poet's daughter indignantly refused to accept this tardy atonement, another relative took the money and built the dike which Firdusi had longed to see.

We know that Persian monarchs made sundry attempts to collect the annals of their country, but these collections were scattered at the time of the Arabian conquest, so that only a few documents were ultimately brought back to Persia. The poem of Firdusi claims to be a complete history of Persia, but it contains so many marvels that, were it not for its wonderful diction, it would not have survived, although he declares that he has written

> What no tide
> Shall ever wash away, what men
> Unborn shall read o'er ocean wide.[1]

The poem opens with the description of a ruler so prosperous that the Spirit of Evil sent a mighty devil (*deev*) to conquer him. Through the efforts of this demon, the King's son was slain, and, as the monarch died of grief, it was his grandson who succeeded him. During a forty-centuries reign this king gave fire to his people, taught them irrigation and agriculture, and bestowed names on all the beasts.

His son and successor taught mortals how to spin and weave, and the demons, in the hope of destroying him, imparted to him the arts of reading and writing. Next came the famous Persian hero Jemshid, who is said to have reigned 700 years, and to have divided the Persian nation into four classes,

[1] The quotations are from Champeon's translation.

priests, warriors, artisans, and husbandmen. During his reign, which is the Age of Gold of Persia, the world was divided into separate parts, and the city of Persepolis founded, where two columns of the ruined royal palace still bear the name of the monarch who instituted the national festival of Persia (Neurouz).

Having accomplished all these wonderful things, Jemshid became so conceited that he wished to be worshipped, whereupon a neighbouring volcano vomited smoke and ashes and innumerable snakes infested the land. Then Prince Zohak of Arabia was sent by the Evil Spirit to drive away Jemshid and to take possession of his throne. Although at first Zohak was very virtuous, the Evil Spirit, having him in his power, began to serve him in the guise of a cook. Once, having succeeded in pleasing him, he begged permission as a reward to kiss the King between his shoulders. But no sooner had this demon's lips touched the royal back than two black serpents sprang up there, serpents which could not be destroyed, and which could only be kept quiet by being fed with human brains.

> "If life hath any charm for thee,
> The brains of men their food must be."

Zohak, 'the Serpent King,' as he is now invariably called, was therefore obliged to prey upon his subjects to satisfy the appetite of these serpents, and, as two men were required daily for that purpose during the next thousand years, the realm was sorely depopulated.

> The serpents still on human brains were fed,
> And every day two youthful victims bled;
> The sword, still ready, thirsting still to strike,
> Warrior and slave were sacrificed alike.

Naturally, all the Persians grew to loathe their monarch, and, when the seventeenth and last child of the blacksmith Kavah was seized to feed the serpents, this man rebelled, and, raising his leathern apron as a standard, rallied the Persians round him. He then informed them that, if they would only fight beneath 'the flag of Kavah'—which is now the Persian ensign—he would give them as king Feridoun, a son of Jemshid, born during his exile. The rebels therefore went in quest of Feridoun, 'the glorious,' in regard to whom Zohak had been favoured with several visions, although he had been brought up in secret, his sole nurse being a faithful cow. When this animal died at last, the grateful Feridoun made a mace of one of its big bones, and armed with that weapon, defeated Zohak, who was chained to a mountain, where he was tortured by visions of his victims for 1000 years. Meantime Feridoun occupied so justly the throne of Persia—where he reigned some five hundred years—that his realm became an earthly Paradise.

At the end of this long reign, Feridoun dispatched his three sons to Arabia in quest of wives, and on their return proceeded to test their mettle by meeting them in the shape of a dragon. While the eldest son retreated, crying that a wise and prudent man never strives with dragons, the second advanced recklessly, without thinking of protecting himself. The third, however, set to work in a businesslike way, not only to rescue his foolhardy brother, but to slay the dragon. On perceiving this, the father resumed his wonted form, and announced that he would divide his realm into three parts, of which the best share, Iran or Persia, was bestowed upon Trij, the son who had shown both courage and prudence.

Not long after this division, the two elder brothers united to despoil the younger, but, although they succeeded in slaying him, his infant daughter was brought up by the aged Feridoun, and in due time gave birth to a son, Minuchir, destined to avenge his grandfather's death by defeating and slaying his great-uncles. Having done this, Minuchir occupied the throne, while his favourite vassal was made governor of one of the newly conquered realms. This swarthy, dark-haired man proved perfectly happy in these new estates until he heard that his wife had given birth to a son with snow-white hair.

"No human being of this earth could give to such a monster birth,
He must be of the demon race, though human still in form and face.
If not a demon, he at least appears a parti-coloured beast."

Such an offspring seeming nothing short of a curse, the father had little Zal exposed on Mount Alborz, where he expected him to perish in a brief space of time.

On the top of this mountain the Simurgh, or Bird of God—a marvellous golden-feathered eagle—had built a nest of ebony and sandal-wood, lined with spices, round which she had piled all manner of precious stones, whose glitter pleased her. Hearing the cry of a babe, this great bird swooped downward, and, fastening her talons in the child's dress, bore him safely away to her eyrie, where she dropped him in the nest beside two eaglets. These little birds proved kind to the young prince, although they were able to leave their nest long before he could walk about and play with the precious stones.

It was only when Zal was about eight years old that his father realized that he had committed a deadly sin, and was correspondingly relieved to learn in a dream that his child had not perished, but had been nursed by the Simurgh. Hastening to the mountain, the father besought the Bird of God to give back his son, whereupon the golden-feathered eagle, after taking affectionate leave of little Zal (upon whom she bestowed a feather which was to be cast into the fire in time of need), bore him back to his father.

> "Having watched thee with fondness by day and by night,
> And supplied all thy wants with a mother's delight,
> Oh, forget not thy nurse—still be faithful to me,
> And my heart will be ever devoted to thee."

The father now brought up young Zal, who soon became so remarkable for strength and bravery that he promised to become the greatest warrior the world had ever known. In early manhood this youth journeyed to Kabul, where he beheld the lovely Rudaveh, who belonged to the race of the Serpent King. The arrival of a young but white-haired warrior caused such a sensation at court that the Princess, who had already fallen in love with him on hearsay, became anxious to meet him.

One day, when the maidens were gathering roses near his pavilion, Zal shot a bird, which, falling in their midst, gave them an occasion to address him. He, too, had heard so much about the loveliness of Rudaveh, that he questioned her attendants and gave them jewels to take to her. Such gifts quickly paved the way for an interview, for Rudaveh immediately sent for Zal. On appearing beneath her window, this lover began so sweet a serenade that the Princess stepped out in her balcony, where, loosening her long black braids, which hung down to the ground, she bade Zal use them to climb up to her. He, however, gallantly refused, for fear he should hurt her, and deftly flinging his noose upward caught it fast in a projection, and thus safely reached the balcony, where this Persian Romeo acceptably wooed his Juliet.

The royal parents, on discovering these clandestine meetings, questioned the young man, who proved his intelligence by solving six riddles, and, after giving satisfactory tokens of his other qualifications, was allowed to marry the Princess, for the oracles predicted that from this union would arise a hero who would honour his native land.

Time now passed happily until the moment came when Rudaveh's life was in imminent danger. Zal flung the golden feather into the fire with so trembling a hand that it fell to one side, so that only one edge was singed. This proved sufficient, however, to summon the faithful Simurgh, who, after rapturously caressing her nursling, whispered in his ear a magic word, which not only enabled him to save the life of his dying wife, but also assured his becoming the happy father of a stalwart son named Rustem.

This boy, stronger and handsomer than any child yet born, required no less than ten nurses, and after being weaned ate as much as five men! Such being the case, he was able, by the time he was eight years of age, to slay a mad white elephant with a single stroke of his fist. Many similar feats were performed during the boyhood of this Persian Hercules, who longed to fight when the realm was finally invaded by the Tartar chief Afrasiab and war began to devastate the land.

> Loud neighed the steeds, and their resounding hoofs
> Shook the deep caverns of the earth; the dust
> Rose up in clouds and hid the azure heavens.
> Bright beamed the swords, and in that carnage wide,
> Blood flowed like water.

When the Persians, in their distress, implored Zal to meet and defeat this dreaded foe, the hero answered that he was too old to perform such a task, but that his son Rustem would fight in his stead. Before sending him forth, however, Zal bade Rustem select a suitable steed, and, from all those paraded before him, the youth picked out a rose-coloured colt called Rakush (lightning) whom no one had ever been able to mount. After lassoing and taming this wonderful steed, which obeyed him alone, Rustem, armed with a mace, set out to meet the foe, sent hither as he knew by the Evil Spirit. After driving away the foe, he placed on the throne Kaikobad, a descendant of the old royal family.

The wise Kaikobad, who reigned peacefully for 100 years, was, however, succeeded by a very foolish son, Kaikous, who, ill satisfied with the extent of his realm, undertook to conquer Mazinderan, which was in the hands of demons, but which he had coveted ever since it had been described by a young bard who sang:

> "And mark me, that untravelled man
> Who never saw Mazinderan
> And all the charms its bowers possess,
> Has never tasted happiness."

On hearing his master propose such a conquest, Zal vainly remonstrated, but the foolish monarch set out, and on arriving in Mazinderan was defeated by the demons, who blinded him and his army and detained them prisoners. No sooner did the news of this calamity reach Zal, than he bade Rustem go and rescue the foolish monarch, adding that, although it had taken Kaikous six months to reach his destination, Rustem could get there in seven days, provided he were willing to brave great dangers.

Of course the hero selected the shorter route, and on the first day slew a wild ass, which he roasted for supper before lying down to rest. The odour of roast meat, however, attracted a lion, which would have made a meal of the sleeping Rustem, had not his brave steed fought with hoofs and teeth until he succeeded in slaying the beast of prey. Awakened only as the fight ended, Rustem reproved his horse for risking his life in this reckless way, and bade him henceforth call for aid.

"Oh, Rakush, why so thoughtless grown
To fight a lion thus alone?
For had it been thy fate to bleed,
And not thy foe, O gallant steed!
How could thy master have conveyed
His helm, and battle-axe, and blade,
Unaided to Mazinderan?
Why didst thou fail to give the alarm,
And save thyself from chance of harm,
By neighing loudly in my ear?
But, though thy bold heart knows no fear,
From such unwise exploits refrain,
Nor try a lion's strength again."

During the second day's journey, Rustem was saved from perishing of thirst by following a stray ram to a mountain stream; and on the third night, having forbidden his horse to attack any foe without warning him, Rustem was twice awakened by the loud neighing of Rakush, who had seen an eighty-yard long dragon draw near. Each time he neighed, however, the dragon disappeared, so Rustem, seeing nought, reproved his horse for breaking his rest. The third time, however, he caught a glimpse of the dragon's fiery eyes, so, attacking him, he slew him, thanks to the help of his horse. The fourth day was signalized by other marvellous adventures, and on the fifth, while journeying through the land of magic, Rustem was met by a sorceress, who tried to win him by many wiles. He accepted the banquet and the cup of wine which she tendered, but he no sooner bade her quaff it in the name of God, than she was forced to resume her fiendish form, whereupon he slew her.

On the sixth day, Rustem, forced to ride through a land where the sun never shone, allowed his intelligent steed to guide him, and thus safely reached on the seventh a land of plenty and light, where he lay down to rest. There, while he was sleeping, the people of Mazinderan captured his wonderful steed. But, following the traces of his struggling horse, Rustem, by dint of great exertions, made them give back Rakush, and forced them to guide him to the cave where the White Demon was detaining his fellow-countrymen prisoners.

In front of this cave Rustem found an array of demons, and, after conquering them all, forced his way into the Persian hell, whence he rescued his companions, whose sight he restored by trickling the blood of the White Demon into their sightless eyes.

Having thus earned the title of 'champion of the world,' Rustem escorted the stupid king home, but this monarch, not satisfied with this blunder, committed one folly after another. We are told that he even undertook to fly, his special make of acroplane being a carpet borne by four starving eagles, fastened to the four corners of its frame, and frantically striving to reach a piece of meat fixed temptingly above and ahead of them.

Time and again the foolish monarch Kaikous was rescued by the efforts of Rustem, who, in the course of his wanderings, finally came to the court of a king whose daughter, loving him by hearsay, had his horse stolen from him. When Rustem angrily demanded the return of his steed, the monarch assured him he should have Rakush on the morrow. But that night the beautiful princess, Tamineh, stole into Rustem's room, and, after waking him, promised he should have his horse provided he would marry her. Charmed by her beauty and grace, Rustem readily consented, and found such attractions in his bride that he lingered by her side for some time.

The moment came, however, when the foolish monarch required Rustem's services, and, as Tamineh was not able at that time to bear the long journey, Rustem bade her a fond farewell, leaving an onyx bracelet bearing the image of the Simurgh, with which he bade her deck their expected child. In due time the lovely princess gave birth to a beautiful boy, whom she called Sorab (sunshine), but, fearing lest Rustem should take him away to train him as a warrior, she sent word to him that she had given birth to a daughter. Girls being of minor importance in Persia, Rustem inquired no further about this child, and was kept so busy serving his monarch that he never once visited his wife while his son was growing up.

For a long time Tamineh jealously guarded the secret of Sorab's birth, fearing lest her young son would want to go forth and do battle too. But when she could no longer keep him at home, she told him the story of her wooing:

> "Listen, my child, and you shall hear
> Of the wondrous love of a maiden dear
> For a mighty warrior, the pride of his day,
> Who loved, and married, and rode away,
> For this is the romance of Rustem."

The lad, who had always cherished a romantic admiration for Rustem, was overjoyed to learn his origin, and departed only after being reminded that he must never fight his father, although about to help the Tartars in a war against Persia. Sorab was doing so because everybody was tired of the foolish king, who was to be overthrown, so that Rustem could be placed on the throne in his stead. To make sure that her son should not fail to recognize his father, Tamineh sent with him two faithful servants who had known Rustem well when he came to woo her.

Meantime Afrasiab, chief of the Tartars, delighted to have Sorab's aid against Persia, cautioned all his warriors not to tell the youth, should his father appear in the opposite army, for he slyly hoped "the young lion would kill the old one," and felt sure that, were he only rid of father and son, he would be able to rule over Persia himself.

In the course of this war young Sorab met with many adventures, fighting once against an Amazon, who by trickery managed to escape from him. However, Sorab kept hoping the time would come when he and his father would meet face to face, and, whenever a fray was about to take place, he always bade his companions scan the ranks of the foe to make sure that Rustem was not there.[1]

Meantime the foolish king, having been worsted in the war, had sent for Rustem, who, in order to reconnoitre, entered the Tartar camp as a spy. There he beheld Sorab, and could not help admiring the young warrior, of whose many brave exploits he had already heard. While thus prowling about the

[1] It is this part of the story which Matthew Arnold has rendered so ably in his *Sohrab and Rustum.*

enemy's tents Rustem was discovered by the two servants whom Tamineh had placed by her son's side, both of whom he killed before they could give the alarm. Thus, when Sorab and Rustem finally came face to face, there was no one at hand to point out the son to the father or inform the son of his close relationship to his antagonist. After the war had raged for some time, Sorab challenged the Persians to a single fight, for he was anxious to distinguish himself, knowing that should he win a great triumph his father would hear of it, and inquire the origin of the youth of whom such tales were told :

> "Come then, hear now, and grant me what I ask.
> Let the two armies rest to-day ; but I
> Will challenge forth the bravest Persian lords
> To meet me, man to man : If I prevail,
> Rustum will surely hear it ; if I fall—
> Old man, the dead need no one, claim no kin.
> Dim is the rumour of a common fight,
> Where host meets host, and many names are sunk ;
> But of a single combat fame speaks clear." [1]

Such was the reputation of Sorab, however, that none of the Persians dared encounter him, and Rustem was urged to undertake this task himself. Fearing lest so youthful an opponent should withdraw if he heard the name of his antagonist, or that he should pride himself too greatly on the honour done him, Rustem went into battle in disguise.

On seeing a stalwart old warrior approach, Sorab felt strangely moved, and, running to meet him, begged to know his name, for he had a premonition

[1] The quotations concerned with this episode are from Matthew Arnold's *Sohrab and Rustum.*

that this was Rustem. The father, too, seized by a peculiar feeling of tenderness for this youth, owned to himself that had he a male descendant he would fain have had him look like Sorab, and therefore tried to make him withdraw his challenge. Notwithstanding Sorab's eager inquiries, Rustem obstinately refused to divulge his name, and, seeing his opponent would not desist, bade him begin the fight without further ado.

> And then he turned and sternly spake aloud,—
> "Rise! wherefore dost thou vainly question thus
> Of Rustum? I am here whom thou hast called
> By challenge forth; make good thy vaunt, or yield!
> Is it with Rustum only thou wouldst fight?
> Rash boy, men look on Rustum's face, and flee!
> For well I know, that did great Rustum stand
> Before thy face this day, and were revealed,
> There would be then no talk of fighting more."

For three consecutive days the battle raged, father and son proving of equal strength and skill. But, although Sorab once overthrew Rustem, he generously stepped aside and allowed the aged warrior to recover his footing. Several times, also, the young man proposed that they should sheathe their swords, for his heart continued to be attracted to his opponent, who, fighting down similar emotions, always taunted his antagonist into renewing the fight.

> He spoke; and Sohrab kindled at his taunts,
> And he too drew his sword; at once they rushed
> Together, as two eagles on one prey
> Come rushing down together from the clouds,
> One from the east, one from the west; their skulls
> Dashed with a clang together, and a din
> Rose, such as that the sinewy woodcutters
> Make often in the forest's heart at morn,
> Of hewing axes, crashing trees,—such blows
> Rustum and Sohrab on each other hailed.

The Death of Sorab
Gertrude A. Steel

It was only on the fifth day that Rustem, forgetting everything in the excitement of the moment, met his foe with his usual war-cry, "Rustem, Rustem." The mere sound of so beloved a name so paralyzed Sorab, that, instead of meeting this onslaught, he sank beneath his father's blow. Then he gasped that, although dying, his adversary could not pride himself upon having fairly won the victory, for nothing short of his father's name could have disarmed him thus.

> "But that beloved name unnerved my arm,—
> That name, and something, I confess, in thee,
> Which troubles all my heart, and made my shield
> Fall; and thy spear transfixed an unarmed foe.
> And now thou boastest, and insult'st my fate.
> But hear thou this, fierce man, tremble to hear:
> The mighty Rustum shall avenge my death!
> My father, whom I seek through all the world,
> He shall avenge my death, and punish thee!"

On hearing these words Rustem anxiously demanded explanation, only to learn that the man he had mortally wounded was his own son, as was only too surely proved by the bracelet decorated with the Simurgh which Sorab exhibited.

> It was that griffin which of old reared Zal,
> Rustum's great father, whom they left to die,
> A helpless babe, among the rocks;
> Him that kind creature found, and reared, and loved;
> Then Rustum took it for his glorious sign.

Not only did broken-hearted Rustem hang over his dying son in speechless grief, but the steed Rakush wept bitter tears over the youth who had so longed to bestride him.

> And awe fell on both the hosts,
> When they saw Rustum's grief; and Ruksh, the horse,
> With his head bowing to the ground, and mane
> Sweeping the dust, came near, and in mute woe

> First to the one, then to the other, moved
> His head, as if inquiring what their grief
> Might mean; and from his dark compassionate eyes,
> The big warm tears rolled down and caked the sand.

In hopes of saving his son, Rustem vainly implored the foolish monarch, Kaikous, to bestow upon him a drop of a magic ointment which he owned. But Sorab expired without this aid in Rustem's arms, and the broken-hearted father burned his remains on a pyre. Then he conveyed to his home Sorab's ashes, and sent the young hero's riderless steed back to his poor mother, who died of grief.

We are told that the foolish king proved so fortunate as to have a noble and generous son named Siawush, of whom he became so jealous that the youth was obliged to leave his home and was brought up by Rustem. The stepmother, who had so poisoned his father's mind against him, plotted Siawush's death as soon as he returned to court, by accusing him of making love to her. In anger the father decreed that Siawush should submit to the test of fire, so huge furnaces were lighted, through which the young man rode unharmed, the Angel of Pity and the spirit of his dead mother standing on either side of him to guard him from injury. Because the stepmother had wrongfully accused Siawush, she too was condemned to pass through the fire, but her stepson, knowing *she* could never stand such an ordeal, pleaded successfully in her behalf.

Not daring to remain at his father's court, this young prince withdrew among the Tartars, where he married Afrasiab's daughter. But such were his qualities and noble deeds, that his wicked father-in-law became jealous of him and slew him. He did not, however, succeed in exterminating the race, for a kind-hearted nobleman, Piran-Wisa, secreted Siawush's little son, and entrusted him to a goat-herd to bring up. When Afrasiab discovered a few years later that this child was still living, he planned to put him to death, until the nobleman assured him that the child was an idiot and would, therefore, never work him any harm. Only half convinced, Afrasiab sent for the youth, Kai-Khosrau, who, duly instructed by his protector, returned such foolish answers to his grandfather's questions, that Afrasiab felt satisfied he was an idiot indeed.

This young prince, having attained manhood, led a rebellion so successfully that he not only dethroned his grandfather, Afrasiab, but also recovered his hereditary throne of Persia. There he reigned for many years, at the end of which he became so anxious to leave this world, that he prayed the good god (Ormudz) to receive him in his bosom. In a dream this divinity informed the King that, as soon as his affairs were in order and his successor named, his wish would be granted. Kai-Khosrau, therefore, made all his arrangements, and set out on the journey to the next world, bidding his friends not try to accompany him, for the road would be too hard for them to travel. In spite of these injunctions, a few faithful followers went with him, until they reached a place where the cold was so intense that they all froze to death, and thus left him to continue alone the journey from which he never returned.

> And not a trace was left behind,
> And not a dimple on the wave;
> All sought, but sought in vain, to find
> The spot which proved Kai-Khosrau's grave.

The successor which Kai-Khosrau had chosen

proved a just ruler until he becamc jealous of his own son, Isfendiyar, who was also a great warrior, and who, like Rustem, accomplished seven great works. He too overcame demons, wolves, lions, enchanters, dragons, and unchained elements, and on one occasion proceeded to rescue two of his sisters, who were detained captives in the fortress of Arjasp, a demon king. Knowing that he could not enter this stronghold by force, Isfendiyar penetrated into it in the guise of a merchant, having hidden in his chests a number of soldiers, who were to help him when the right moment came. Thanks to their aid and to the fact that he began by intoxicating his foe, Isfendiyar triumphed.

The time came, however, when Isfendiyar was ordered by his father to bring Rustem to court in chains. This task proved most distasteful to the Prince, who, on approaching Rustem, explained that he was not a free agent. As the old hero obstinately refused to be manacled, the two warriors began fighting, and at the end of the day Rustem and his steed were so severely wounded that Isfendiyar felt sure they would not be able to renew the fight on the morrow.

It happened, however, that the aged Zal, on seeing his wounded son, remembered his partly burned feather, and promptly cast it into the fire. Immediately the Simurgh appeared, and with one touch of her golden wings healed the horse, and used her clever beak to draw the lance out of Rustem's side. Having thus healed her nursling's son, the Simurgh vanished, leaving Rustem and his steed in such good condition that they were able to renew the battle on the morrow. This time, Isfendiyar perished beneath Rustem's blows, exclaiming that the hero was not to blame for his death and that he fell victim to his father's hate. In token of forgiveness, he begged Rustem to bring up his son, a wish which was piously carried out by the brave warrior as long as he lived.

Because it had been written in the stars that " he who slew Isfendiyar would die miserably," Rustem was somewhat prepared for his tragic fate. It seems that his young half-brother finally became so jealous of him that he plotted to kill him by digging seven pits lined with swords and spears. These were hidden in a road along which Rustem must travel when he came in the King's name to claim tribute. Falling into the first pit, Rustem set his spurs to Rakush's sides ; and the brave steed, although wounded, leaped out of this trap, only to tumble into a second and third. From pit to pit Rustem and his dauntless horse landed at the bottom of the seventh, fainting from their many wounds.

The treacherous stepbrother now drew cautiously near to ascertain whether Rustem were dead, whereupon our hero begged for his bow and arrows, declaring he wished to ward off the wild beasts as long as he remained alive. The unsuspecting brother, therefore, flung the desired weapons down into the pit, but no sooner were they within reach, than Rustem fitted an arrow to the string, casting such a baleful look at his stepbrother that this coward hastened to take refuge behind a tree. No obstacle could, however, baulk the righteously angry Rustem, who sent his arrow straight through the trunk into his brother's heart, thus punishing the murderer for his dastardly trick. Then, returning thanks for having been allowed to avenge his wrongs, Rustem breathed his last beside his faithful steed.

On hearing that his son had perished, Zal sent an army to lay Kabul waste, and, having recovered the corpses of Rustem and of his steed, laid them piously to rest in a magnificent tomb in Seistan.

INDIAN EPICS

BESIDES the two great classical epics (*Mahàkavyas*)—the *Mahabharata* and the *Ramayana*—Indian literature claims eighteen Puranas, each of which bears a distinctive title. These Puranas treat mainly of 'ancient legendary lore,' and contain many tales of gods and sages, as well as descriptions of the Hindu world, with Mount Meru as its centre, and also of the deluge.

Many of the incidents of the two great epics inspired later poets to compose what are known as *kavyas*, or court epics. Six of these by Bahrtruhari are termed Great Court Epics (*Mahàkavyas*), and another, by the poet Asvaghosha, describing the doings of Buddha at length, was translated into Chinese between 414 and 421 A.D. The Golden Age for the court epics (which were written from 200 B.C. to A.D. 1100) was during the sixth century of our era.

In the fifth century A.D. the poet Kalidasa composed a nineteen-canto epic, entitled *Raghuvamça*, wherein he related at length the life of Rama, as well as of Rama's ancestors and of his twenty-four successors. This poem abounds in striking similes, as does also the same poet's *Kumarasambhava*, or Birth and Wooing of the War God Siva. There are, however, cantos in all these poems which are too erotic to meet with favour among modern readers. Kalidasa is also the author of an epic in Prakrit, wherein he sings of the building of the bridge between India and Ceylon and of the death of Ravana.

We are told that the *Ramayana* inspired the greatest poet of Mediaeval India, Tulsi Das, to compose the *Ram Charit Manas*, a play wherein he gives a somewhat shorter and very popular version of Rama's adventures. This work still serves as a sort of Bible for 100,000,000 of the people of Northern India.

The poet Kaviraja (*c.* A.D. 800) composed an epic wherein he combines the *Ramayana* and *Mahabharata* into one single poem. This is a Hindu *tour de force*, for we are told that "the composition is so arranged that by the use of ambiguous words and phrases the story of the *Ramayana* and the *Mahabharata* is told at one and the same time. The same words, according to the sense in which they are understood, narrate the events of each epic."

THE RAMAYANA

This Hindu epic, an older poem than the *Mahabharata*, was composed in Sanscrit some five hundred years before our era, and is contained in seven books, aggregating 24,000 verses. It is often termed 'the *Odyssey* of the East,' and relates events which are said to have occurred between 2000 and 900 B.C. The poem is generally attributed to Válmikí, a hermit on the bank of the Ganges, who, seeing one bird of a happy pair slain, made use of a strange metre in relating the occurrence to Brahma. This god immediately bade him employ the same in narrating the adventures of Rama, one of the seven incarnations of the god Vishnu.

> Praise to Válmikí, bird of charming song,
> Who mounts on Poesy's sublimest spray,
> And sweetly sings with accents clear and strong
> Rama, aye Rama, in his deathless lay.[1]

[1] The quotations in short lines are taken from the translation by Griffeth, and those in long lines from that by Romesh Dutt.

The poem opens with a description of the ancient city of Ayodhya (Oude), beautifully situated on the banks of a river and ruled by a childless rajah.

In bygone ages built and planned
By sainted Manu's princely hand,
Imperial seat! her walls extend
Twelve measured leagues from end to end;
Three in width, from side to side
With square and palace beautified.
Her gates at even distance stand,
Her ample roads are wisely planned.
Right glorious is her royal street,
Where streams allay her dust and heat.
On level ground in even row
Her houses rise in goodly show.
Terrace and palace, arch and gate
The queenly city decorate.
High are her ramparts, strong and vast,
By ways at even distance passed,
With circling moat both deep and wide,
And store of weapons fortified.

The Rajah Dasaratha, a descendant of the moon, was 60,000 years old when the story begins. Although his reign had already extended over a period of 9000 years,—during which his people had enjoyed such prosperity that it is known as the Age of Gold,—the King, still childless although he had 750 concubines, decided to offer a great horse sacrifice (*asvatmedha*) in hopes of obtaining a son to celebrate his funeral rites and thereby enable him to enter heaven.

That the ceremony might be properly performed, a horse had to be turned out to wander at will for a year, constantly watched by a band of priests, who prevented any one laying a hand upon him, for, once touched, the animal was unfit to be offered up to the gods. This horse sacrifice having been duly performed, the happy Rajah was informed by the gods that four sons would uphold his line, provided he and three of his wives quaffed the magic drink they gave him.

Having thus granted the Rajah's prayer, the lesser gods implored their chief Indra to rid them of the demons sent by Ravana, the Satan of the Hindus. This evil spirit, by standing on his head in the midst of five fires for 10,000 years in succession had secured from Brahma a promise that no god, demon, or genius should slay him. By this extraordinary feat he had also obtained nine extra heads with a full complement of eyes, ears, and noses, hands and arms. Mindful of his promise, Brahma was at a loss to grant this request until he remembered that he had never guaranteed Ravana against attack by man or monkey. He therefore decided to beg Vishnu to enter the body of a man and conquer this terrible foe, while the lesser gods helped him in the guise of monkeys.

> "One only way I find
> To slay this fiend of evil mind.
> He prayed me once his life to guard
> From demon, god, and heavenly bard,
> And spirits of the earth and air,
> And I, consenting, heard his prayer.
> But the proud giant in his scorn
> Recked not of man of woman born;
> None else may take his life away
> And only man the fiend can slay."

At Brahma's request, Vishnu not only consented to become man, but elected to enter the body of the Rajah's eldest son—one of the four children obtained in answer to prayer. In the meantime he charged his fellow gods diligently to beget helpers for him, so they proceeded to produce innumerable monkeys. The poem next informs us that Rama, son of the Rajah's favourite wife, being a god,—an incarnation of Vishnu,—came into the world with jewelled crown and brandishing four arms, but that, at his parents' request, he concealed these divine attributes, assumed a purely human form, and cried lustily like a babe. Two other wives of the Rajah, having received lesser portions of the divine beverage, gave birth to three sons (Bharata, Lakshmana, and Satrughna), and the news that four heirs had arrived in the palace caused great rejoicings in the realm.

These four princes grew up full of promise, Rama in particular developing every virtue, and showing even in childhood marked ability as an archer. Such was his proficiency in athletic sports that a hermit besought him, at sixteen, to rid his forest of the demons which were making life miserable for him and his kin. To enable Rama to triumph over these foes, the hermit bestowed upon him divine weapons, assuring him they would never fail him.

> And armed with these, beyond a doubt,
> Shall Rama put those fiends to rout.

The hermit also beguiled the weariness of their long journey to the forest by relating to Rama the story of the Ganges, the sacred stream of India. We are told that a virtuous king, being childless, betook himself to the Himalayas, where, after spending 100 years in austerities, Brahma announced that he should have one son by one of his wives and 60,000 by the other, adding that his consorts might choose whether to bear one offspring or many. Given the first choice, the favourite wife elected to be the mother of the son destined to continue the royal race, while the other brought into the world a gourd, wherein a hermit discovered the germs of 60,000 brave sons, all of whom, thanks to his care, grew up to perform wonders in behalf of their father and brother.

On one occasion, a horse chosen for sacrifice having been stolen, the father dispatched these 60,000 braves in quest of it, and, as they were not able to discover any traces of it on earth, bade them dig down to hell. Not only did they obey, but continued their search until they worked their way down to the four elephants on whose backs the Hindus believe that our earth peacefully reposes. Here, the diggers disturbed the meditations of some god, who, in his anger, burned them up. The poor father, anxious to purify the ashes of his dead sons, learned that he would never be able to do so until the Ganges—a river of heaven—was brought down to earth. By dint of penance and prayer, the bereaved parent induced Vishnu to permit this stream—which until then had only flowed in heaven—to descend to earth. The King was warned that the river, in coming down, would destroy the world unless some means were found to stem the force of its current. Our clever Rajah met this danger by persuading the god Siva to receive the cataract on the top of his head, where the sacred waters, after threading their way through his thick locks, were divided into the seven streams which feed the sacred springs of India. Thus safely brought to earth, the Ganges penetrated to hell, where it purified the ashes of the 60,000 martyrs, and ever since that time its waters have been supposed to possess miraculous powers.

For sin and stain were banished thence,
By the sweet river's influence.

The hermit also related how the gods procured the Water of Life (*Amrita*) by churning the ocean, using Mount Meru as a dasher, and a huge serpent as the rope whereby to twirl it around.

Led by this hermit, Rama not only slew the ravaging monsters, but went on to take part in a tournament, where King Janak offered his daughter, Sita, in marriage to any archer who would span a bow which he had obtained from Siva. On arriving at the place where this feat was to be performed, Rama saw the huge bow brought forth on a chariot drawn by 5000 men, and, although no one else had even been able to raise it, took it up and bent it until it broke with a crack which terrified all present. By this feat young Rama won the hand of Sita, a beautiful princess, whom her father turned up from the soil while ploughing one day, and who is hence the Hindu personification of Spring.

The wedding of Rama and Sita was honoured by the presence of both kings, and Rama's three brothers were made as happy as he by receiving the hands of three of Sita's sisters, the father telling each bridegroom:

"A faithful wife, most blest is she,
And as thy shade will follow thee."

When the four bridal couples returned to Ayodhya, Dasaratha decided to name his eldest son assistant king, and therefore gave orders to prepare for the ceremony. The mere rumour that Rama was about to be crowned aroused the jealousy of the King's youngest wife, Kaikeyi, who, instigated by an evil-minded, hunch-backed maid, sent for her aged

Rama breaks the Bow of Janak
Evelyn Paul

spouse and reminded him how once, when he was ill, he had promised in return for her care to grant any two boons she asked. The infatuated monarch, seeing her grief, rashly renewed this promise, swearing to keep it by Rama's head.

> As some wild elephant who tries
> To soothe his consort as she lies
> Struck by the hunter's venomed dart,
> So the great king, disturbed in heart,
> Strove with soft hand and fond caress
> To soothe his darling queen's distress,
> And in his love addressed with sighs
> The lady of the lotus eyes.

Hearing him confirm his former oath, the favourite wife bade him banish his heir to the forest for fourteen years and appoint her son as viceroy in his brother's stead. In vain the old king pleaded; the favourite wife insisted so vehemently that when morning dawned the bewildered old Rajah sent for Rama to ask his advice. Although this prince fully expected to be crowned that day, he was too virtuous not to perceive that a promise must be kept at any cost, so without a murmur he prepared to go to the forest of Dandaka and dwell there in hermit garb fourteen years.

> "The orders of my sire," he cried,
> "My will shall ne'er oppose:
> I follow still, whate'er betide,
> The path which duty shows."

His first duty, however, was to return to his palace to inform his wife that they must part; but, on hearing what had occurred, Sita piteously begged to share his fate, although he eloquently described the hardships to which she would be exposed should she venture to accompany him. Her devotion was, however, proof against all that he could urge, for she declared with tears there was no happiness for her save at his side.

> "With thee is heaven, where'er the spot;
> Each place is hell where thou art not."

Hearing this declaration, Rama finally consented to take her with him, and, bidding farewell to father and mother, left the city, accompanied by his wife and his favourite brother, Lakshman, and escorted by his mourning subjects.

His father, broken-hearted at parting with his favourite son, took to his bed, which he was never to leave again, confiding to Rama's mother that he was being sorely punished for a sin of his youth. It seems that, while out hunting one night, hearing a gurgle by a stream, and fancying that some wild beast was there drinking, he let fly a shaft, which only too surely reached its goal. Startled by a human cry, the Rajah rushed down to the river, only to discover that he had mortally wounded a youth who had come down to draw water for his blind parents.

> "Then in the dusk I heard the sound of gurgling water;
> Quickly I took my bow, and, aiming toward the sound, shot off the dart.
> A cry of mortal agony came from the spot,—a human voice
> Was heard, and a poor hermit's son fell pierced and bleeding in the stream."

Before dying this lad implored his slayer to hasten back to the hermitage with water, as the old people were longing to quench their thirst. On hearing footsteps, the blind parents peevishly reproached their son for tarrying, and, when the unfortunate murderer tried to explain what had occurred, cursed him vehemently, declaring that he would some day experience the loss of a son. It was, therefore, in fulfilment of this curse that the aged Dasaratha died thirteen days after Rama's departure.

Meantime the banished prince, riding in one of his father's chariots, had reached the junction of the Jumna and the Ganges, where he spent the first night of his exile beneath a banyan on the banks of the sacred stream. There he built a raft, by means of which he crossed to the other side, and from there sadly watched his faithful subjects depart homeward. Then he plunged into the forest, arranging that Sita should always tread its narrow paths between him and his brother, to make sure that no harm should befall her.

The Indian poet now favours us with a wonderful description of the tropical forest, with its huge trees, brilliant flowers, strange birds and monkeys, all of which gives the reader a vivid impression of the colour, beauty, perfume, and luxuriance of the tropics.

> On rocky heights beside the way
> And lofty trees with blossoms gay;
> And streamlets running fair and fast,
> The royal youths and Sita passed.

The exiles, wandering thus in single file, finally arrived at Citra-kuta, where they joined a colony of hermits, built a rustic booth, and dwelt happily for some time. One day the rumour of a coming host roused their curiosity, and Lakshman, descrying a long procession from the top of a high tree, excitedly warned Rama that his brother was probably coming to annihilate them.

Rama, who always ascribes good motives to every one, now declares it is impossible this should be true, and feels sure that his brother is coming for some affectionate purpose. Greeting Bharata kindly, therefore, he soon discovers that his previsions are correct, for the young prince, after announcing his father's death, implores Rama to return and reign over Ayodhya. He not only protests that he will never supplant his senior, but reviles his mother for having compelled her husband to drive Rama into exile.

Although all present unite in entreaties, Rama, too virtuous to break a promise, decides to remain in the forest the allotted fourteen years and to resume his regal state only at the end of that time. He adds that during his banishment he will live in such a fashion that his exile will prove a blessing to his people.

"Many a blessing yet will spring
From banished Rama's wanderings."

Rama then urges his brother to act meanwhile as vice-regent; whereupon Bharata, taking Rama's golden sandals, proclaims that they alone shall occupy the throne beneath the royal umbrella, although he consents to rule in his brother's name. This settled, the gorgeous procession slowly wends its way back to Ayodhya, where for fourteen years every one does homage to Rama's golden sandals.

Life in the hermitage continues its peaceful course, the royal ascetics being disturbed only by the demons (*Rakshasas*) who haunt the forest and try to injure the hermits, simply because they are good. Sita is perfectly happy in this humble home because she enjoys the constant presence of her husband, who, taking her one day to visit an aged female ascetic, implores this woman to bestow a boon upon his faithful spouse. The old woman then and there endows Sita with eternal youth and beauty, declaring that no matter what hardships she encounters, she will always be as dainty and young as at present.

One of the female demons finally becomes so anxious to win Rama's love that she disguises herself as a beautiful creature in hopes of fascinating him. Angry because all her efforts fail, she next tries to injure Sita, whereupon Rama, by cutting off her nose and ears, forces her to resume her usual shape. In her anger this demon bids her brothers avenge her wrongs, whereupon fourteen fiends attack Rama, who, having slain them all, is almost immediately afterward forced to face thousands of demons. He defeats them single-handed, while his brother watches over Sita, hidden in a neighbouring cave.

The massacre of 21,000 of his fiends in three hours' time naturally enrages Ravana, whose abode is in Ceylon, in a golden palace which has such high walls that no one can peep over them. This King of Demons, who is also called the "Courage of the Three Worlds," has the power of increasing his stature until he can reach up to the stars with his score of arms. Owing to his ten heads, his appearance is terrifying, especially as his eyebrows are composed of live black snakes which writhe continually. No sooner does his sister appear before him, reporting that she has been mutilated by Rama, who has besides slain hosts of his subjects, than Ravana swears revenge, adding that he will first kidnap Sita, for his sister's description of her matchless charms has fired his imagination.

In his golden chariot Ravana, therefore, flies to the forest, where he bids his sister change herself into a wonderful deer, and in that shape lure Rama away, to enable him to abduct Sita. The three hermits are, therefore, calmly seated before their hut when a deer darts past, exhibiting so unusual a pelt that Sita, fired with the desire to possess it, urges Rama to pursue it. To gratify her whim, Rama starts out to track this game, calling to his brother to mount guard over his wife during his absence. Lured farther and farther away from home, Rama finally brings down his quarry, which, in falling, calls for help in a voice so exactly like his own that his brother, hearing the despairing accent, is torn between the desire to rush to his rescue and the necessity of remaining to protect Sita. But the latter, sure that her husband is in danger, so vehemently urges her brother-in-law to leave her that he finally dashes off. A moment later Sita sees an old hermit draw near to beg for alms. While she is entertaining this holy guest, he frightens her by suddenly announcing that he is Ravana, King of the Demons. As Sita resists all his advances, Ravana, suddenly resuming his wonted shape, snatches her up in his arms and whisks her off in his flying chariot. Notwithstanding the rapidity of his course, the King of the Vultures, seeing them dart through the air and hoping to rescue the frantic Sita, attacks Ravana, only to fall mortally wounded to earth. Because Sita—the personification of vegetation—has now been abducted by the demon—who typifies winter—the whole earth shows signs of mourning, and the two brothers hurry back to the hut, their hearts filled with nameless apprehensions.

> Like streamlet in the winter frost,
> The glory of her lilies lost.
> With leafy tears the sad trees wept
> As a wild wind their branches swept.
> Mourned bird and deer; and every flower
> Drooped fainting round the lovely bower.

> The sylvan deities had fled
> The spot where all the light was dead.

Reaching their hermitage and finding their worst fears justified, both brothers set out in quest of Sita, and soon come across the dying vulture, who reports what he has seen, and bids them, after burning his body, find the monkey king, Sugriva, who will aid them. After piously fulfilling the brave vulture's last wishes, Rama and his brother visit the monkey monarch, who reports that, as the demon flew over his head, Sita flung down a few of her ornaments, begging that they might be taken to Rama. An alliance is now concluded between Rama and Sugriva, and, as each party pledges himself to help the other, Rama begins by slaying the brother and chief foe of the monkey king, who in his turn undertakes to trace Sita.

To discover where she may be, Hanuman, the monkey general, sets out, and, following Sita's traces, discovers that she has been carried to Ceylon. On arriving at the southern point of the Indian peninsula and finding some two hundred miles of water between him and this island, Hanuman, son of the God of the Winds, transforms himself into a huge ape, and in that shape takes a flying leap from the top of Mount Mandara (the fabled centre of the earth) to the top of Mount Sabula, which overlooks the capital of Ceylon. Then, reconnoitring from this point, the monkey general perceives that Ravana's palace is so closely guarded that he can only steal into it in the guise of a cat. Prowling through the royal premises, he searches for Sita until he finally discovers her in a secluded garden, bitterly mourning for her spouse.

In spite of the fact that she has already been some

time in Ravana's power, he has not yet succeeded in winning her affections, and dares not use violence against her lest he incur the wrath of the gods. It is evident, however, that his patience is at an end, for Hanuman overhears him threaten to chop Sita to pieces unless she will yield to his wishes and become his wife within the next two months.

> "My cooks shall mince thy limbs with steel
> And serve thee for my morning meal."

When Sita is left alone, Hanuman, in the guise of a tiny monkey, climbs down to her side, exhibits Rama's ring, which he has brought as a token, and receives from her in return a jewel, after he has assured her that she will soon be delivered.

About to leave Ceylon to report what he has seen, it occurs to the monkey general to do some damage to the foe. In the guise of an immense baboon, he therefore destroys a grove of mango trees, an act of vandalism which so infuriates Ravana that he orders the miscreant to be seized and fire to be tied to his tail. But no sooner has the brand been set alight than the monkey general, suddenly transforming himself into a tiny ape, slips out of his bonds, and scrambling up on the palace roof sets it on fire as well as all the houses in Lanka, his flaming tail serving as a torch.

> As earth with fervent heat will glow
> When comes her final overthrow,
> From gate to gate, from court to spire,
> Proud Lanka was one blaze of fire,
> And every headland, rock, and bay
> Shone bright a hundred leagues away!

Then, satisfied with the damage he has done, Hanuman hastens back to the seashore, whence by another prodigious leap he lands in India, to inform Rama and Sugriva, the monkey king, of the success of his expedition.

A huge monkey army now sets out under Rama's guidance, but general and warriors are equally dismayed on reaching the sea to find an insurmountable obstacle between them and their goal. In answer to Rama's fervent prayers, however, the God of the Sea, rising from the waves, promises that any materials cast into his waters shall be held in place, to form a bridge whereby they can cross to Ceylon. All the monkeys now bring stones and tree-trunks, which they hurl into the sea, where, thanks to the efforts of the Hindu architect Nala, they are welded together and form a magic bridge. It is by means of this causeway that Rama invades Ceylon. When Ravana hears the foe is approaching, he musters an army, of which the poem gives a wonderful description. Then begins the dire combat; Rama and his forces finally prove victorious, and our hero, after slaying Ravana's son, fights with the demon himself, whose heads he proceeds to cut off. He is justly dismayed, however, to see they have the power of springing up again as soon as hewn, until remembering at last his magic bow, he makes such good use of it that he annihilates the demon, whose numerous wives wail as he falls.

As many of Rama's adherents have perished in battle, he now proceeds to call them back to life, and graciously receives the praise they bestow upon him for having rid the world of demons.

Soft from celestial minstrels came
The sound of music and acclaim;
Soft, fresh and cool, a rising breeze
Brought odours from the heavenly trees;

And, ravishing the sight and smell,
A wondrous rain of blossoms fell;
And voices breathed round Reghu's son,
"Champion of gods, well done, well done."

It is only then that Rama consents to see Sita, who, thanks to her gift of eternal beauty, is still so lovely that all present are awed. But, instead of embracing her, Rama coldly declares that, although he crossed the seas for her sake and slew her foes, she is no longer worthy to dwell in his sight since she has been an inmate of Ravana's harem. In vain Sita urges that she has been faithful throughout. Rama refuses to credit her purity; so the poor little wife, preferring death to disgrace, begs permission to die on a funeral pyre. Even then the stern husband shows no signs of relenting, but allows her to enter a fierce fire, whence the God of the Flames bears her out unharmed, and restores her to her husband, declaring that, as her chastity has withstood this fiery test, he can receive her without compunction.

By this time the prescribed fourteen years of exile have run their course, so husband and wife set out for home, crossing the ocean bridge in Ravana's magic car, and flying all over India, of which the poet gives a wonderful panoramic description. Rama's return to Ayodhya is joyfully welcomed by Bharata, who proudly shows him the golden sandals which have occupied the throne all this time.

Rama's reign proves a golden age for India, but, although all seem happy, some doubt lingers in regard to the propriety of Sita's return. When a famine finally devastates the land, one of the ministers ascribes this scourge to the fact that Rama has taken back a guilty wife. Rama, therefore, banishes the

The Triumph of Sita

Evelyn Paul

536

faithful Sita, who returns to the forest and to the protection of the hermits, where she gives birth to twin sons, Kusa and Lava, the destined singers of Válmikí's wonderful song. These youths are, however, brought up in the forest in total ignorance of their august descent.

Twenty years have passed since Rama repudiated his wife, when he decides to offer a horse sacrifice. But, the steed which he selects having been captured by two young men, Rama angrily orders them to be put to death. As the victims resist all efforts to seize them, the King in person goes forth to capture them. On approaching near enough, he haughtily demands their names and origin, whereupon the youths rejoin that their mother is Sita and their tutor Válmikí, but that they do not know their father's name. These words reveal to Rama that he is face to face with his own sons, but, although he rejoices, he still finds it difficult to believe that Sita can have been faithful. He therefore determines that before she is reinstated she must undergo a second trial by fire; but Sita, who no longer feels any desire to belong to so heartless a spouse, flatly refuses to accompany him, until Válmikí informs her that it is a wife's duty to obey.

Still wearing the crown of eternal youth and beauty, Sita now appears before Rama, in whose presence she implores the earth to open and receive her, and thus prove that she has ever been true to her marriage vows. A moment later the King and his court see the earth heave and open, and behold the Goddess of the Earth, who, taking Sita by the hand, announces that she is about to convey her to realms of eternal bliss. Then Sita and the goddess disappear, the earth closes once more, and the gods chant the praises of the faithful wife, showering flowers upon Rama, who grovels on the ground in his agony. A broken-hearted man, he then returns to his palace with his two sons, the first to sing this poem, whose verses are so sacred that those who listen to a few of them are forgiven many sins, while those who hear the whole epic are sure to achieve Paradise.

He shall be
From every sin and blemish free:
Whoever reads the saving strain,
With all his kin the heavens shall gain.

Because the poem is so sacred, its author enjoined upon the youths to recite it often, a task which they faithfully performed as long as they lived, and which other bards have continued until to-day in all parts of India.

Recite ye this heroic song
In tranquil shades where sages throng;
Recite it where the good resort,
In lowly home and royal court.

We are told besides that—

As long as mountain ranges stand
And rivers flow upon the earth,
So long will this Ramayana
Survive upon the lips of men.

Rama is finally visited by the God of Time, who offers him the choice of remaining on earth or returning to heaven. When he wisely chooses the latter alternative, Rama is bidden to bathe in sacred waters, and thence is translated to the better world.

THE MAHABHARATA

The longest poem in existence, is composed in Sanscrit, and, although begun before the *Ramayana*, was completed only about one hundred years later. It consists of some two hundred and twenty thousand lines, divided into eighteen sections (*parvans*), each of which forms a large volume. Although the whole work has never been translated into English verse, many portions of it have been reproduced both in verse and prose.

The Hindus consider this one of their most sacred books, attribute its authorship to Vyasa, and claim that the reading of a small portion of it will obliterate sin, while the perusal of the whole will insure heavenly bliss. Its name signifies 'the great war,' and its historical kernel, including one-fifth of the whole work, consists of an account of an eighteen days' battle (in the thirteenth or fourteenth century B.C.) between rival tribes. The poem is, besides, a general repository of the mythological, legendary, and philosophical lore of the Hindus, and reached its present state of development only by degrees and at the end of several centuries.

Bharata, the real founder of the principal Indian dynasty, is so famous a character that the Hindus often designate their whole country as 'the land of Bharata.' We are told that Rajah Dushyanta, a descendant of the Moon, while hunting one day, beheld the beautiful Sakuntala, daughter of a sage, whom he persuaded to consent to a clandestine marriage. But after a short time the bridegroom departed, leaving his bride a ring as a pledge of his troth.

Absorbed in thoughts of her absent lover, Sakuntala once failed to notice the approach of a sage, who cursed her, saying she should be forgotten by the man she loved, but who, relenting after a while, declared this curse would be annulled when her husband beheld his ring.

Some time after this, on the way to rejoin her spouse to inform him that she was about to become a mother, Sakuntala, while bathing in a sacred pool, accidentally dropped this ring. On appearing without it before Dushyanta, he sternly denied all acquaintance with her and ordered her to be driven out into the jungle, where she soon gave birth to their son Bharata.

The lad was about six years old when a fisherman found in the stomach of a fish the lost ring, which he carried to the Rajah. On beholding this token, Dushyanta, remembering all, hastened to seek poor Sakuntala, whom he discovered in the jungle, watching her boy fearlessly play with lion cubs. Proud of such a son, the Rajah bore his family home; and Bharata, after a long reign, had a son, Hastin, founder of Hastinapur, a city on the bank of the Ganges about sixty miles from the modern Delhi.

A grandson of this Hastin married the Goddess of the Ganges, who was doing penance on earth, and their children were animated by the souls of deities condemned for a time to assume human form. In order to enable these fellow-gods to return to heaven as soon as possible, Ganga undertook to drown each of her babes soon after birth, provided the gods would pledge themselves to endow one of her descendants with their strength, and would allow him to live, if not to perpetuate his species.

After seeing seven of his children cast into the water without daring to object, the Rajah, although he knew his goddess-wife would leave him if he found fault with anything she did, protested so vehemently against the loss of his eighth son that his wife disappeared with the child. But a few years later this son, Bhishma the Terrible, having grown up, was restored to his father.

To comfort himself for the loss of his first wife, the King now married the beautiful daughter of a fisherman, solemnly promising that her son should succeed him, for Bhishma voluntarily relinquished all right to the throne and took a vow to remain celibate. The new wife's main attraction seems to have been a sweet odour, bestowed by a saint, who restored her virginity after she had borne him a son named Vyasa, the author of this poem.

By the Rajah the fishermaid now had two sons, one of whom was slain at the end of a three years' fight, while the other began his reign under the wise regency of Bhishma. When it was time for his royal stepbrother to marry, Bhishma sent him to a Bride's Choice (*Swayamvara*), where three lovely princesses were to be awarded to the victor. Without waiting to win them fairly, the young prince kidnapped all three and, when the disappointed suitors pursued him, Bhishma held them at bay by shooting ten thousand arrows at once, and thus enabled his stepbrother and brides to escape.

Although thus provided with three royal wives, our prince was soon deserted by one of them and was never fortunate enough to have children by the two others. After he had died, custom required that his nearest kinsman should raise issue for him, so, owing to Bhishma's vow, Vyasa, who was fabulously ugly, undertook to visit the two widows. One of them, catching a glimpse of him, bore him a blind son (Dhritarashtra), while the other was so frightened that she bore a son of such pale complexion that he was known as Pandu the White.

Neither of these youths being deemed perfect enough to represent properly the royal race, Vyasa announced he would pay the widows another visit; but this time they hired a slave to take their place, so it was she who brought into the world Vidura, God of Justice. Because one prince was blind and the other the offspring of a slave, the third, Pandu, was set upon his throne by his uncle Bhishma, who in due time provided him with two lovely wives.

With these the monarch withdrew to the Himalayas to spend his honeymoon, and while there proved unfortunate enough to wound a couple of deer who were hermits in disguise. In dying they predicted that he would perish in the arms of one of his wives, whereupon Pandu decided to refrain from all intercourse with them, graciously allowing them instead to bear him five sons by five different gods. These youths, known in the poem as the sons of Pandu, the Pandavs (or the Pandavas), are the main heroes of India. As a prediction made by an ascetic was bound to come true, the King, momentarily forgetting the baleful curse, died in the embrace of his second wife, who, in token of grief, was burned with his remains, this being the earliest mention of a suttee.

In the meantime the blind prince had married a lady to whom a famous ascetic had promised that she should be mother to one hundred sons! All these came into the world at one birth, in the shape of a lump of flesh, which the ascetic divided into one hundred and one pieces, each of which was enclosed in a pot of rarefied butter, where these germs gradually developed into one hundred sons and one daughter.

As long as Pandu sojourned in the Himalayas, the blind prince, Dhritarashtra, reigned in his stead, but when he died, his surviving widow brought to the capital (Hastinapur) her five divine sons, the Pandavs. There the blind uncle had them brought up with their cousins, the hundred Kurus (or Kauravas), with whom, however, they were never able to live in perfect peace. Once, as the result of a boyish quarrel, a Kuru flung Bhima, one of the Pandavs, into the Ganges, where, instead of sinking, this hero was inoculated by serpent-bites with the strength of 10,000 elephants before he returned to his wonted place at home.

The young princes, who had all been trained to fight by their tutor, Drona, and who had already given proofs of their proficiency in arms, were finally invited by the blind monarch to give a public exhibition of their skill. The poem gives us a lengthy description of this tournament, expatiating on the flower-decked booths reserved for the principal spectators, and dwelling particularly on the fact that the blind monarch, unable to see with his own eyes, made some one sit beside him to describe all that was going on.

After the preliminary sacrifice offered by the tutor, the skill of the princes, as archers, was tested on foot, on horse-back, in howdahs, and in chariots; then they indulged in mock fights with swords and bucklers, closely watched by Drona, who pronounced his favourite, Arjuna, the third Pandav, the finest athlete ever seen.

> Still the princes shook their weapons, drove the deep resounding car,
> Or on steed or tusker mounted waged the glorious mimic war!

Mighty sword and ample buckler, ponderous mace the princes wield,
Brightly gleam their lightning rapiers as they range the listed field,
Brave and fearless is their action, and their movements quick and light,
Skilled and true the thrust and parry of their weapons flaming bright!

Thereupon, from the ranks of the spectators, emerged Karna, son of a charioteer, who challenged Arjuna to fight with him, but the Prince refused on the score that they were not of equal rank. Still a legend assures us that Karna was a child of the Sun-god, set afloat by his mother on the river Jumna, whence this Hindu Moses, floating down into the Ganges, was rescued and brought up by the charioteer, his reputed father. Meanwhile the four Pandav brothers were greatly elated by the eulogy bestowed upon their brother, but their jealous cousins became so enraged that, when the time came for the youths to face each other in club exercises, the sham battle degenerated into a real fight.

With ponderous mace they waged the daring fight.
As for a tender mate two rival elephants
Engage in frantic fury, so the youths
Encountered, and amidst the rapid sphere
Of fire their whirling weapons clashing wove,
Their persons vanished from the anxious eye.
Still more and more incensed their combat grew,
And life hung doubtful on the desperate conflict;
With awe the crowd beheld the fierce encounter
And amidst hope and fear suspended tossed,
Like ocean shaken by conflicting winds.

At last the horrified tutor separated the contestants, whom he soon after sent off separately to war against a neighbouring rajah. In this conflict the one hundred

Kurus were badly worsted, while the five Pandavs scored a brilliant triumph. They also subdued several other kings, thereby so rousing the jealous hatred of their uncle and cousins that these finally began to plot their death. The five Pandavs and their mother were therefore invited to a feast in a neighbouring city (Allahabad), where the Kurus arranged that they should be burned alive in their booth. But, duly warned by Vidura, the Pandavs had an underground passage dug from their hut to the forest, by means of which they escaped, unaware that a beggar woman and her five children—who had sought refuge in the empty hut—would be burned to death in their stead.

Disguised as Brahmans, the five brothers and their mother now dwelt for a time in the jungle, where they proceeded to slay some demons, to marry others, and to perform sundry astounding feats of strength. We are told, for instance, that whenever the mother and brothers were tired, the strongest of the Pandavs, Bhima, carried them all with the utmost ease.

While in the jungle they were visited by their grandfather Vyasa, who bade them attend the Bride's Choice of Draupadi, daughter of a neighbouring king, who—Minerva-like—came into the world full grown.

> Human mother never bore her, human bosom never fed,
> From the altar sprang the maiden who some prince will wed!

As she was passing fair, her father decided that the suitor whom she favoured would have to prove himself worthy of her by spanning a bow which no one as yet had been able to bend, and by sending an arrow through a rapidly revolving wheel into the eye of a gold fish stationed beyond it.

Owing to the loveliness of Draupadi, many rajahs

flocked to the tournament to compete for her hand, and the five Pandavs betook themselves thither in Brahman garb. After the preliminary exercises, the beautiful Princess—to whom all her suitors had been duly named—gave the signal for the contest to begin. The mere sight of the huge bow proved enough to decide several of the contestants to withdraw, but a few determined to risk all in hopes of obtaining Draupadi's hand. No man, however, proved able to bend the bow until Arjuna stepped forward, begging permission to try his luck. While the rajahs were protesting that no Brahman should compete, this Pandav spanned the bow and sent five successive shafts straight to the goal, amid the loud acclamations of all present.

> He grasped the ponderous weapon in his hand
> And with one vigorous effort braced the string.
> Quickly the shafts were aimed and swift they flew;
> The mark fell pierced; a shout of victory
> Rang through the vast arena; from the sky
> Garlands of flowers crowned the hero's head,
> Ten thousand fluttering scarfs waved in the air,
> And drum and trumpet sounded forth his triumph.

The beautiful Princess, captivated by the goodly appearance of this suitor, immediately hung round his neck the crown of flowers, although the defeated rajahs muttered that a mere Brahman should not aspire to the hand of a princess. In fact, had not his four brothers, aided by Krishna (a divine suitor), stood beside him, and had not the King insisted that there should be no disturbance, the young winner might have had a hard time. Then, as the Princess seemed perfectly willing, the wedding was celebrated, and the five brothers returned to the humble hut where they lived on alms, calling out to their mother that they had won a prize! On hearing these tidings, the mother—without knowing what the prize was—rejoined, "Share it among you," an injunction which settled for good and all that Draupadi should be common wife to all five. But the legend adds that this came to pass mainly because the maiden had prayed five times for a husband, and that the gods were answering each of her prayers separately.

Shortly after this fivefold marriage, which assured the Pandavs a royal ally, Bhishma persuaded the blind Rajah—who had meantime discovered that his nephews were not dead—to give them one half of his realm. Taking up their abode there, the Pandavs built the city of Indraprastha (Delhi) on the banks of the Jumna, before they decided that the eldest among them (Yudhishthira) should be king, the others humbly serving as his escort wherever he went.

One day this eldest Pandav went to visit the eldest Kuru, a proficient gambler, with whom he played until he had lost realm, brothers, wife, and freedom. But, when the victor took forcible possession of the fair Draupadi, and publicly stripped her of her garments, the gods, in pity, supplied her with one layer of vesture after another, so that the brutal Kuru was not able to shame her as he wished. Furious to see the treatment their wife was undergoing at the victor's hands, the five Pandavs made grim threats, and raised such a protest that the blind uncle, interfering, sent them off to the forest with their wife for twelve years. He also decreed that, during the thirteenth, all must serve in some menial capacity, with the additional condition that, if they were discovered by their cousins they should never regain their realm.

'Tis no fault of thine, fair princess! fallen to this servile state,
Wife and son rule not their actions, others rule their hapless fate!
Thy Yudhishthir sold his birthright, sold thee at the impious play,
And the wife falls with the husband, and her duty—to obey!

During the twelve years which the Pandavs spent in the forest, with the beautiful and faithful Draupadi (who was once carried away by a demon but rescued by one of her spouses), they met with many adventures. Not only did they clear the jungle, rescue from cannibals the jealous cousins who came to humiliate them, and perform other astounding feats, but they were entertained by tales told by Vyasa, among which are a quaint account of the Deluge, of the descent of the Ganges, a recitation of the *Ramayana*, and the romance of Nala and of Savitri, of which brief sketches are given at the end of this section. All this material is contained in the 'Forest Book,' the third and longest *parvan* of the *Mahabharata*, wherein we also find a curious account of Arjuna's voluntary exile because he entered into Draupadi's presence when one of his brothers was in her company. To atone for this crime, Arjuna underwent a series of austerities on the Himalayas, in reward for which his father Indra took him up to heaven, whence he brought back several weapons, among which we note Siva's miraculous bow.

In the meantime his four brothers and Draupadi had undertaken pious pilgrimages to all the sacred waters of India, and had learned various useful trades and arts before they too visited the Himalayas. There Arjuna joined them in Indra's chariot, and led them to the top of a mountain, whence they beheld the glittering palace of Kuvera, God of Wealth.

After the twelve years' sojourn in the jungle were ended, the Pandavs, thanks to divine aid, entered the service of a neighbouring king as teachers of dice and music, as charioteer, cook, cow-herd, and maid. There the five men and their wife remained for a whole year, without being discovered by their enemies, and, toward the end of their sojourn, rendered so signal a service to their master that he offered his daughter in marriage to Arjuna. Although this prince virtuously refused to accept her for himself, he bestowed her upon a son begotten during his exile.

Having completed their penance, the Pandavs returned home, to demand of the Kurus the surrender of their realm. As these greedy cousins refused to relinquish their authority, both parties prepared for war. Seeing the Kurus had ten allies, the Pandavs became anxious to secure some also. The most powerful person in the region being the Rajah Krishna, one of the Kurus hastened to his palace to bespeak his aid, and, finding him asleep, seated himself at the head of the bed. A moment later one of the Pandavs arrived, and modestly placed himself at the foot of the sleeping monarch's couch. On awakening, Krishna, of course, saw the Pandav first, but, after listening impartially to both petitioners, informed them that one party should have the benefit of his advice and the other the aid of his 100,000,000 soldiers. The greedy Kuru immediately bespoke the use of the army, while the Pandav was only too glad to secure the advice of Krishna (an embodiment of all the gods), who throughout the war acted as Arjuna's charioteer.

All preparations finished, the Great War (Mahabharata) began, the two families pitted against each other meeting on the plain of Kurukshetra (the modern Panipat) where the battle was fought. After many speeches, and after erecting fortifications which bristled with defences and were stocked with jars of scorpions, hot oil, and missiles, the two parties drew up rules of battle, which neither was to infringe under penalty of incurring the world's execration.

Even Nature now showed by unmistakable signs that a terrible conflict was about to take place, and when the two armies—which the Hindus claim numbered several billion men—came face to face, Krishna delayed the fight long enough to recite with Arjuna a dialogue of eighteen cantos called the *Bhagavad-gita*, or Divine Song, which contains a complete system of Indian religious philosophy.

The Pandavs, having besought the aid of the monkeys, were informed that they would derive great benefit by bearing a monkey banner, so it was round this standard that they marched on to victory.

> The sons of Pandu marked the coming storm
> And swift arrayed their force. The chief divine
> And Arjuna at the King's request
> Raised in the van the ape-emblazoned banner,
> The host's conducting star, the guiding light
> That cheered the bravest heart, and as it swept
> The air, it warmed each breast with martial fires.

Throughout the war the Pandav forces were directed by the same general, but their opponents had four. A moment after the first collision, the sky was filled with whistling arrows, while the air resounded with the neighing of horses and the roaring of elephants; the plain shook, and clouds of dust, dimming the light of the sun, formed a heavy pall, beneath which Pandavs and Kurus struggled in deadly fight. This frightful conflict lasted eighteen days, the battle always stopping at sunset, in order that the combatants might recover their strength.

> And ever and anon the thunder roared,
> And angry lightnings flashed across the gloom,
> Or blazing meteors fearful shot to earth.
> Regardless of these awful signs, the chiefs
> Pressed on to mutual slaughter, and the peal
> Of shouting hosts commingling shook the world.

The Kurus' general, Bhishma, fell on the tenth day,—after a terrible fight with Arjuna,—riddled with so many arrows that his body could not touch the ground. Although mortally wounded, he lay in this state, his head supported by three arrows, for fifty-eight days, and was thus able to bestow good advice on those who came to consult him.

> Darker grew the gloomy midnight, and the princes went their way;
> On his bed of pointed arrows, Bhishma lone and dying lay.

He was succeeded as leader of the Kurus by the tutor Drona, who during his five days' generalship proved almost invincible. But, some one suggesting that his courage would evaporate should he hear that his son was dead, a cry arose in the Pandav ranks that Aswathaman had perished! Unable to credit this news, Drona called to the eldest Pandav —who was strictly truthful—to know whether it was so, and heard him rejoin that it was true in regard to the elephant known by that name, but not of the man.

> Said Yudhishthir: "Lordly tusker, Aswa-thaman named, is dead";
> Drona heard but half the accents, feebly dropped his sinking head!

The poor father, who heard only a small part of the sentence—the remainder being drowned by the sound of the trumpets—lost all courage, and allowed himself to be slain without further resistance.

The whole poem bristles with thrilling hand-to-hand conflicts, the three greatest during the eighteen days' battle being those between Karna and Yudhishthira, between the eldest Kuru and Bhima, and between Karna and Arjuna. During the first sixteen days of battle, countless men were slain, including Arjuna's son by one of his many wives. Although the fighting had hitherto invariably ceased at sunset, darkness on the seventeenth day failed to check the fury of the fighters, so when the moon refused to afford them light they kindled torches in order to find each other. It was therefore midnight before the exhausted combatants dropped down on the battle-field, pillowing their heads on their horses and elephants to snatch a brief rest, so as to be able to renew the war of extermination on the morrow.

On the eighteenth day—the last of the Great War—the soil showed red with blood and was so thickly strewn with corpses that there was no room to move. Although the Kurus again charged boldly, all but three were slain by the enemies' golden maces. In fact, the fight of the day proved so fierce that only eleven men remained alive of the billions which, according to the poem, took part in the fight. But during that night the three remaining Kurus stole into the Pandav camp, killed the five sons which

Draupadi had born to her five husbands, carried off their heads, and laid them at the feet of the mortally wounded eldest Kuru, who at first believed that his cousins had been slain.

The battle ending from sheer lack of combatants, Yudhishthira ordered solemn funeral rites, which are duly described in the poem.

> "Pious rites are due to foemen and to friends and kinsmen slain,
> None shall lack a fitting funeral, none shall perish on the plain."

Then, no one being there to dispute it, he took possession of the realm, always dutifully according precedence to his blind uncle, who deeply mourned his fallen sons.

Wishing to govern wisely, Yudhishthira sought the wounded general, Bhishma, who still lay on his arrowy bed in the battle-field, and who, having given him rules for wise government, breathed his last in the presence of this Pandav, who saw his spirit rise from his divided skull and mount to the skies "like a bright star." The body was then covered with flowers and borne down to the Ganges, where, after it had been purified by the sacred waters, it was duly burned.

The new king's mind was, however, so continually haunted by the horrors of the great battle-field that, hoping to find relief, he decided to perform a horse sacrifice. Many chapters of the poem are taken up in relating the twelve adventures of this steed, which was accompanied everywhere by Arjuna, who had to wage many a fight to retain possession of the sacred animal and prevent any hand being laid upon him. Then we have a full description of the seventeen ceremonies pertaining to this strange rite.

Victor of a hundred battles, Arjun bent his homeward way,
Following still the sacred charger free to wander as it may,
Strolling minstrels to Yudhishthir spake of the returning steed,
Spake of Arjun wending homeward with the victor's crown of
meed.

Next we learn that the blind king, Dhritarashtra, still mourning the death of his sons, retired to the bank of the Ganges, where he and his wife spent their last years listening to the monotonous ripple of the sacred waters. Fifteen years after the great battle, the five Pandavs and Draupadi came to visit him, and, after sitting for a while on the banks of the sacred stream, bathed in its waters as Vyasa advised them. While doing so they saw the wraiths of all their kinsmen slain in the Great Battle rise from the boiling waters, and passed the night in conversation with them, although these spirits vanished at dawn into thin air. But the widows of the slain then obtained permission to drown themselves in the Ganges, in order to join their beloved husbands beyond the tomb.

These and other mighty warriors, in the earthly battle slain,
By their valour and their virtue walk the bright ethereal plain !
They have cast their mortal bodies, crossed the radiant gate of
heaven,
For to win celestial mansions unto mortals it is given !
Let them strive by kindly action, gentle speech, endurance long,
Brighter life and holier future unto sons of men belong !

Then the Pandav brothers and their wife took leave of the blind king, whom they were destined never to see again, for some two years later a terrible jungle fire consumed both cottage and inmates. This death was viewed by the Pandavs as a bad omen, as was also the destruction of Krishna's capital because his people drank too much wine. Krishna himself was slain by accident, while a hurricane or tidal wave sweeping over the "City of Drunkenness" wiped it off the face of the earth.

Having found life a tragedy of sorrow, Yudhishthira, after reigning thirty-six years, decided to abdicate in favour of Arjuna's grandson, and to start on a pilgrimage for Mount Meru, or Indra's heaven. As the Hindu universe consists of seven concentric rings, each of which is separated by a liquid from the next continent, he had to cross successive oceans of salt water, sugar-cane juice, wine, clarified butter, curdled milk, sweet milk, and fresh water. In the very centre of these alternate rings of land and liquid rises Mount Meru to a height of 64,000 miles, crowned by the Hindu heaven, toward which the Pandav was to wend his way. But, although all their subjects would fain have gone with them, the five brothers, Draupadi, and a faithful dog set out alone in single file, "to accomplish their union with the Infinite."

With steadfast hearts they cross the salt ocean and come within sight of the mighty mountain Himavat. Beyond its lofty peaks they come to a great ocean of sand, and at last draw near to Meru, "king of mountains." But as they hasten on, intent on their union with the Infinite, Draupadi's heart fails her, and with faltering footsteps she falls to the earth.

Thus, during this toilsome journey, one by one fell, never to rise again, until presently only two of the brothers and the dog were left. The eldest Pandav, who had marched on without heeding the rest, now explained to his companion how Draupadi sinned through excessive love for her husbands, and that their fallen brothers were victims of pride, vanity, and falsehood. He further predicted that his companion would fall, owing to selfishness, a prediction which was soon verified, leaving the eldest Pandav alone with his dog.

On his arrival, Indra bade this hero enter heaven, assuring him that the other spirits had preceded him thither, but warning him that he alone could be admitted in bodily form. When the Pandav begged that his dog might enter too, Indra indignantly rejoined that heaven was no place for animals, and inquired why the Pandav made more fuss about a four-legged companion than about his wife and brothers. Thereupon the Pandav replied that he had no power to bring the others back to life, but considered it cowardly to abandon a faithful living creature. The dog, listening intently to this dialogue, now resumed his proper form—for it seems he was the King's father in a former birth—and, having become human once more, he too was allowed to enter Paradise.

Beneath a golden canopy, seated on jewelled thrones, Yudhishthira found his blind uncle and his cousins, but failed to discern any trace of his brothers or Draupadi. He, therefore, refusing to remain, begged Indra's permission to share their fate in hell; so a radiant messenger was sent to guide him along a road paved with upturned razor edges, which passed through a dense forest whose leaves were thorns and swords. Along this frightful road the Pandav toiled, with cut and mangled feet, until he reached the place of burning, where he beheld Draupadi and his brothers writhing in the flames. Unable to rescue them, the Rajah determined to share their fate, so bade his heavenly guide return to Paradise without him. This, however, proved the last test to which his great heart was to be

"Along this frightful road the Pandav toiled"
Evelyn Paul

subjected, for no sooner had he expressed a generous determination to share his kinsmen's lot, than he was told to bathe in the Ganges and all would be well. He had no sooner done so than the heavens opened above him, allowing him to perceive, amid undying flowers, the fair Draupadi and his four brothers, who, thanks to his unselfishness, had been rescued from hell.

The grandson of Arjuna reigned at Hastinapur until he died of a snake-bite, and his son instituted snake sacrifices, at which this epic was recited by a bard who learned it from the mouth of Vyasa.

There is a continuation of the poem, in three sections, called the *Harivamça*, which relates that Krishna is an incarnation of Vishnu, and describes his exploits and the future doom of the world.

The Story of the Deluge

The detached stories in the *Mahabharata* are a quaint account of the Deluge, where we learn that an ascetic stood for 10,000 years on one leg, before a small fish implored him to save him from the big ones in the stream. This ascetic placed the petitioner first in an earthen vessel of water, then in a tank, then in the Ganges, "the favourite spouse of the ocean," and finally in the sea, for this fish rapidly outgrew each receptacle. On reaching the ocean, the fish informed the ascetic, *with a smile*, that the dissolution of the earth was near. He also bade him build an ark provided with a long rope, told him to enter in it with seven other sages and seeds of every kind, and promised to appear as a horned fish to save him from destruction. When the flood came, the horned fish, seizing the rope, dragged the ark to the top of the Himalayas, where it rested securely. There it declared, "I am Brahma who saved you," and directed the ascetic, aided by his learned companions, to create everything anew by means of the seeds.

The Story of Nala and Damayanti

The romantic story of Nala and Damayanti was told to comfort the eldest Pandav for having gambled away all his possessions. It seems that once, while hunting, Nala released a golden bird, because it promised to win for him the affections of Princess Damayanti. Pleased with this prospect, Nala let the bird go, and watched it fly in the direction of Damayanti's palace. There the bird, caught by the Princess, praised Nala so eloquently that Damayanti fell in love with him, and, in order to meet him, announced that she was about to hold a Bride's Choice. On his way to this tournament, Nala met four gods, all anxious to marry the beautiful Princess, and they, after obtaining his promise to perform their wishes, bade him steal unseen into the palace and bid the Princess choose one of them as a spouse.

The broken-hearted Nala, forced to sue for the gods, made known their request to Damayanti, who declared that she did not intend to marry any one but himself, as she meant to announce publicly at the Bride's Choice on the morrow.

"Yet I see a way of refuge—'tis a blameless way, O king;
Whence no sin to thee, O rajah,—may by any chance arise.
Thou, O noblest of all mortals—and the gods by Indra led,
Come and enter in together—where the Swayembara meets;
Then will I, before the presence—of the guardians of the world,
Name thee, lord of men! my husband—nor to thee may blame accrue."

She was, however, sorely embarrassed on arriving there to find five Nalas before her, for each of the gods had assumed the form of the young prince after the latter had reported what Damayanti had said. Unable to distinguish between the gods and her lover, Damayanti prayed so fervently that she was able to discern that four of her suitors gazed at her with unwinking eyes, exuded no perspiration, and cast no shadow, while the fifth betrayed all these infallible signs of mortality. She, therefore, selected the real Nala, upon whom the four gods bestowed invaluable gifts, including absolute control over fire and water.

The young couple were perfectly happy for some time, although a wicked demon (Kali)—who had arrived too late at the Bride's Choice—was determined to trouble their bliss. He therefore watched husband and wife in hopes of finding an opportunity to injure them, but it was only in the twelfth year of their married life that Nala omitted the wonted ablutions before saying his prayers. This enabled the demon to enter his heart and inspire him with such a passion for gambling that he soon lost all he possessed.

His wife, seeing her remonstrances vain, finally ordered a charioteer to convey her children to her father's home, and they had barely gone when Nala came out of the gambling hall, having nothing left but a garment apiece for himself and his wife. So the faithful Damayanti followed him out of the city into the forest, the winner having proclaimed that no help should be given to the exiled king or queen. Almost starving, Nala, hoping to catch some birds which alighted near him, flung over them as a net his only garment. These birds, having been sent by the demon to rob him of his last possession, flew away with the cloth, calling out to him that they were winged dice sent by Kali.

> Over them his single garment—spreading light, he wrapped them round:
> Up that single garment bearing—to the air they sprang away;
> And the birds above him hovering—thus in human accents spake,
> Naked as they saw him standing—on the earth, and sad, and lone:
> "Lo, we are the dice, to spoil thee—thus descended, foolish king!
> While thou hadst a single garment—all our joy was incomplete."

Husband and wife now wander on, until one night Nala, arising softly, cut his wife's sole garment in two, and, wrapping himself in part of it, forsook her during her sleep, persuading himself that if left alone she would return to her father and enjoy comfort. The poem gives a touching description of the husband's grief at parting with his sleeping wife, of her frenzy on awakening, and of her pathetic appeals for her husband to return.

Then we follow Damayanti in her wanderings through the forest in quest of the missing Nala, and see her join a company of hermits, who, being spirits sent to comfort her, predict, before they vanish, that her sorrows will not last forever. Next she joins a merchant caravan, which, while camping, is surprised by wild elephants; these beasts trample the people to death and cause a panic. The merchants fancy this calamity has visited them because they showed compassion to Damayanti, whom they now think a demon and wish to tear to pieces. She, however, has fled at the approach of the wild elephants, and again wanders alone through the forest, until she finally comes to a town, where, observing her wan and distracted appearance, the people follow her hooting.

The Queen-mother, looking over the battlements of her palace and seeing this poor waif, takes compassion on her, and, after giving her refreshment, questions her regarding her origin. Damayanti simply vouchsafes the information that her husband has lost all through dicing, and volunteers to serve the Rani, provided she is never expected to eat the food left by others or to wait upon men.

Before she had been there long, however, her father sends Brahmans in every direction to try and find his missing daughter and son-in-law, and some of these suspect that the Rani's maid is the lady they are seeking. When they inform the Rani of this fact, she declares that if Damayanti is her niece, she can easily be recognized, as she was born with a peculiar mole between her eyebrows. She, therefore, bids her handmaid wash off the ashes which defile her in token of grief, and thus discovers the birth-mole proving her identity.

Damayanti now returns to her father and to her children, but does not cease to mourn the absence of her spouse. She, too, sends Brahmans in all directions, singing, "Where is the one who, after stealing half of his wife's garment, abandoned her in the jungle?" Meantime Nala has saved from the fire a serpent, which by biting him has transformed him into a dwarf, bidding him at the same time enter the service of a neighbouring Rajah as charioteer, and promising that after a certain time the serpent poison will drive the demon Kali out of his system. Obeying these injunctions, Nala becomes the charioteer of a Rajah, and while with him hears a Brahman sing the song which Damayanti taught him. He answers it by another, excusing the husband for having forsaken his wife, and, when the Brahman reports this to Damayanti, she rightly concludes that her Nala is at this Rajah's court.

She, therefore, sends back the Brahman with a message to the effect that she is about to hold a second Bride's Choice, and the Rajah, anxious to secure her hand, asks his charioteer whether he can convey him to the place in due time. Nala undertakes to drive his master 500 miles in one day, and is so clever a charioteer that he actually performs the feat, even though he stops on the way to test his master's knowledge of figures by begging him to count the leaves and fruit on the branch of a tree. Finding that the Rajah has accurately guessed them at a glance, Nala begs him, in return for his services as charioteer, to teach him the science of numbers, so that when he dices again he shall be sure to win.

On arriving at the court of Damayanti's father, Nala is summoned into the presence of his wife, who, although she does not recognize him in his new form, insists that he must be her spouse, for no one else can drive as he does or has the power which he displays over fire and water. At this moment the sway of the demon ends, and Nala, restored to his wonted form, rapturously embraces his wife and children.

> Even as thus the wind was speaking,—flowers fall showering all around:
> And the gods swee music sounded—on the zephyr floating light.

Then, thanks to his new skill in dicing, Nala recovers all he has lost, and is able to spend the rest of his life in peace and happiness with the faithful Damayanti.

The Story of Savitri and Satyavan

Once upon a time a king, mourning because he was childless, spent many years fasting and praying in hopes that offspring would be granted him. One day the Goddess of the Sun rose out of his sacrificial fire to promise him a daughter, more beauteous than any maiden ever seen before. The King rejoiced, and, when this child was born, every one declared little Savitri the prettiest maiden ever seen. As she grew up she became more and more beautiful, until all the surrounding kings longed to marry her, but dared not propose. Seeing this, her father conferred upon her the right to select her own spouse, and the Princess began to travel from court to court inspecting all the marriageable princes. One day, in the course of these wanderings, she paused beneath a banyan tree, where a blind old hermit had taken up his abode. He was in the act of telling the Princess that he dwelt there with his wife and son, when a young man appeared, bringing wood for the sacrifice. This youth was Satyavan, his son, who was duly astonished to behold a lovely princess.

On returning home, Savitri informed her father that her choice was made, for she had decided to marry the hermit's son! This news appalled the King, because the Prime Minister assured him that Satyavan—the son of a banished king—was doomed to die at the end of the year.

Knowing the unenviable lot of a Hindu widow, the King implored Savitri to choose another mate, but the girl refused, insisting that she would rather live one year with Satyavan than spend a long life with any one else.

The marriage therefore took place, and, as the

hermit and his son had vowed to remain in the jungle until they should be reinstated in their realm, the Princess dwelt in their humble hut, laying aside her costly garments and wearing the rough clothes which hermits affect.

In spite of poverty, this little family dwelt happily beneath the huge banyan tree, the Princess rigidly keeping the secret that her husband had but a year to live. Time passed all too swiftly, however, and as the year drew toward an end the little wife grew strangely pale and still, fasted constantly, and spent most of her time praying that the doom of death might be averted. When the fatal day drew near, she was so weak and faint that she could hardly stand; but when Satyavan announced that he was going into the forest to cut wood, she begged leave to accompany him, although he objected that the way was too rough and hard for her tender feet. By dint of coaxing, however, Savitri obtained his consent; so hand in hand she passed with her husband through the tropical woods.

While Satyavan was felling a tree, he suddenly reeled and fell at her feet, fainting. In a moment Savitri was bending over him, holding his head in her lap and eagerly trying to recall life in his veins. Then she suddenly became aware of Yama, God of Death, with blood-red clothes, cruel eyes, and the long black noose with which he snares the soul and draws it out of the body. In spite of Savitri's pleading, he now drew out Satyavan's soul and started off with his prize, leaving the youthful body pale and cold on the ground.

But the little wife, instead of staying with the corpse, followed Yama, imploring him not to bear off her husband's soul! Turning around, Yama sternly

Savitri and Yama

Evelyn Paul

564

bade her go back, since no human mortal could tread the road he was following, and reminded her that it was her duty to perform her husband's funeral rites. She, however, insisting that wherever Satyavan's soul went she would go, painfully followed the King of Death, until in pity he promised to grant her anything she wished, save her husband's soul. Thereupon Savitri begged that her blind father-in-law might recover sight and kingdom, boons which Yama immediately granted, telling Savitri to go and bear the news to her father-in-law, for the way he had to tread was long and dark.

Weak and weary as she was, Savitri nevertheless persisted in following Yama, until he again turned, declaring that he would grant any boon, save her husband's life, to comfort her. The little wife now begged that her father might have princely sons, knowing he had long desired an heir. This favour also was granted, before Yama bade her go back to light and life; but Savitri still insisted that was impossible, and that as long as she lived she must follow her beloved!

Darkness now settled down on the forest, and although the road was rough and thorny Savitri stumbled on and on, following the sound of Yama's footsteps although she could no longer see him. Finally he turned into a gloomy cavern, but she plodded on, until she so excited his compassion that he promised her one more boon, again stipulating that it should not be the soul which he held in his hand. When Savitri begged for children, sons of Satyavan, Yama smiled and granted her prayer, thinking he would now surely be rid of her at last. But Savitri followed him on into the depths of the cavern, although owls and bats made the place hideous with their cries. Hearing her footsteps still behind him, Yama tried to frighten her away, but she, grasping the hand which held her husband's soul, laid her tear-wet cheek against it, thereby so touching the god's heart that he exclaimed, "Ask anything thou wilt and it shall be thine."

Noticing this time that he made no reservation, Savitri joyfully exclaimed that she wished neither wealth nor power, but only her beloved spouse! Conquered by such devotion, Death relinquished into her keeping Satyavan's soul, and promised that they should live happy together and have many sons.

"Adieu, great God!" She took the soul,
No bigger than the human thumb,
And running swift, soon reached her goal,
Where lay the body stark and dumb.
She lifted it with eager hands
And as before, when he expired,
She placed the head upon the bands
That bound her breast, which hope new fired,
And which alternate rose and fell;
Then placed his soul upon his heart,
Whence like a bee it found its cell,
And lo, he woke with sudden start!
His breath came low at first, then deep,
With an unquiet look he gazed,
As one awakening from a sleep,
Wholly bewildered and amazed.

Miss Toru Dutt

Before long warmth and strength returned to Satyavan, who went home with Savitri, "and they lived happy ever after," for all the boons which Yama had promised were duly granted.

CHINESE AND JAPANESE POETRY

WHITE ASTER

EPICS as they are understood in Europe do not exist in either China or Japan, although Orientals claim that name for poems which we would term idylls.

A romantic tale, which passes as an epic in both countries, was written in Chinese verse by Professor Inouye, and has been rendered into classical Japanese by Naobumi Ochiai. It is entitled *The Lay of the Pious Maiden Shirakiku* (Shirakiku=White Aster).

The first canto opens with an exquisite description of an autumn sunset and of the leaves falling from the trees at the foot of Mount Aso. Then we hear a temple bell ringing in a distant grove, and see a timid maiden steal out weeping from a hut in the extremity of the village to gaze anxiously in the direction of the volcano, for her father left her three days before to go hunting and has not returned. Poor little White Aster fears some harm may have befallen her sire, and, although she creeps back into the hut and kindles a fire to make tea, she turns her head at every sound in the hope that her father has come back at last. Stealing out once more only to see wild geese fly past and the rain-clouds drift across the heavens, White Aster shudders and feels impelled to start in quest of the missing man. She, therefore, dons a straw cloak and red bamboo hat, and, although night will soon fall, steals down the village street, across the marsh, and begins to climb the mountain

> Here the steep path winds with a swift ascent
> Toward the summit:—the long grass that grew
> In tufts upon the slopes, shrivelled and dry,
> Lay dead upon her path;—hushed was the voice
> Of the blithe chafers.—Only sable night
> Yawned threatening from the vale.[1]

While she is searching, the rain ceases and the clouds part, but no trace of her missing father does she find. Light has gone and darkness has already invaded the solitude, when White Aster descries a faint red gleam through the trees and hears the droning voice of a priest chanting his prayers. Going in the direction of light and sound, White Aster soon approaches a ruined temple, standing in the midst of a grove of cypress and camphor trees, amid bleached bones and mouldering graves overhung by weeping-willows.

Her light footfall on the broken steps, falling upon the ear of the recluse, makes him fancy that some demon is coming to tempt him, so seizing a light he thrusts it out of the door, tremblingly bidding the "fox ghost" begone. In the East, foxes being spirits of evil and having the power to assume any form they wish, the priest naturally takes what seems a little maiden for a demon. But, when he catches a glimpse of White Aster's lovely innocent face and hears her touching explanation, he changes his opinion:

> "Tis clear she comes of noble family:
> Her eyebrows are as twin half-moons: her hair
> Lies on her snowy temples, like a cloud:
> In charm of form she ranks with Sishih's self,
> That pearl of loveliness, the Chinese Helen."

Taking his visitor gently by the hand, he leads her

[1] The quotations are from the Rev. A. Lloyd's translation.

into the sanctuary, where he seats her at Buddha's feet, before inquiring who she is and what she is doing at night in the wilderness. White Aster timidly explains that, although born in one of the southern islands and cradled in a rich home, the pleasant tenor of her life was suddenly interrupted by the outbreak of war. Her home sacked and destroyed, she and her mother barely escaped with their lives. Taking refuge near a ruined temple, they erected a booth to shelter them, where the girl who had always been lapped in luxury had to perform all kinds of menial tasks. But even under such circumstances her life proved pleasant compared to what she suffered when news came that her father had rebelled against the King, and that he and his adherents had been crushed in the war. No poppy-draught could enable the two poor women to forget such terrible tidings, and it is no wonder the poor mother pined away.

> "As the stream
> Flows to the sea and nevermore returns,
> So ebbed and ebbed her life. I cannot tell
> What in those days I suffered. Nature's self
> Seemed to be mourning with me, for the breeze
> Of Autumn breathed its last, and as it died
> The vesper-bell from yonder village pealed
> A requiem o'er my mother. Thus she died,
> But dead yet lives—for, ever, face and form,
> She stands before my eyes; and in my ears
> I ever seem to hear her loving voice,
> Speaking as in the days when, strict and kind,
> She taught me household lore,—in all a mother."

Having carefully tended her mother to the end, poor little White Aster lived alone, until one day her father suddenly appeared, having found at last a way to escape and rejoin them. He was broken-hearted on learning of his wife's death, and, hoping to comfort him, White Aster paid him all manner of filial attentions. She could not, however, restore happiness or peace to the bereaved man, who, besides mourning his wife, keenly regretted the absence of his son Akitoshi, whom he had driven from home in anger when the youth proved wild and overbearing.

During this artless narrative the recluse had exhibited signs of deep emotion, and, when White Aster mentioned the name of her brother, he clasped his hands over his face as if to conceal its expression. After listening to her tale in silence, he kindly bade White Aster tarry there until sunrise, assuring her that it would not be safe for her to wander in the mountain by night. Little White Aster, therefore, slept at Buddha's feet, shivering with cold, for her garments were too thin to protect her from the keen mountain air. As she slept she dreamt of her father, whose wraith appeared to her, explaining that a false step had hurled him down into a ravine, whence he had vainly been trying to escape for three days past.

The second canto opens with a description of a beautiful red dawn, and of the gradual awakening of the birds, whose songs finally rouse the little maiden, who again sets off on her quest.

> Now the red dawn had tipped the mountain-tops,
> And birds, awaking, peered from out their nests,
> To greet the day with strains of matin joy;
> The while, the moon's pale sickle, silver white,
> Fading away, sunk in the western sky.
> Clear was the air and cloudless, save the mists
> That rolled in waves upon the mountain-tops,
> Or crept along the gullies.

Skirting the trunks of mighty trees, stealing beneath whispering pines, White Aster threads different parts of the solitude, where she encounters deer and other timid game, seeking some trace of her father. She is so intent on this quest that she does not mark two dark forms which gradually creep nearer to her. These are robbers, who finally pounce upon White Aster and drag her into their rocky den, little heeding her tears or prayers; and although the maiden cries for help, echo alone repeats her desperate calls.

The brigands' lair is beneath an overhanging cliff; here they have erected a miserable booth whose broken thatch is supplemented by the dense foliage of the ginkgo tree overshadowing it. In front of this hut runs a brawling stream, while the rocks all around are hung with heavy curtains of ivy, which add to the gloom and dampness of the place.

> Here the sun
> Ne'er visits with his parting rays at eve,
> But all is gloom and silence save the cry
> Of some belated bird that wakes the night.

Having brought their prisoner safely into this den, the robbers proceed to eat and drink, dispensing with chop-sticks, so wolfish is their hunger. Meantime they roughly jeer at their captive, who sits helpless before them, tears streaming down her pale cheeks. Having satisfied their first imperious craving for food and drink, the brigands proceed to taunt their prisoner, until the captain, producing a koto or harp, bids her with savage threats make music, as they like to be merry.

> "Sit you down,
> And let us hear your skill; for I do swear
> That, if you hesitate, then with this sword
> I'll cut you into bits and give your flesh
> To yonder noisy crows. Mark well my words."

So proficient is our little maiden on this instrument, that her slender fingers draw from the cords wonderful sounds which hold all living creatures spellbound. Even the robbers remain quiet while she plays, and are so entranced that they fail to hear the steps of a stranger, stealing near the hut armed with sword and spear. Seeing White Aster in the brigands' power, this stranger bursts open the door and pounces upon the robbers, several of whom he slays after a desperate conflict. One of their number, however, manages to escape, and it is only when the fight is over that White Aster—who has covered her face with her hands—discovers that her rescuer is the kind-hearted recluse. He now informs her that, deeming it unsafe for her to thread the wilderness alone, he soon followed her, intending to tell her that he is her long-lost brother. Then he explains how, after being banished from home, he entered the service of a learned man, with whom he began to study, and that, perceiving at last the wickedness of his ways, he made up his mind to reform. But, although he immediately hastened home to beg his parents' forgiveness, he arrived there only to find his native town in ruins. Unable to secure any information in regard to his kin, he then became a recluse, and it was only because shame and emotion prevented his speaking that he had not immediately told White Aster who he was.

> " Much then my spirit fought against itself,
> Wishing to tell my name and welcome you,
> My long-lost sister: but false shame forbade
> And kept my mouth tight closed."

His tale ended, the recluse and his sister leave the robbers' den, and steal hand in hand through the dusk, the forest's silence being broken only by the shrill cries of bands of monkeys. They are about to emerge from this dark ravine, when the robber who had escaped suddenly pounces upon the priest, determined to slay him in order to avenge his dead comrades. Another terrible fight ensues, which so frightens poor little White Aster that she runs off, loses her way in the darkness, and in spite of all her efforts is unable to return to her brother's side.

The third canto tells how, after wandering all night, White Aster finally emerges at dawn on the top of a cliff, at whose base nestles a tiny village, with one of the wonted shrines. Making her way down to this place, White Aster kneels in prayer, but her attitude is so weary that an old peasant, passing by, takes pity upon her and invites her to join his daughter in their little cottage. White Aster thus becomes an inmate of this rustic home, where she spends the next few years, her beauty increasing every day, until her fame spreads all over the land. Hearing of her unparalleled loveliness, the Governor finally decides to marry her, although she is far beneath him in rank, and sends a matrimonial agent to bargain for her hand. The old rustic, awed by the prospect of so brilliant an alliance, consents without consulting White Aster, and he and the agent pick out in the calendar a propitious day for the wedding.

When the agent has departed, the old man informs his guest how he has promised her hand in marriage, adding that she has no choice and must consent. But White Aster exclaims that her mother, on her way to the temple one day, heard a strange sound in the churchyard. There she discovered, among the flowers, a tiny abandoned girl, whom she adopted, giving her the name of the blossoms around her.

> "Once," she said,
> "Ere morn had scarce begun to dawn, I went
> To worship at the temple: as I passed
> Through the churchyard 'twixt rows of grave-
> stones hoar,
> And blooming white chrysanthemums, I heard
> The piteous wailing of a little child.
> Which following, I found, amidst the flowers,
> A fair young child with crimson-mouthing lips
> And fresh soft cheek—a veritable gem.
> I took it as a gift that Buddha sent
> As guerdon of my faith, and brought it up
> As my own child, to be my husband's joy
> And mine: and, as I found thee couched
> Amidst white-blooming asters, I named thee
> White Aster in memorial of the day."

The little maiden adds that her adopted mother made her promise never to marry any one save her so-called brother, and declares that she is bound in honour to respect this maternal wish. The Governor, anxious to secure this beautiful bride, meantime sends the agent hurrying back with a chest full of gifts, the acceptance of which will make the bargain binding. So the clever agent proceeds to exhibit tokens which so dazzle the old peasant that he greedily accepts them all, while admiring neighbours gape at them in wonder.

Poor little White Aster, realizing that it will be impossible to resist the pressure brought to bear upon her, steals out of the peasant's house at midnight, and, making her way across damp fields to the river, climbs up on the high bridge, whence she intends to fling herself into the rushing waters. She pauses, however, to utter a final prayer, and, closing her eyes, is about to spring when a hand grasps her and a glad voice exclaims that she is safe! Turning around, White Aster gazes with wondering eyes upon the recluse, who ever since he escaped from the brigand's clutches has vainly sought her everywhere. He declares that they shall never part again and tenderly leads her home, where she is overjoyed to find her father, who still mourns her absence.

Thankful for the return of his child, the father relates how, having fallen into a ravine—where he found water and berries in plenty—he vainly tried to scale the rocks, to escape from its depths and return home. All his efforts having proved vain, he was about to give way to despair, when a band of monkeys appeared at the top of the cliff and by grimaces and sounds showed him how to climb out by means of the hanging vines. Trusting to these weak supports, the father scaled the rocks, but on arriving at the summit was surprised to discover no trace of the monkeys who had taught him how to escape. He remembered, however, that while hunting one day he had aimed at a mother monkey and her babe, but had not injured them because the poor mother had made such distressing sounds of despair. He adds that it was probably in reward for this act of mercy that the monkeys saved his life.

> "I spared her life;
> And she, in turn, seeing my sorry plight,
> Cried to me from the rocks, and showed the way
> To flee from certain death."

Thus, this epic ends with a neat little moral, and with the comforting assurance that White Aster, her father, and her husband lived happy ever afterward.

AMERICAN EPICS

WHEN Europeans first landed in North America, they found that continent occupied by various tribes of Indians, speaking—it is estimated—some 600 different languages or dialects. At first no systematic effort could be made to discover the religion or traditions of the native Americans, but little by little it was discovered that they boasted a rich folk-lore, and that their nature-myths and hero-tales were recited by the fireside from generation to generation. There were tribes in different degrees of evolution between savagery and the rudimentary stages of civilization, so also there are more or less rude myths and folk-tales in the samples with which we have thus become familiar.

Among the more advanced tribes, Indian folk-lore bears the imprint of a weirdly poetical turn of mind, and ideas are often vividly and picturesquely expressed by nature similes. Some of this folk-lore is embodied in hymns, or what have also been termed nature-epics, which are now being carefully preserved for future study by professional collectors of folk-lore. Besides a few very interesting creation myths and stories of the Indian gods, there is a whole fund of nature legends of which we have a characteristic example in Bayard Taylor's *Mon-da-min*, or ' Creation of the Maize,' and also in the group of legends welded into a harmonious whole by Longfellow in the ' American-Indian epic ' *Hiawatha.*

The early European settlers found so many material obstacles to overcome, that they had no leisure for the cultivation of literature. Apart from letters, diaries, and reports, therefore, no early colonial literature exists. But, with the founding of the first colleges in America—Harvard, Yale, William and Mary, the College of New Jersey, and King's College (now Columbia)—and with the introduction of the printing press, the American literary era may be said to begin. Early attempts at epics were made by Anne Bradstreet—the Morning Star of American Poetry—by Michael Wigglesworth, by Timothy Dwight, and by Barlow, whose voluminous *Columbiad* contains some praiseworthy passages.

In 1819 appeared Washington Irving's *Sketch-Book*, which contains the two classics, *Legend of Sleepy Hollow* and *Rip Van Winkle*, which are sometimes quoted as inimitable samples of local epics in prose. Cooper's Leather-stocking series of novels, including *The Deerslayer*, *The Last of the Mohicans*, *The Pathfinder*, *The Pioneers*, and *The Prairie*, are also often designated as "prose epics of the Indian as he was in Cooper's imagination," while some of his sea-stories, such as *The Pirate*, have been termed 'epics of the sea.' Bryant, first-born of the famous group of nineteenth-century American poets, made use of many of the Indian myths and legends in his verse.

It is, however, Longfellow, America's most popular poet, who has written the nearest approach to a real epic, in *The Song of Hiawatha*, composed in 1855, in the metre of the *Kalevala*. Its introductory lines explain that the Indian legends it embodies originated:

> In the birds'-nests of the forest,
> In the lodges of the beaver,
> In the hoof-prints of the bison,
> In the eyrie of the eagle.

THE SONG OF HIAWATHA

This nature song relates how the Master of Life, having traced the pathway which all the waters on earth were to travel, called an assembly of the 'Prophets of the Nations,' and, after stating his regret that they could not abide in peace together, promised to send them

> "A Deliverer of the nations,
> Who shall guide you and shall teach you,
> Who shall toil and suffer with you."

The Master of Life further added that, if they followed this prophet's teachings, they should "multiply and prosper," while if they disregarded them, they should "fade away and perish." This warning given, the Master of Life ascended heavenward in the smoke of his peace-pipe.

The epic next describes the four winds of heaven, ascribing the greatest power to the West Wind, and tells of his impetuous wooing of Wenonah, only daughter of Nokomis, a daughter of the Moon. But the West Wind proves fickle and soon forsakes Wenonah, who, dying, leaves her little son, Hiawatha, to old Nokomis. The grandmother rocks the babe in an Indian cradle, and, as he grows older, relates for his entertainment the Indian legends, and teaches him the language of the stars, the winds, the trees, the birds, and the fishes. The marvellous story-teller Iagoo fashions Hiawatha's first bow and arrows, and sends him forth to slay a deer, which supplies a feast for the whole village.

After becoming skilled in all "manly arts and labours," Hiawatha determines to seek the father who betrayed his mother. A long journey brings the youthful adventurer to "the portals of the sunset," and face to face with his father, who boastfully declares that naught can harm him, save a certain black rock. In return, Hiawatha asserts that he fears naught but the bulrush. The West Wind, in conversation with Hiawatha, admits that it was he who caused Wenonah's early death, and a three days' battle ensues, during which father and son belabour each other with rock and bulrush and cause great confusion upon earth, without either being able to gain any advantage.

At last the West Wind bids his son return to earth, and free it from all harm; when his labours are ended and death draws near, he shall return and share his father's kingdom. Wending his way homeward, Hiawatha notes the tumultuous signs of his recent conflict with his father, and pauses to purchase arrow-heads from an old Indian, whose beautiful daughter bears the name of Minnehaha, or Laughing Water.

On his return to Nokomis, Hiawatha goes into the forest to undergo the usual seven days' fast, or Indian initiation into manhood. During this period, youthful warriors concentrate their thoughts upon the object which they most covet, so Hiawatha broods over the needs of his people, who, in the season when the birds fly southward, when the fish hide beneath the ice, when the game vanishes, and roots, berries, and wild rice can no longer be gathered, suffer from a woeful lack of food.

On the fourth day of this voluntary fast, Hiawatha is suddenly confronted by the green-clad, yellow-plumed warrior Mondamin, who declares that since he prays only "for profit of the people, for advantage of the nations," his prayer shall be answered, provided he wrestles three evenings in succession with his interlocutor, and triumphs over him at last.

Weak from fasting, Hiawatha wrestles manfully, night after night, and although old Nokomis tempts him to sustain his strength by surreptitiously tasting food, Hiawatha remains firm. The last wrestling bout ends with the death of Mondamin, whom Hiawatha carefully buries, ere he returns home to partake of food.

Then, still mindful of his adversary's instructions, Hiawatha mounts guard over the grave, from whose brown turf green blades spring forth, grow and flourish until, when autumn comes, Hiawatha is able to harvest the yellow ears of Mondamin, or Indian maize, the precious gift from the Great Spirit, which enables the Indians to subsist when other food is unobtainable.

Not satisfied with having bestowed the priceless boon of Indian corn upon his people, Hiawatha often discusses with his friends Chibiabos, a musician, and Kwasend, an athlete, "how the tribes of men might prosper."

Having decided to undertake a special fishing feat, Hiawatha begs from the trees of the forest the necessary materials for a perfect canoe, in which he sails out on the Big Sea Water, to angle for the King of Fishes, a wily sturgeon. Angered at last by Hiawatha's taunts, the King of Fishes swallows both canoe and angler! Swinging his canoe sideways, as it is slipping down the sturgeon's gullet, Hiawatha wedges it so fast, that it chokes the King of Fishes, whose carcass, drifting ashore, is attacked by flocks of ravenous gulls. They soon bare the sturgeon's ribs, and Hiawatha, rapturously greeting the light of day, escapes from his prison. By his directions Nokomis allows the birds to feed on the sturgeon's carcass by day, but at night takes her share of the flesh and boils it, to secure a supply of oil for winter use.

Hiawatha, hearing that Pearl Feather, the slayer of Nokomis' father, guarded by fiery serpents, dwells in the midst of pitch-black waters, whence he sends out deadly miasmic fevers, determines to seek and slay him. Properly equipped, our hero sets out in his magic canoe, shoots the fiery serpents, and, notwithstanding the baleful fogs, pestilential mosquitoes, and treacherous fireflies, reaches the island in the Black Waters where Pearl Feather's wigwam stands. Loudly challenging the Magician to confront him, Hiawatha strings his bow and replies to his opponent's rude gibes, by saying:

> "Big words do not smite like war-clubs,
> Boastful breath is not a bow-string,
> Taunts are not so sharp as arrows,
> Deeds are better things than words are,
> Actions mightier than boastings!"

In spite of Hiawatha's magic mittens and well-directed arrows, he fights in vain until he has but one arrow left, which a woodpecker bids him aim at Pearl Feather's upstanding tuft of hair, his only vulnerable spot. Waiting until his adversary stoops to pick up a stone, Hiawatha's last arrow slays the Magician, and the bloody tuft of hair thereafter adorns the woodpecker's head! Sailing homeward with the Magician's wampum shirt and store of skins, Hiawatha enriches his people, who again hail him as their deliverer.

It is shortly after this encounter that Hiawatha reasons :

"As unto the bow the cord is,
So unto the man is woman ;
Though she bends him, she obeys him,
Though she draws him, yet she follows;
Useless each without the other ! "

But when Nokomis suggests some fitting mate he declines, and sets out for the Arrow-maker's wigwam, intending to sue for Minnehaha, who is meanwhile dreaming of the young warrior whom she has seen but once. Arriving with a deer, which he has slain on the way, Hiawatha, after giving an account of his birth and youth, proposes that a lasting peace be cemented between the Ojibway and Dacotah tribes by his marriage with Minnehaha.

The proposal being duly referred to the maiden herself, she consents, and on the morrow, she and Hiawatha, hand in hand, begin their homeward journey through the forest while the old Arrow-maker moralizes :

"Thus it is our daughters leave us !
Those we love and those who love us !
Just when they have learned to help us,
When we are old and lean upon them,
Comes a youth with flaunting feathers,
With his flute of reeds, a stranger,
Wanders piping through the village,
Beckons to the fairest maiden,
And she follows where he leads her,
Leaving all things for the stranger ! "

During their wedding journey the young couple receive the congratulations and benedictions of birds, beasts, and the sun, and their arrival at the abode of Nokomis is followed by wedding rejoicings, with feasting, the bestowal of gifts, story-telling, singing, and dancing.

In the happy days that follow, Hiawatha hunts and fishes, while Minnehaha waits upon old Nokomis and plants the corn. By Hiawatha's directions, she steals forth at night, clad only in her tresses, draws a magic circle round the cornfields, and blesses the grain. Not content with this spell and blessing, Hiawatha fashions snares to catch the ravens that dig up the seeds. One of these captives he tethers to his wigwam, as a living warning to other crows. The seeds, thus protected, sprout, grow, and bear many golden ears, which are husked in autumn by the assembled Indians.

Seeing how even the memory of great deeds fades from the minds of old men, Hiawatha invents picture writing, using as materials birch bark, tanned hides, smooth rocks, polished tree-trunks and mineral pigments. He instructs his people in the science of signs, and teaches each family to inscribe its special mark on its wigwam hides and totem poles.

Wise as Hiawatha is, he cannot save his careless young friend Chibiabos from the Evil Spirits lurking beneath the ice on the Big Sea Water. But, having seen the ice crack beneath him and the sweet singer vanish, Hiawatha composes a lament for him; then, aided by his friends, he calls up his spirit from the waters, and sends it on, duly shod and provisioned, to the Islands of the Blessed.

The Village Dancer, Pau-Puk-Keewis, jealous of the fame of the Story-teller, teaches the Indians how to gamble, and wins all their possessions; on his way home he kills Hiawatha's crow, tumbles all his household goods into an untidy heap, and, perching himself upon a neighbouring headland, begins to slaughter the gulls, "Hiawatha's chickens."

Informed of these misdeeds, Hiawatha follows the trail of the mischief-maker, who, hoping to elude pursuit, changes himself first into a beaver, then into an aquatic bird, and finally takes refuge within a mountain, where Hiawatha attacks him with thunderbolts and condemns his spirit, in punishment, to dwell in the winds and be blown hither and thither over the face of the earth.

The Hiawatha epic finally describes how Winter came down from the Northland, shrouding the North in snow, so that hunters could secure no game, and locking the waters fast beneath ice so thick that no fish could be obtained. The Indians began to feel the pinch of hunger, then, overcome by cold, fever, and famine, many died.

Like the other braves, Hiawatha vainly ranged the forest and plain on snow-shoes, hoping to find game, and while he wildly implored the Great Spirit to give him food, the spectres of Fever and Famine stalked into his wigwam, and laid low his beloved Minnehaha. In her feverish ramblings she retraced her happy childhood and blissful wedding journey, then died, uttering a despairing cry which summoned the empty-handed Hiawatha to her lifeless body.

After watching beside the beloved form seven days and nights, Hiawatha and Nokomis wrapped it in the softest furs, and consigned it to a snowy grave, over which for four days they kept a fire burning to give her comfort during her long journey to the Islands of the Blessed.

The poet now personifies this cruel Winter as an

The Departure of Hiawatha
Nancy Smith

aged chief, who, sitting in his comfortless wigwam, is surprised by the arrival of a young warrior—Spring; the coming of the latter is accompanied by the melting of snow and ice, by the return of wild-fowl and four-footed game, and by the sprouting of leaf and blossom.

Then, too, appears the Story-teller, Iagoo, relating how he has seen, sailing over the ocean, a great, white-winged canoe, manned by 100 pale-faced and heavily bearded warriors. The people all laugh at this as one of Iagoo's flights of fancy, until Hiawatha assures them that the Great Spirit revealed to him, in a vision, the coming of the white men, destined to overrun and transform the whole country. He adds that if the Indians make friends with the strangers and keep the peace among themselves, they shall prosper, while if they do not, they shall be swept westward—

> "Wild and woeful,
> Like the cloud-rack of a tempest,
> Like the withered leaves of autumn."

Early summer having brought back comfort and plenty to his people, Hiawatha tarried only long enough to welcome the Pale-faces, whose Black-robed chief tells the Indians of the birth, life, death, resurrection, and ascension of the Saviour. Then, rising from the side of these sleeping guests, Hiawatha bids Nokomis care for them hereafter, as he himself is bound

> "On a long and distant journey,
> To the portals of the sunset."

By the time all his farewells are spoken and his canoe launched, the evening sun is setting, and as

Hiawatha sails westward, the farewell sighs of his people waft him on his way :

Thus departed Hiawatha,
Hiawatha the Belovèd,
In the glory of the sunset,
In the purple mists of evening,
To the region of the home-wind,
Of the North-west wind, Keewaydin,
To the Islands of the Blessèd,
To the Kingdom of Ponemah,
To the Land of the Hereafter.

INDEX

INDEX

INDEX

C

INDEX

INDEX

D

INDEX

F

INDEX

INDEX

I

INDEX

K

L

INDEX

O

INDEX

P

INDEX

S

INDEX

T

INDEX

X

Y

Z